Praise for VICKI

"*Don't Jump* is a delicious roman à clef àla Carrie Fisher, with the emotional honesty and deft writing of a modern Dorothy Parker. It has an intelligence without snobbery, a wit beyond crudity, a sensitivity without preachiness ... and is funny as all hell." ★★★★★

Hubert O'Hearn, *San Diego Book Review*

"The warmth and wit of Vicki's writing knocked me out! In a good way. Not like Cosby. (Too soon?)"

Tom Bergeron, Emmy Award Winning Host, *Dancing With The Stars*

"If you've ever read Vicki Abelson's whip-smart, mind-twisting and hilariously profane screeds on Huffington Post, you know that pulling punches is not exactly in her skill set. Well, brace yourself for *Don't Jump*— her volcanic portrait of a woman under siege—by booze and drugs, an unrelenting social life, and a fair dose of self-destruction. At turns howlingly funny and surprisingly touching, it lights a match to the traditional heart-on-the-sleeve 'memoir,' giving birth to what may become a whole new genre of confessional literature. Is the book's heroine actually Abelson or a fabrication of her wonderfully warped worldview? Who cares? From the first page to the last, *Don't Jump* throws you on the bed and rips your clothes off—and that never sucks."

Bruce Kluger, Op-Ed Columnist *USA Today*

"I've had the pleasure of attending several live readings of various chapters of Vicki Abelson's *Don't Jump* and with each listen, there was one question that continued to rack my brain: Why isn't Vicki famous already? Not only does Vicki deserve a one-woman Broadway show for her candor, sparkling wit and razor-sharp cultural commentary on everything from celebrity crushes to menopause—she's a delicious mash-up of Carrie Fisher-meets-Sandra Bernhard—but her writing deserves its own special place in the canon of those artists whose words leap from the page and stay with you long after you've finished reading. A raucous, rowdy, thought-provoking read from a writer who is sure to leave her mark."

Malina Saval, Features Editor at *Variety*

"A funny, silly, frothy read. Vicki's voice is completely unique, and wildly exceptional. A tough book to put down."

Mike Binder, Writer, Director, *Upside of Anger*

"I jumped, I went 'all in.' I was hooked from the self-deprecating prologue until the epiphany at the end. A novel? My a*s. Nothing can be that vivid, that honest or that funny unless every moment was lived. I'm trying to figure out how someone whose life experiences suggest serious ADD could write 377 pages. May I add, the fastest, most absorbing 377 pages I can recall... ever. Now I know why nothing I write is ever published; I'm not this good."

Gary Kroeger, Actor, *Saturday Night Live*, Congressional Contender

"Vicki Abelson's *Don't Jump* grabs your attention, your emotions, and your funny bone immediately—much as its author does if you're lucky enough to meet her—and it never lets go, as it guides you on a trip that is certainly humorous, but also painfully honest and revealing. It seems limiting to call *Don't Jump* a novel, as it also manages to be a journal, a guide, to the human heart and the damaging things that can happen to those who possess and utilize it. It is also a sort of self-help book, and one of the lessons it teaches you is that humor and honesty will get you through almost anything. Take this journey—brilliant, self-lacerating, bracing, illuminating—and notice how you've been changed by it."

James Grissom, Author, *Follies of God*

"So powerful, so touching, so witty, so reminiscent of, well, me."

Alan Zweibel, Original *Saturday Night Live* Writer,
Thurber Prize Winner for *The Other Shulman*

"Do jump for *Don't Jump* Vicki Abelson's funny, rowdy, touching fictional (?) memoir of sex, drugs, rock 'n' roll, stand-up comedy, and overbearing mamas kept me up till dawn several nights in a row, bleary-eyed but unwilling to put it down. Her insights into the worlds of entertainment and addiction are remarkable, and she negotiates the path from hilarious to deeply moving (and back) with finesse and precision. Add to that the fun of figuring out who she's really writing about, and *Don't Jump* is a wonderfully engaging ride through a world most of us only get to see from the outside"

Jim Beaver, Actor, *Deadwood*, *Justified*, *Supernatural*,
Author, *Life's That Way*

"Vicki Abelson's *Don't Jump* is as smart, sexy and honest as the woman herself. I fell in love with Vicki all over again reading about Andi, a balls-to-the-wall rock-and-roll-goddess who wears her heart—and her men—on her sleeve. An authentic, compelling roller coaster ride."

Gigi Levangie Grazer NY Times Bestselling Author, *The Starter Wife*

"Wow! Just plain Wow! What an amazing book Vicki Abelson has written - deeply touching, searingly honest, wildly funny yet powerful like a kick in the stomach, and as bittersweet and raw as life. I read it in one sitting, didn't mean to but couldn't stop!"

Henry Jaglom, Filmmaker, Author, *My Lunches With Orson*

"Vicki Abelson is a force of nature who brings her wealth of pain, joy and life experience to all those who are smart enough to open themselves to the wisdom of this book."

Rob Morrow, Actor, *Northern Exposure*, *Numb3rs*

"I was bewitched by this story. *Don't Jump* captured me from the first and never me go. Vicki's voice is clear and easy, her humor natural and familiar and I felt she was speaking only to me. She actually made me wish I'd known her then! Now it seems I did. And as I got closer to the end, like every great love affair I've ever had—literary and otherwise—I started to ration out pages, moments with it, to draw it out as long as I could."

James Morrison, Actor, *24*

"If Vicki Abelson's life is anything like that of her heroine, Andi, it's a helluva lot more fun and dangerous, sweet and sad, than yours or mine. And apparently, Vicki's life is exactly like Andi's. Like Vicki's electric prose, it's a life that sizzles. Andi/Vicki displays a wicked sense of humor and an ability to evolve, no matter how many slings and arrows are hurled her way. Yes, there's angst and wailing, but also belly laughs along with the cruel truths. Wise and witty, *Don't Jump* is an awe-inspiring debut for a woman (and writer) who walks the walk on a high-wire above a raging falls."

Paul Levine, Bestselling Author, *Bum Rap*

"Fell out of my chair! What a ride. It's no easy feat getting published these days—even harder to write something you'll be proud of for the rest of your life. You can check that off your bucket list!"

Chris Lemmon, Actor, Author, *A Twist of Lemmon,*
A Tribute to My Father

"I'd certainly see *Don't Jump* when adapted as a magnificent one person show, much like *Tru*, which won so many awards when it played on Broadway. So, someone please think about the prospect of bringing this to life for all to see on stage, TV, a movie. Great work, dear Vicki... may it have a long life!"

Robert Morse, Tony, Emmy & SAG Award Winner,
How to Succeed in Business, *Tru*, *Mad Men*

"It's rare coming across writings like Vicki's. There is such a natural lyricism in her prose, flowing like water in a mountain brook, which is, time and again, punctuated with wisdom, humor and raw awakening. Her life in faux memoir, or memoir in disguise of fiction, is a soulful search for meanings in life, and for insights through her own trials through the rugged contours of her own experiences, bearing witness to some of the most important and provocative celebrities that she came in contact with through many of her own professional transformations. In the end, and hidden deep within her tales, rises a gifted storyteller, who will not only make you cringe, but laugh and cry all at the same. Her comedy hides tragedy and tragedy is told through comedy. Hers are the best kind of tales, which gladden our hearts and enlighten our souls. Hers are the kind we celebrate and cherish."

Da Chen, Author, New York Times Bestseller, *Brothers*

"Vicki Abelson's brave, funny and thought-provoking book about fighting your demons in a world gone mad is liable to change your life. Be warned, you may be subjected to truth and honesty. And should you become addicted— you may find yourself all the better for it."

Frank Howson, Screenwriter, *Boulevard of Broken Dreams*, Award Winning Director

"Abelson is a force of nature… impetuous, caustic, and incendiary… yet you feel a continual sense of contentment and calm with her at the helm, like you're being guided by someone who you could trust with your life. If you don't need another person in your world that you grow to care about deeply, then don't bother buying this book."

Gregor Collins, Author, *The Accidental Caregiver: How I Met, Loved and Lost Legendary Holocaust Refugee Maria Altmann*

"Ms. Abelson writes with heartbreaking compassion, vein-opening honesty and tragicomic hilarity—or what might have happened if Nora Ephron had gone on a speed bender and written a female version of Frederick Exley's classic *A Fan's Notes*. So jump now into Ms. Abelson's generosity of spirit and an unforgettable heroine in a novel (memoir?) that'll finally launch both to that all-elusive fame."

John Jeter, Author, *Rockin' A Hard Place*

"*Don't Jump* is a rock and roll testimonial to the strength of the human spirit, enlightening all who read it."

Anson Williams, Actor, Author, *Singing to a Bulldog: From Happy Days to Hollywood Director*

"If you don't see parts of yourself in Vicki Abelson's wildly entertaining, wickedly funny and at times, heartbreakingly honest 'semi' fictional journey through the rapids of rock and roll, standup comedy, marriage, children, addiction and overbearing parents, the only plausible explanation I can come up with is that you are a goldfish."

John Hartnett, Author, *The Barber's Conundrum and Other Stories:*
Observations on Life from the Cheap Seats

"If you haven't had the rare opportunity to take Vicki Abelson to bed with you, now's your chance. She's a hot read."

Michael O'Keefe, Actor, *Masters of Sex*, *Homeland*,
Academy Award Nominee, *The Great Santini*

"The most common phrase in Hollywood is 'I know.' Miss Abelson skewers that myth like Jumping Jill Flash in a sitcom hurricane."

Michael Des Barres, Rock Star, Actor, Sirius Radio Show Host

"A hurtling subway ride through the worlds of comedy and rock clubs in the 80s and 90s. I have never read a book that felt like it MADE me read it fast, as if the narrative and I were hurtling along on a gritty, graffiti-covered New York subway train. The author's memoir is thinly veiled as fiction, and provides an engrossing read in vivid detail, reminding me of my single days as a student in New York in the early 80s. She captures all the joys, and mostly the anguish, of being a single girl. Engrossing and recommended."

Stephanie Weaver, Author, *Golden Angels: A Pet Loss Memoir*,
The Migraine Relief Diet

"Actually do Jump... and get Vicki Abelson's book. I can highly recommend: as a writer, a reader and a jumper! Vicki will take you to places, people and things without your permission and return you with speed and safety. She's the real deal trip. Enjoy her ride."

Carrie White, Author, *Upper Cut: Highlights of My Highlights*
of My Hollywood Life

"Do jump... into the pages of Vicki's book. You'll love it!"

Gordon G.G. Gebert, Bestselling Author, *Kiss & Tell*

"You will love following the adventures of Vicki Abelson's delightfully flawed heroine as she navigates her hilarious and touching way toward success and happiness. A generous, engaging read—like the author herself."

Eve Pell, Author, *Love, Again: The Wisdom of Unexpected Romance*

"*Don't Jump*—like bungee jumping—without the bungee. Keep your eyes open, it's a great ride."

Rex Smith, Pop Star, Actor, *Pirates of Penzance*

"Screw the title! By the end of the first page of Vicki Abelson's *Don't Jump* that's all I wanted to do—jump into her next thrilling encounter, the surprise lurking right around the next page and the inspirational manner in which she takes it in—whether it was a good, bad or indifferent experience. Hell, jump, I say—there is enough pure joy, quite obviously, in the woman who wrote this book that you're gonna bungee jump right up and read the whole damn thing all over again. And learn even more the second time around! Especially swear words."

J. Marshall Craig, Author, *Between Rock and a Home Place*

"Vicki Abelson has her thumb on the pulse! Her writing reverberates with deep feeling for the travails women face but never takes her subject matter too seriously to keep the laughs from flying! A joyous read that gave this gay man a lot of pleasure!"

Leslie Jordan, Actor, *Will & Grace,*
Author, *My Trip Down the Pink Carpet*

"Vicki Abelson, always a champion for women writers, now, with *Don't Jump*, leads by example."

Scott Carter, Exec Producer, *Real Time With Bill Maher*

"What can I say? I've been waiting for this book for 3 years and Vicki doesn't disappoint! This "based on a true story" is more than a journey—it's a romp that reads so quickly leaving you wanting more. Do you hear me, Miss Abelson? More. So immediately get to writing the next book please. You know how I hate to wait."

Harvey Helms, Author, *Blush: The Unbelievably Absurd Diary Of A Gay Beauty Junkie*

"Vicki Abelson's *Don't Jump* is more than one rockin' rollin' woman's blast from the past. Through Andi, Abelson's comedianne/rockgirl with a heart of gold and a gut for irony, we get a front row seat to all the sex, lies, and celebrity of New York's club scene in the '80s. It's more than a fast read. It's an adrenaline rush."

Josie Brown, Author, *The Housewife Assassin* Series

"I met her on the phone and then in person. My, what an energy? What stood out for me was this beautiful worldly lady had more passion, conviction and a fabulous sense of humor to rally anyone's worst enemy. It's called trust. It's obvious that Vicki Abelson is a down to earth mama that has faced her demons and come out on the other side shouting "I"m a survivor." Her experiences have given her the ability and insight to be there for others and that she has done in spades. A winner in life that crossed my path to remind me, when things are well done. Congratulations dear friend."

Thaao Penghlis, Actor, *Days of Our Lives*, Author, *Places: The Journey of My Days, My Lives*

"Vicki is what they call a "Larger than Life" person. She's passionate, funny, outspoken, brave and driven. This book makes you feel like you've just climbed onto the rollercoaster ride that is Vicki's mind."

Kathleen Wilhoite, Actor, *ER*, *Gilmore Girls*

"Everybody says Vicki's a rock star... *Don't Jump* proves she's better than that: she's a rock star *woman*!"

Jackie Collins, NY Times Bestselling Author, *Hollywood Wives*

"A wonderful, revealing story told by a vulnerable and truly lovable woman. By only 75 pages in, I could see there are years of work ahead of us."

Vicki's Therapist

"Damn! That was gonna be the title of my book."

Vicki's Daughter

"Vicki wrote a book?"

Vicki's Mom

RANDOM™ CONTENT

Beverly Hills, CA 90210
www.RandomContent.com

Published 2015

FIRST EDITION

Front cover design by Lawrence O'Flahavan
Inside flaps designed by D.J. Markuson
Author photo: ©Carlos Alejandro Photography

Library of Congress Cataloging-in-Publication Data
Abelson, Vicki
Don't Jump: Sex, Drugs, Rock 'n' Roll... and My Fucking Mother / Vicki Abelson—1st ed.
pages cm
ISBN: 978-0-9915368-3-2 (trade paperback) — ISBN: 978-0-9915368-4-9 (electronic)
1. Abelson, Vicki 2. Contemporary Fiction I. Title
PN2015949436
[B]

This book is a work of fiction. Names, characters, places, and incidents either are products of the author's imagination or are used fictitiously with respect and affection.

Printed in Canada

DON'T JUMP

a novel

VICKI ABELSON

RANDOM
CONTENT
PUBLISHING

For **Harry** & **Samantha Abelson**
and my father, **Larry Katz**

"I always wanted a happy ending... Now I've learned, the hard way, that some poems don't rhyme, and some stories don't have a clear beginning, middle and end. Life is about not knowing, having to change, taking the moment and making the best of it without knowing what's going to happen next. Delicious ambiguity."

~ Gilda Radner

DON'T JUMP

AUTHOR'S NOTE

Dearest Reader,

I apologize in advance if I offend your sensibilities. I bastardize the English language all over the friggin' place—break rules of etiquette, convention and grammar... and, even spelling oft times.

I'm inconsistent as hell because I'm a control freak. I want to dictate where you roll, pause and stop. If you just would've sprung for the audio book we wouldn't be having this discussion.

I allowed myself certain liberties because being wrong, sometimes felt right.

A couple of times, I make references that aren't relevant to the time frame. Because they work. I'm sorry. Shoot me. From the left. That's my "good" side.

You may even come across something like this—I cross ~~shit~~ out, because I want you to know what Andi's *really* thinking.

My publisher and editor hate my guts.

I pray you will love me.

Somebody has to.

My mother's got a damn good reason to bail, no?

I love you.

Do too.

You're reading it, ain'tcha?

Gratefully and alanonically,*
Vicki

*alanonically
\'al\uh\non\-i-k(ə-)lē\ adverb
: compulsively needing to control people, places, and things.

The end, from the beginning

I'm a narcissistic blowhard with low self-esteem.

I'm also a wife, a mother, a daughter, a sister, a friend, a woman and an addict.

And I'm 50... plus.

How the hell did that happen? I feel young. When I look down at myself, I still look kind of young. It's only when I catch a glimpse of myself in good light that I can see it—the years etched subtly on my skin. Avoiding mirrors like the plague, I can delude myself, as I do about so many things.

Married eighteen years to the same guy, we've got two great kids, two cars and two homes. What the hell do I have to complain about?

Give me a second.

All I ever wanted was to be loved, admired, respected, adored, worshipped...

What?!?

My life hasn't exactly gone according to plan. Ever since I was a little girl, I saw myself surrounded by fame, fortune and celebrity. It never dawned on me that it wouldn't be my own. I always imagined by now I'd be somebody—well, I am somebody, but I thought I was going to be *somebody*—like Jennifer, Sandra, Meg or Julia.

And, why the hell is Julia Roberts living my life anyway?

Our birthdays are only a few hours apart—give or take a couple of years. We're both Scorpios—why aren't I goofing around with George Clooney?

I covet so many things, dammit—a career, a sex life, a flat tummy.

Don't judge me.

Oh, g'head.

I'm as shallow as a puddle.

But I have had a bit of an awakening.

It began about thirteen years ago—totally not by choice.

ONE

SURRENDER

"Ma, would you set the table *please?*" I pleaded, for the third time.

My mother was busy reading the paper.

The New York Post, like Cookie, supported George W. Bush and the air strikes in Afghanistan.

In spite of being a lifelong pacifist, I, too, found myself getting caught up in the post 9/11 fever. I was tasting blood, which was totally freaking me out, and I wasn't exactly sure why. Was it because I was fundamentally opposed to violence, or because—*shivers down my spine*—it placed me on the same political side as my ultra-conservative, right-wing mother?

It was October 8th, 2001—exactly four weeks to the day since the twin towers had come tumbling down. The city was trying to get back to its normal routine after a few insanely tumultuous weeks. Likewise, my mother and I had resumed our Monday ritual and gone grocery shopping. She was joining us for supper, as she often did. I was in the kitchen putting the finishing touches on the salad, hoping for some help.

"Maaaaa…"

Jack, my seven year-old, raced by me, trying to pry a toy microphone out of his little sister Sydney's hand. He succeeded and she collapsed in tears. Softening at the sight of his sobbing baby sister, Jack gave Sydney back the microphone, helped her up, and while putting a protective arm around her shoulder, whispered, "Okay, you can be Justin first." Pressing play on the portable cassette deck, N'Sync's, "Tearin' Up My Heart" rang out. Syd, doing her best pre-pubescent karaoke, let it rip.

I couldn't help but smile. They loved each other so—nothing like my brother Jeff and me. I can't remember a time we weren't at odds, except perhaps the early '70s, when we shared some joints, a few friends, and were too stoned to remember that we didn't like each other.

"I changed my mind," Sydney shrieked. "I don't wanna be Justin, I wanna be Britney!"

My little one, who fancied herself Britney Spears, started singing with conviction, "I'm not that innocent."

"Not that innocent?" You're three! And, it's time for dinner. Go wash your hands."

Nobody moved.

"Ma, dinner's ready, would you get the kids over here please?"

Silence.

"Ma!" I barked. My fuse was short. When wasn't it lately?

Finally setting the newspaper aside, Cookie got up and began dancing with Jack.

"Ma, are you kidding me? It's getting late, you know it's a school night."

With a loud smooch on his forehead, as sort of a defiant punctuation, Cookie finally made her way into the kitchen, gathering dishes and silverware to set the table.

Just as she and the kids sat down to eat in the dining room, the phone rang. "Daaaaaddy, is it daddy?" Sydney asked, thrilled at the thought.

Lifting the receiver, I heard the familiar, "Marge…" sounding strangely unfamiliar.

Winking at Sydney, I quickly turned my back. I could hear the fear in his voice. I could almost smell it. While holding my suddenly aching stomach, I whispered, "What's wrong, what's happened?"

I could tell it was bad; after ten years of marriage, you just know those things.

"I got a call to go see Lenore," he said, trying to mask his terror.

Lenore was the office hammer. When Lenore rang, it was never good news. We'd heard of others getting "the call." As much as we prayed otherwise, we knew what was coming.

I tried to comfort him. "I'm sure it's nothing," I said, trying to convince myself, as well. "Call me the second you get back to your office."

"I will," he replied, already sounding defeated.

Wanting desperately to say something encouraging, all I could muster was, "I love you."

"You too," he replied distractedly, before hanging up.

After pacing around our tiny Manhattan kitchen, I tried to sit down at the dining room table, but I couldn't eat, couldn't sit still.

"Something wrong, Andi?" Cookie asked, noticing my discomfort. (Andi's my name. Marge is a term of endearment my funny boy's been calling me since we got hitched. He, in turn, is my Homer.)

I didn't make eye contact, but I knew, she knew, something was very wrong. Never good at hiding my feelings, I said shakily, "Nah, everything's fine." Pushing my food around the plate, I attempted to take a bite.

The phone rang again. Leaping from my chair, I slipped into the kitchen, clutching the ringing receiver, terrified to push the "on" button.

"It's done," he said.

"What's done?" I asked, as casually as I could manage, attempting to suppress my hysteria, the acid in my stomach backing all the way up to my eyeballs.

"I've been let go," he said.

Silence.

"Just come home."

All I wanted in that moment was to make it go away—the fear, the pain, the shame—Homer's and mine.

How could I help? What could I say? I wanted to hold him, tell him that it was going to be all right, infuse some hope, but from where? Who was going to comfort and convince me?

I tried to think of a way to go back in time and undo—undo what? What had he done? What action, what word, what deed? I don't believe in regrets. Everything happens for a reason. But, what the fuck!

And, what the hell was I going to tell my mother?

I didn't say anything.

Cookie knew something was up, but mercifully held her tongue. That was the surest tip-off that she knew it was bad. Gratefully, she left shortly after dinner.

A couple of hours later, the kids were still up, watching some completely inappropriate music videos on MTV, while I was holed up in the bathroom, crying my ass off and shitting my brains out.

Hearing the key in the lock, I quickly got my act together.

Homer walked in, balancing a few cardboard boxes, trying desperately to hold them and himself together.

We didn't say a word.

We'd survived our share of heartbreaks, but this—what would we do with this?

─────── **Three's company, two** ───────

Homer worked for Robert Holloran, the cranky, pioneering, television genius. Even casual viewers knew he was difficult—that's part of his charm.

Holloran had handpicked Homer for the job of a lifetime: head writer for one of the most influential TV shows in America. But, with the perks came stomachaches, nosebleeds and a steady supply of Xanax. Now, with his fourth Emmy pending, and a recent salary bump, he was informed that his job was being eliminated—with no warning and no cause given. We were left to surmise that Marty, an ambitious, self-admitted control freak, wanted his job back and had finally succeeded. Homer had replaced Marty four years earlier, but Marty had returned in a limited capacity, only it was becoming less and less limited by the minute. Holloran and Marty were great friends, which was something Holloran didn't have many of, by his own choosing. Holloran adored Marty, who spent his workdays entertaining Holloran, as Holloran prepared to entertain America.

It was always amusing to watch Marty work. Obsessed with pleasing Holloran (and anyone else of importance), he reminded me of a medieval court jester, desperate for a laugh—at risk of death with failure.

Known around the office as a formidable foe, Marty appeared threatened even though he had recommended Homer as his replacement. I think Marty genuinely liked and respected him, but his ego was far bigger than his heart or his body. He had a tall case of the short man blues.

Marty had been working on Holloran to get rid of Homer ever since he'd passed the baton to him and noticed that Holloran seemed fine with the adjustment. One of the most easy-going, laid back sort of guys in the business, Homer was totally non-threatening, except with his talent, which was a powerful weapon, indeed.

After September 11th, Holloran was showing the public a sensitive side for, perhaps, the very first time—telling the nation how he couldn't fathom the cruelty of the world's situation, how he could never understand the inhumanity of the cowardly terrorists. But at the same moment that Holloran was soothing America, he was wielding his axe on Homer.

He didn't do the dirty work himself; he had people who did that sort of thing for him. Once Homer got the word from Holloran's minion, he never saw Holloran face to face again. Holloran was shielded from discomfort, as he was from so many things.

Holloran felt everyone's pain after 9/11, everyone's except ours. The devastation didn't end with our little family, either. Another writer with kids, who'd put in almost a decade of service on Holloran Hour, was let go the following week. What could either of them possibly have done, just then, to make it so imperative to shake up their lives and their family's lives at that precise moment in time? *The man knew our children.*

The world was upside down. Landing a new job was going to be about as easy as getting Jocelyn Wildenstein's eyes shut.

The official word was that Holloran was re-thinking things and making some changes. In a business of perpetual uncertainty, four plus years in one place seemed like a lifetime. Still reeling from 9/11, this shock sent us right back under the covers.

There we were, the four of us, squished into the center of our king-sized bed which, sadly, for the first time in a long time, seemed too big. Over the past year, the ever growing distance between Homer and me played out in the gap on the Serta Sleeper. Now, we couldn't get close enough—tossing and turning, no one sleeping.

Fighting back tears, I wondered what in the hell I was going to fill in on forms that demand "Employer's Address." Homer was worrying about money, his prospects and what the hell he had done. The kids were frightened, although they weren't exactly sure why. We'd yet to share this latest news, but we were acting weird, and they could sense it.

Jack and Syd had been frequent guests in our bed for the past month, anyway. *"What if Bin Laden finds us and blows us up?"* Now, it appeared it was about to become a regular occurrence. The old mattress wasn't seeing much action anyway, but I did think about giving it the old college try. Only, I really didn't know how to go about it.

We'd been struggling in couple's therapy for months. Fay, our therapist, kept suggesting, "Quit your job, get away from Holloran—he's destroying your self-esteem, your health, your marriage and your life." We'd laugh in unison, one of the only times we were truly in synch in those days and demand another solution. Say goodbye to the money and the perks? No freakin' way.

Ironically, looking back that was just about the same time Holloran started pulling away from Homer and me. Iced us is more like it. Holloran was an interesting sort of guy. If he liked you, his loyalty and devotion were unparalleled. If you fell from grace, there was an unapproachable coldness that was irreversible. Once you did something that offended Holloran, there was no discussion and no forgiveness. It was over. Forever. We never did find out what, if anything, Homer, or maybe even I, did to offend him, or what ammunition we'd given Marty, but it kept us up almost every night for months.

—————— Idle worship ——————

When Homer and I got together in the late '80s, one of the many things we had in common was that we worshipped Rob Holloran. Soon to be a megastar, at that point he was still an acquired taste. Holloran had been my hero for a long time. We'd had a close encounter about ten years prior, when I was a star-struck young actress/waitress and he was up and coming and quite the gentleman.

Holloran was dining with his sidekick, Mitch Newman, at The Café, where I was waitressing. They weren't in my section, but I didn't let that deter me. Scribbling a note on a menu, I quoted one of his regular catch phrases, so he'd know I was a *true* fan. "Darn the luck, you're not in my station. Come back!" I signed off, "Love, Andi," and handed it to his waiter for delivery.

He quickly replied, "Thanks for the free dinner, Awfi." My handwriting has always been completely illegible, even to me.

Posting myself by the exit, so he'd have to pass me on his way out, I held the scribbled menu so he'd know who I was. He introduced himself and Mitch to me before leaving. What a rush.

Almost twenty years later, I had Homer bring my saved treasure into rehearsal. The following week I flipped out when a letter from Holloran Hour, addressed to me, arrived in the mail. Tearing it open, it read: "Dear Andi, I got a kick out of seeing the menu. Thanks for thinking of me. Best Regards, Rob Holloran." Rob Holloran was thanking me for thinking of him? No shit.

For four years when Holloran heard the name Andi, I was, perhaps, the first person that came to his mind. It doesn't get much better than that, at least not for me. I got to see him fairly regularly and even exchanged witty banter.

At my third Holloran Christmas party he began holding the annual holiday obligation on the set of his show to ease his discomfort. It seemed to work.

Entering the room, moving briskly, his assistants flanking his sides, he stopped momentarily here and there to say a quick hello and share a few words with his underlings. Heading straight towards me, he smiled as he extended his arm. I slipped my hand in his, blushing as our eyes locked. Without moving his gaze, he lifted my hand to his lips, placing a gentle kiss.

"Hello, lovely Andi."

Wanting desperately to appear cool, trying murderously hard not to swoon, I replied, "Hello, Rob, thanks for having me."

I winked, far more confidently than I felt.

Not a traditionally handsome man, more flawed in person than on television, he was still an imposing presence. He had *the funny* and he had *it*, the great intangible. It was a damn attractive combination.

As soon as we got home, I couldn't decide what to do first. Whipping out my dictionary, I dialed my best friend, Maryann.

"Holy shit, holy shit, holy shit!" I babbled, unable to be any more articulate than that.

"Andi, what's up? I take it this is good news?"

"I'll say," I sighed, finally taking in some much needed oxygen.

"Rob Holloran kissed my hand and called me lovely!"

"That's huge," Maryann said, duly impressed.

"I've got my Webster's, what the hell does it actually mean?" Finding the page, I read aloud:

> "**love'ly** adj **1** having physical or mental traits that arouse affection or admiration; **2** beautiful; **3** *colloq* delightful **4** beautiful young woman; SYN *adj* comely, fair, exquisite, attractive, enchanting, captivating (cf. *beautiful*)."

"Ah..." I sighed, allowing myself the moment's enjoyment.

"Did I mention that HE KISSED MY FUCKING HAND when he said it?" I added, laughing and screaming at the same time.

"I believe you might have mentioned it."

"So I did. But, I believe it bears repeating."

All the weed in the world couldn't have gotten me higher than that simple turn of phrase.

He did not however, admire my scent. That was the compliment that eluded me, the one he showered on Julia, Cher, Isabella and countless other exquisite, successful women.

I coveted their smell, their careers, their flat tummies.

Even Julia's only human; she must have days when she feels *less than*. On one of those days, if you gave us each a scene of Chekhov, I think I could take her. There's just the little matter of her gorgeous legs, the Oscar, and that damn twenty million-dollar smile.

Hooked on a bad feeling

Not unlike Julia, I started out as a promising, young actress. I began doing school and community theatre as a kid in the Bronx. Although not always getting the part I sought, I was usually pretty lucky.

For a drama education major at the University of Arizona, freshman and sophomore year were pretty much torture. Not part of the *in* crowd, I was left un-cast in all the major productions. The rejection was palpable. Final auditions usually came down to popular-pretty-waspy girl and me. No matter how strong my reading, popular-pretty-waspy girl got the part.

Junior year things drastically improved when Doug Fusco, a young, new professor, cast me as Candy Star in the main stage production of *One Flew Over the Cuckoo's Nest*. He was the first person at the U of A to believe in me. It was a huge turning point after a long period of insecurity, aided by my then boyfriend, who tolerated my acting aspirations as he did a trip to the dentist.

An eccentric local director, who'd started his own small theatre company, saw the play and began chatting me up. Bruno was an outcast, with a reputation for chasing and casting young, vulnerable actresses who weren't very talented. He was sort of the Brian DePalma of Tucson. Although only 25, he looked about 50. It seemed creepily inappropriate for him to be running after young co-eds.

At the start of senior year, he seemed to be following me everywhere.

"Hey, Andi," he called after me, one September afternoon, as I tried to ditch him in the Student Union. Bruno didn't even go to the University of Arizona; he took some classes at the local community college. *Who needed to be seen with him?*

Continuing on my way, with pretended purpose, I felt a sudden, gentle, yank on my waist length hair. "Andi, I wanted to talk to you about starring in my next production." Raunchy reputation or not, those were delicious words for a starving young actress.

"Really. What play're you doing?"

"Terrance McNally's *Bad Habits,*" he said, with a smile.

I knew the play well—two hysterical one acts, sandwiched together.

"What part do you see me as?" I asked, afraid to hope.

"April Pitt in the first act and Nurse Benson in the second."

The leads. Not the female leads. The leads. Period. It'd been a long time since I'd had one of those, let alone two.

With the script in hand, he invited me to do a scene with him on the spot. After reading aloud almost the entire play, he said, "It's yours."

Whatever momentary concern I might have had about Bruno's motives was immediately dispelled.

"I'm looking to build an ensemble and I think I just found my core. Interested?" Sensing my trepidation, he added, "No monkey business. Promise."

Only the week before, I'd been dumped by my boyfriend and lost yet another role to one of the drama department's popular-pretty-waspy girls.

"I'm in."

I owe Bruno a lot. At the height of my insecurity, he bolstered my confidence.

Not only did he provide my first paycheck as an actress, he also encouraged me to help choose the leading man. I hoped whoever played Roy would take my mind off my broken heart. It was the seventies, before AIDS, when sex *was* the date.

On the last day of auditions, depressed—desperately trying to figure out whom, out of the last four-dozen uninspiring hopefuls would be my leading man, in swaggered Frank. At first, all I could see were his cowboy boots and perfectly faded, snugly fit, Levi's. As he got directly under the stage lights, I audibly gasped as I beheld a magnificent specimen. Not breathing, not moving, I wondered if he was aware of how awestruck I felt. I know Bruno was. He was laughing as he introduced us. Frank had starred in one of Bruno's first productions and somehow had slipped Bruno's mind until they ran into each other, playing darts, at The Bum Steer Saloon, the night before.

Eventually inhaling, I allowed myself to shamelessly take him in, top to bottom. Thick, sandy hair—wild, but not too long—framed his chiseled face, which was sprinkled with freckles. The greenest, most intense eyes I'd ever seen were amusedly looking right through me. To say he was handsome would be a tremendous injustice. He was gorgeous. Tall, but not *too*, he stood about six feet. Trim, he had the body of a guy who worked it, without working out.

When he spoke, I could have come right there. He had the deepest, most resonant, manly voice I'd ever heard. Could talent possibly come in that package?

Before he even began reading, Bruno crossed his arms, put his feet up and grinned. Within seconds, I knew why.

Frank instantly captured the character's swagger. Standing close under the lights, his emerald eyes twinkling, despite my outward calm, he knew, immediately, that he had me. Going back and forth, as if we'd been doing it forever, the scene was a fight between a husband and wife. Who knew it would foreshadow the next ten years of our lives?

He got the part.

We were April and Roy Pitt. The Pitts. And that's exactly what our life eventually became.

The first year was a whirlwind. Co-starring in six of Bruno's productions in a row, our photos appeared in local newspapers and magazines. One night, while out to dinner at a local restaurant, a couple of high school girls began giggling and staring at us. On our way out the door, they ran up behind us, paper and pen in hand. Our picture had just appeared on the cover of *Tucson Tonight*, but wanting our autograph probably had more to do with Frank's good looks than either of our talents. Regardless, my success, both onstage and in love, had my ex-boyfriend, an actor who wasn't acting, and who'd been dumped by his old married lady girlfriend, beside himself. Pity.

It didn't take long for our passion to turn on us. I was young, jealous and insecure. Frank was smart, controlling, drunk, abusive and opinionated—very opinionated. He worked me like nobody's business. So, of course, I married him.

At our engagement party, he got totally wasted and flirted with so many women that he spent the entire next day on the phone apologizing. I knew I should call the whole thing off, but as soon as my mother made that suggestion, I smoked a few joints and wed him out of spite. I showed her.

For the duration of our years together, I lived with a knot in my stomach the size of Bermuda. Pot paranoia didn't help. So unsure of what was real, I didn't trust my own judgment at all. I trusted him even less. In no time, he had me convinced I was stupid, petty and worthless. Eventually, I lived up to all his expectations.

The Café

I yearned for someone to gaze into my eyes and drink me in, instead of a case of beer.

At Frank's urging, after college, we left Tucson, making a brief stop in Colorado. Never intending to live in New York again, I was as angry with myself for agreeing to go—as I was with Frank for forcing my hand.

In my early twenties, I was unwilling to make the commitment to use my degree to teach drama. I wanted the opportunity to pursue my acting career and that meant finding work as a waitress.

I set my sights on The Café, one of New York's hippest hot spots. It was the late '70s and Mervin Oz, an enormous mountain of a man with an uncanny creative vision, had masterminded an amazing eclectic circus. It was the original meat market, New York's first true singles scene. Determined to get the gig, I did *The Secret*, when it was still a secret. Setting up an interview as soon as I returned to New York, there was one little problem. The only prior waitressing experiences I'd had were in an ice-cream parlor and a pub. Except for transporting maybe a half dozen cocktails at a time, I'd never carried a real tray in my life. I knew little of wine, beyond Sangria and Boone's Farm. Thanks to my mom, I had a fair knowledge of food.

To my great good fortune, Jan Holland, the snappy British manager who had a fabulous and filthy sense of humor, interviewed me. I was warned he would require me to explain the creation of a single dish (it was to be the deal maker, or breaker). To my sheer good luck he asked me to list the ingredients and preparation for Steak Tartare. I was weaned on the delicacy although, for my mother and me, it was basically the raw beef we devoured while she palm-formed hamburgers. But, she had treated me to PJ Clarke's a couple of times, where they prepared the dish tableside. I lustily recalled the fresh ground sirloin, capers, anchovies, egg yolks, Dijon, Worcestershire and Tabasco.

As serious as Jan was pretending to be, I gave him my most dazzling smile, trying to still my quivering hands. I think he knew how nervous I was, but he was very kind, or, maybe, he just wanted to have another girl around. The Café was a tough gig, long hours maneuvering through packed crowds, up and down stairs, carrying enormous trays loaded with silver-lidded, heavy china dishes. It was not for the weak, the faint hearted, or the inexperienced.

Primarily a boys club, the staff consisted mostly of aspiring actors and "lifers," gay men looking to make the most money in the least amount of hours, to leave them plenty of time for The Anvil, Fire Island and the Cape. Then there were the debonair foreign men of all nationalities, usually with families and without green cards; and lastly, two women. Me, being one—Sandra, the other.

Sandra was attractive, tough and looking for a husband. As I posed no threat, thanks to Frank, she tolerated my being added to the roster, even though I muscled in on some of her regulars. For that, she regarded me with a certain disdain.

I was terrified when I actually had to face lifting my first stainless steel nightmare. After confiding my secret to Joe, a sweet, vivacious aspiring opera star who was pretty new himself, he took me aside, gave me a few pointers and a demonstration. It wasn't long before I was sashaying down the stairs with my right arm completely extended to the sky, the tray perfectly balanced, maneuvering through the crowd by gently guiding people out of the way with my extended left hand, while shouting over the din, "coming through."

I loved the guys I worked with. We were family. And, being family there were also those I couldn't stand and vice versa. Sharing secrets, cigarettes, Caesar salads and sweat, work was actually fun. We dished and sampled the wares, from the finest ports and cigars to imported truffles. Many of the customers were disgracefully self-important and rude, but there were also the celebrities and the "hitters," and they were a constant. The Café was *the* place to see and be seen. Everyone who was anyone in the '70s to mid-'80s hung there. The energy was sizzling, especially after dark. From rock stars and comedians to movie stars, politicians and sports heroes—they all came and then they came back. For a stargazer like me, it was paradise.

I had the opportunity to serve and flirt with an amazing cast of characters on a regular basis. Tom Jones was very knowledgeable and appreciative of fine food and liquor. He was charming and an amazing tipper. Woody Allen came in two weeks after I'd paraded past him at a cattle call. This time he smiled at me with genuine interest. I'd never really cared for Robert Plant onstage, but up close and personal he was very impressive. I batted my eyes and sashayed suggestively all evening. Dustin Hoffman was adorable, talky, flirty fun. Bill Murray held court in the dining room and lived up to his funny boy status. George Carlin came in right after his heart trouble, alone, and was polite, warm and generous. James Woods was full of sex appeal and flirty confidence. Arnold Schwarzenegger enjoyed one of his first dates with Maria Shriver. Phil Simms came in at the height of his fame, surrounded by an enormous entourage. Warren Beatty checked out every woman in sight. Crosby, Stills and Nash rolled in at the top of their game—David more interested in trips to the limo than eating, Graham about as gracious as any human being I've ever had the pleasure to meet. The list goes on, and on and on. It was a gas.

As their waiters, we were in the power position. Any bad behavior could justify spitting in their food, or Visine-ing them—an old, horrible waiter trick, where you put a small dose of eye drops in a nasty customer's food or drink and guarantee them a very long and unpleasant night in the bathroom.

One night, while waiting at the service bar for a cocktail order, I noticed one of the bartenders stooped down close to the ground, with his back to the customers. As he turned around and stood up, I saw he was holding a full bottle of beer and zipping his fly. *WHAT?* I didn't find any of that funny and never engaged in such behavior, however, I knew a few co-workers who had not only done so, but also boasted of it. I knew, and so did a lot of the savvy customers. So for the most part, the celebs were on their best behavior: charming, friendly and accessible. Many of them were regulars who had their favorite table, and sometimes, if you were lucky enough, their favorite server. Being one of only two women, I got favored quite a bit, and got to know some of them pretty well—one, in particular.

TWO

HOPE

———— The Athlete ————

Scotty Fitzgerald was at the height of his game, both on and off the court, when I started at The Café in the late '70s. The top-ranked tennis player on the men's tour, he was number one in the world. Cocky did not even begin to describe him. A sometime fan, I usually found him to be unsportsmanlike and obnoxious.

Scotty came to The Café whenever he was in New York. Surrounded by a big group of guys, he was always loud and flirtatious. I was having none of it. I looked up to just about everyone with talent who had the balls and determination to make it. It was my quest, and anyone who had gotten there, had my admiration and respect. I'd never been a star-fucker. Anyone successful wasn't needy enough for me.

As the months passed, I began watching Scotty with increased interest. In spite of myself, as I got to know him, I was won over by his charms. I'd been with Frank for a few years and we were well into our decline.

At first I'd only think about Scotty when he was in town, or when I saw him on TV. I read the sports pages first in those days. I was Yankee baseball and Reggie Jackson crazy. Without warning, Scotty became my *raison d'etre*.

He soon met and minutes later married a beautiful woman with a somewhat checkered past. There were rumors she'd gotten in a family way, but I don't know if it was true or just jealous hearsay. Being married didn't stop Scotty from driving every woman in his path wild. He calmed down a lot when he became a husband, even more so when he had kids, but a flirt is a flirt is a flirt.

As the years passed, the smiles became more familiar and we'd exchange casual conversation. I'd congratulate him on his latest accomplishment and there were many of those. We were polite and respectful of his marriage and mine. As time marched on there would almost always be a touch of some kind—an accidental stroke of fingers while removing a menu, a playful push while rising from a chair, an unintentional brushing of bodies at the crowded exit.

For years I wondered if it was just my imagination, or if this was his flirt with every woman. I believed not. I was different. Yet doesn't every woman think that at the mercy of the truly charming? I wanted to believe it was real; that after all those years, and all those smiles, we were sharing a fantasy. I needed a fantasy. Frank and I were in hell, fighting every moment. We hadn't touched, kissed, or even been civil to each other in longer than I could remember.

Scotty had a few lean years where the young up-and-comers were giving him a run for his money. Coupled with a series of injuries, he was hardly winning games, let alone championships. Yet his popularity soared. He'd mellowed with age. It agreed with him. Where he was once angry and opinionated, he was now funny and self-deprecating. No longer the bad boy, he was a class act. The beloved.

It had been years since Scotty had won the US Open that he'd once owned. He hadn't even come close. After many disappointments, a miracle happened. He was back in it. After each round victory, he'd come to The Café. We'd cheer him. He'd give me a wink. Before I knew it, he was back on center stage in the finals.

Working that night, I was glued to the bar TV. We all were. After an incredible match, the unthinkable happened—Scotty regained the title. The old man ruled once more. Forever ingrained in fans' minds—and on front pages everywhere—was the dramatic image of Scotty falling to his knees, fists raised in victory, his head turned to the heavens in gratitude.

Less than an hour later, his entourage entered. There were about eight of them, including his wife, Cathy, who was at his side. I was thrilled to be working "Star Central" that night.

As I delivered his appetizer, I leaned in slightly, looked directly into Cathy's eyes and said "I'm so happy for you." She smiled warmly. (I'd been around her plenty over the years and tenderness was not something she displayed publicly, but that night was different.) I stole a quick look at Scotty. He smiled slyly, shooting me a knowing "thanks." From my station I nervously watched him for hours, as all who passed extended their congratulations. Everyone at The Café loved Scotty. He was our boy.

When it was time to call it a night, his party, one by one, took their leave until it was just Scotty and his friend Wally picking up the rear. Cathy was already outside and out of sight. Standing at the hosts' podium at the front of the restaurant, I was hoping to say goodbye, when, without warning, Scotty leaned in and planted a big, juicy, open-mouthed kiss right on my shocked, receptive lips. IN FRONT OF EVERYONE. My knees buckled.

The topper was that, unbeknownst to me, there were photographers everywhere and one of them had captured the moment. The kiss was years in the waiting. I HAD TO HAVE THAT PICTURE.

It took me a few hours to come out of my kiss-induced stupor and track down the *Daily News* shutterbug.

"Hi, I'm Andi Stone. I work at The Café…"

Before I could get the sentence out, he jumped in, "I was expecting your call."

He delivered the print to me a few days later.

"Thank you," I said, blushing, "what can I give you…"

"Your joy."

The next year, Scotty won the US Open again, against even greater odds, and returned to The Café to celebrate. I knew he'd come, win or lose, and brought the picture with me. As he was leaving (again alone, bringing up the rear…had he planned it this way?) I offered him the photo.

Grabbing my pen, he wrote what I thought was an autograph, smiled, and left. As he was turning the corner I looked down and saw, "Let's do it again!" I dropped to my knees in dramatic imitation of him and screamed to the heavens…"Take me now Lord, I'm ready." That feeling is something that, even now, gives me the same flood of excitement it did then.

Sometime later, maybe a year or more, Scotty came in with Wally. Wally was always with Scotty when he came to The Café. Come to think of it, he seemed to be in the stands whenever Scotty played in New York. I knew that because I never missed an opportunity to watch him on TV. With ESPN and the increasing popularity of the sport (in large part thanks to Scotty), there was televised coverage almost constantly. I was now undeniably, absolutely obsessed. I ached for him to play locally, searching his schedule daily. The knots in my stomach when I saw an impending extensive road trip made me physically ill. But, the butterflies of excitement when we were next on his agenda forgave all. Cathy wasn't with him on this trip and, now that his children were getting older, that was more common than not.

I wasn't waiting on him on this particular night. He was holding court at table 100—*the* table at The Café. I found an excuse—or twenty, to pass by. Each time I'd steal a glance and find him staring at me unabashedly.

"Hey there," he said finally, as I sauntered by with a tray of cocktails. I blushed.

Returning up the stairs, he called out after me, "Did you hear about the Polish guy who won a gold medal and had it bronzed?"

I let go a laugh, more from the cuteness of his wanting to please me than the actual joke.

On my next pass he said, "Would you like to join us?"

Would I like to join you?

As far as I knew, this was a first.

I raced to Jan Holland, the manager.

"Scotty wants me to join him—to sit and have dinner with him!" I spat out, frantically. "What should I say?"

"Say yes, immediately! Turn over your tables and do your duty!" He added, with a wink.

"Yes, sir!" I said, giving him a soldier's salute, my guts bursting.

Racing up the stairs to the bathroom, I smoked a quick cigarette to calm my nerves. Ripping off my apron, I cursed myself for not wearing civvies to work. Freshening my make-up (in those days serious business–it was the '80s), I spritzed on a ton of perfume, trying to cover the odor of searing food that was stuck to my clothes and pores. Tearing ass downstairs, trying to appear calm, my mind and heart were racing.

In all the years we'd known each other, we'd never spoken more than a few words. Here we were chatting, laughing and flirting as if we'd just met. (All under the amusedly watchful eye of our chaperone, Wally. We were married after all, and not to each other.) It was the first time we were both sitting and together—it was thrilling.

Telling jokes and being charming, he was absolutely everything I'd hoped for and more—smart, funny and sharp. I was really in trouble now.

After the meal (food…there was food? Who cared about food?), I asked, "Mind if I smoke?" (In the olden days, there were typewriters instead of computers—and ashtrays on restaurant tables.)

"Yes," he said.

Shocked and embarrassed, I realized I probably reeked of cigarettes.

Andy Kaufman had just died of lung cancer. He'd never even smoked. Recounting Scotty's disdain, the next morning I took my butts and flushed them down the toilet. Funny how years of parental begging were meaningless, yet momentary scorn from the target of my lustful desire undid years of bad behavior. If only I could've applied that same discipline to pot, junk food, and laziness. But, it wasn't a question of strength of character; Lord knows I didn't have any of that. Scotty simply didn't want me to smoke, and that was reason enough for me.

Snapping me out of my nicotine jones, Scotty said, "We'll take you home. I want to get some fresh air. Mind if we walk part of the way?"

Mind? You mean spend more time with you?

He was walking serpentine. I lived a good three miles away. Even having spent a good part of the night running up and down stairs, hoisting heavy trays, I could've walked all night, and still have begged for more.

After a mile or so, Scotty hailed a cab. First Wally slid in, then Scotty on the bump, and then me. Wally was a big guy. We were pretty squished back there. I could feel the entire side of Scotty's body pressing against mine. We were both too aware of any possible impropriety to actually touch on purpose, but you could have lit the city of New York with the electricity we were generating.

As the cab pulled up to my building, I freaked. What the fuck should I do?

Scotty looked at me with apology, and said, "Goodnight, Andi."

It wasn't a kiss, but, at that moment, I knew he wanted it just as much as I did. He's a guy—maybe, more.

I didn't imagine that I was as important to Scotty as he was to me. But it was easy to delude myself. In all the years since he'd been married, I'd never seen him flirt with anyone but me. I guess there could've been a waitress like me in every city. I'd certainly misread signals before.

The next day, basking in the glow of the night's memory, I was reading Page Six. A blind item sneaked up and then screamed at me. "There's trouble in paradise in a certain sports hero's marriage. A trial separation has begun."

Could Scotty be the one they were talking about? Was that why he risked inviting me to join him at the highly visible Table 100, flirting with me in the presence of everyone, our every move watched?

It had to be him. How else could he have left the restaurant with me for all to see without worry of repercussions?

It was too much to hope for. Hope for? Was I so selfish to be wishing for the end of his marriage? Shamefully, yes, I was. And what about my marriage? It seemed as if daily, Frank and I barely escaped being the brutal double homicide story on the cover of the *New York Post*.

In my wildest, craziest fantasy I envisioned riding off into the proverbial sunset with Scotty.

Suddenly panicked, I realized I wasn't scheduled to work for the next three days. Whenever he was in town, Scotty came in every night. He was now free and I wouldn't be there. As if on cue, my pal Michael, working that night called me on his break.

"Scotty's here. He's looking for you, girl."

"Shit!"

I paced around my apartment trying to figure out what the hell to do. Frank was home and I couldn't think of one good reason, or a bad one, to get all decked out and leave.

"What's up with you, Andi?"

"Nothing, dammit!" I snapped at Frank, like a sea turtle in heat.

About an hour later, Michael called me back.

"Scotty sat on table 110 with his friend. He didn't look happy. That new slut, Stephanie, was waiting on him. Whoring it up like crazy. She ended up leaving with him, telling everyone who'd listen that Scotty was taking her to Xenon. But I gotta tell you, he did NOT look happy. I'm sorry, doll."

"After all the time I've invested in him, it just isn't fair."

Scotty left town the following day.

The slut gloated for weeks.

I was thinking about him way too much, but it was saving my life. It gave me something to hope for.

Comedy 101

When I moved back to New York after college in '78, my acting career was then limited to a series of NYU undergraduate films, with budgets smaller than a week's waitressing wage. Non-union, I couldn't even audition for legitimate roles. Thanks to my friend Kenny, an aspiring location scout, in '83 and '84 I did a few taped pieces for *After Midnight Live*.

My first spot was with Sonny Gold, just prior to his becoming a comedy legend. He was working on a new character, Charlie Rapp—a failed, aging, insult comic. Hired as an extra, I was asked to provide my own wardrobe—show biz speak for, "you're not important enough for us to get you a costume." I spent days in the thrift shops looking for just the right dress and accessories. I was supposed to be a tacky New Jersey gal out for a big night on the town. I teased my hair and packed on the make-up, I found the perfect black velvet dress with rhinestone accoutrements and some really tacky glass jewelry. In a room filled with extras—I was determined to be noticed.

I loved Sonny—was a really big fan (a continuing theme with me).

On the set, after watching him work the room, I made my move.

"You look faaabulous!" I said, eyes twinkling, legs shaking. Like I was the first one to ever use that. But, it worked. He turned to me, winked, and the next thing I knew I was sitting in the front row and he was talking to me throughout the shoot. After about sixteen hours he suggested a new bit of business and said, "Let's use the chick in velvet."

It took a few seconds for my brain to compute. My SAG card! I'd finally be able to audition for actual roles in films and television, not just show up for open cattle calls. At the time, I dreamt of being Debra Winger, doing movies like *Urban Cowboy, An Officer and a Gentleman* and *Terms of Endearment*—plenty of emoting and lots of romance.

All I had to do was a featured bit of business, or say at least five lines on camera and I was guaranteed my union card—carte blanche to superstardom. This was to be, at last, my all access pass to John Travolta, Richard Gere and John Lithgow. John Lithgow?

Having attended college in Tucson, where just about every Western movie and television show was made in those days, I'd certainly had my opportunity. While the rest of my classmates were wisely doing small parts in films and getting their SAG cards the easy way, I was too high falutin', doing theatre. I couldn't do both?

Sonny was giving me a second chance. Making it up as he went along, he blindfolded me, spun me around, while flirting and cracking wise. Even though the laugh was at my expense, I was loving it. He gave me about twenty seconds of airtime on the most talked about show on television.

We took photos together during the break and I even got comfortable enough to make him laugh a few times. It was one for the record books.

The next morning, I called everyone I knew.

That Saturday night, after our weekly poker game, Frank, me, and a handful of our closest friends sat around, eating, drinking, smoking weed and laughing—awaiting my big moment. Following a commercial, about fifteen minutes into the show, there was Sonny and then, quick—there I was! We all screamed.

And then, in a flash, I was gone.

As luck would have it, the only one who got to see my bit was the editor with the scissors, and the janitor sweeping me off the floor.

"What the fuck, Andi? Where'd you go?"

"To the moon, Frank" I replied, garnering a laugh, as I'd hoped. What I really wanted was to die.

The phone started ringing off the hook.

"Andi, what happened??"

"Where the hell were you? I stayed up till midnight for nothing."

"I thought you said you did a bit with Sonny Gold."

Not only did I have to handle my own pain and disappointment, I also had to explain it to my mother, my father, my brother and just about everyone in my phone book.

"That's show biz."

"Yeah, I stayed up, too."

"I did do a bit with Sonny. I guess they cut it. Maybe I wasn't in the budget."

Over and over I answered the same questions, while my stomach churned, my heart tore in two, and my ego tried to buy into the witness protection program.

As painful as it was to explain the cutting room to everyone, that time with Sonny was worth it all. The exhilaration of him picking me in that room full of actors (extras), and the week spent anticipating my debut, were brilliant.

When I got the photos developed, there we were, cozy as can be, snuggling in character.

I sent "Charlie Rapp" a copy of it, with a note of thanks, in care of Sonny. I got one back from "Charlie" with the picture now signed. Twenty years later, Homer brought the photo into the Holloran green room and showed it to Sonny, who smiled, and reminisced about the day.

Even though my bit never made it to air and I didn't get my SAG card, he remembered. And, so did I.

I was invited to be an extra on *After Midnight Live* a couple of more times. Attentive and prepared, each time I got upgraded, but my bits ended up in the grinder. A lesson learned the hard way, if it's not in the original script, it usually doesn't make it to air. Each time I'd tell my family and friends (less so with every appearance, or, non-appearance, as it were), and the calls afterwards would be fewer and not quite as surprised. Except for my mother. We always ran the same script.

"What happened? I thought you said you were going to be on *After Midnight Live* tonight."

"I was supposed to be. I filmed it."

"I guess you just weren't good enough."

Fade to guts joining the footage on the cutting room floor.

A short time later, my dad, an entertainer who never reached the level of success he'd imagined for himself (maybe it's hereditary), took matters into his own hands, producing a series of local variety shows on Long Island. Frank and I performed a vignette from Neil Simon's *The Good Doctor*. Still waitressing, it was a way to stay in the biz, between courses.

At one of my dad's shows, up and coming comic, Rick Weston, was the featured comedian. We got there just as he was ending his set, but rushing for our scene, I didn't get to meet him. About a week later, I got a call from my father.

"Guess what?" he asked, giddy with joy.

"What dad?" I responded happily, anticipating good news.

"Roxlyn and I are going to be in Rick Weston's independent feature film."

My dad had never done a film. He'd never even used the word "film." He was a singer, not an actor. His wife, Roxlyn, was a pen and ink artist. To my knowledge, she'd never acted a day in her life—unless you consider false sincerity acting.

"Is Rick still casting?"

Caught off guard, my dad, stammered, "Um, I think casting's over."

"Please call him and ask."

I couldn't fathom why he hadn't recommended me, his struggling actress daughter. I was hurt and confused.

I bugged him about it for days and he kept changing the subject. My father had always seemed proud of my work. My recent appearances on *After Midnight Live*, as miniscule and insignificant as they ended up, still got me attention and, in their aftermath, sounded impressive. Maybe that was hard for him? All his years in show business had never afforded him national exposure. Either consciously or subconsciously, he didn't want me involved because he wasn't making the call. I finally freaked out and demanded an explanation.

"Dad, why aren't you calling Rick?"

"I will," he said.

"So you've been saying." I couldn't mask my hurt.

He called the next day.

"There are only bit parts left, but Rick will see you for one of them tomorrow."

See me? Not read me? Shit. What else was new? I was the queen of "bits."

It turned out Rick was in an improv group with Steve Sullivan. They'd written the screenplay as a vehicle for themselves. Steve had been partners with Sonny Gold before he hit the big time. At the audition, we exchanged Sonny stories—mine, minus the little detail of the cutting room floor. The combination of my *After Midnight Live* spots, the photo of Sonny and me (always in my wallet), my drama degree and acting resume, gave me a certain cred. A little fudge goes a long way.

"Sorry we found you so late in the game," Rick said, appearing sincere.

Steve, head down, added, "We only have a really minor role left to cast. It's similar to Suzanne Somers' part in *American Graffiti*, only smaller."

That didn't sound so terrible. She was really memorable in it.

"How much smaller?"

"A lot. And no lines." He instinctively ducked when he said it.

They had me read some dialogue, I guess to be polite.

"During the opening scene of the movie, you drive up alongside me, wink, smile, wave—blow a kiss and tear ass out of there. Intent on following you, I gun my engine and stall. Short, cute, over."

There were a couple of minor complications.

While I was waitressing at The Café one night, Dave Righetti stopped in shortly after pitching his no-hitter. I was a hardcore fan to begin with, and he was awfully cute. I went up to talk to him and showed off my Yankees baseball/Dave Righetti knowledge.

Wanting to be nice, I guess, he said, "You look like Stevie Nicks." I was flattered, even though I knew it was bullshit.

Racing to the ladies room to check my hair and make-up—vital for a good flirt—I was so intent on checking myself in the mirror that I ran smack into the door of the bathroom stall. For years I maintained that someone had opened the door into me, too vain and embarrassed to admit I was shamelessly eyeing my reflection, and broke my own fucking nose. I wasn't even stoned. At that moment.

It bled like hell—the bridge bone protruding at an unimaginable angle. I'd always wanted a nose job. Maybe it was a blessing?

I had to be awake for the surgery, so I could move my eyes and face, to ensure that when they re-broke my nose, they could reset it properly. Re-broke? Reset?

I was sedated, almost to the land of oblivion. They explained that they were going to strap me down, just in case—in case *what?*

As Dr. Moss lifted the hammer towards the heavens (Yes, a hammer—a big, steel hammer. I could've built a house with that sucker and a bucket of nails.) he said, "You might feel a little pressure, but no actual pain."

CRACK!

A little pressure? That'd be like the cops telling Rodney King he might "feel a little tap."

Like Malcolm McDowell in *A Clockwork Orange*, I was forced to watch the horror—the hammer coming down, again and again and again, unable to look away, or stop it. But he only had to look. I had to feel. Smack! Whack! Crack! No amount of sedation could ease the discomfort—or the pain. Yes, there was pain, Dr. Moss, you fucking liar.

Three weeks later, I was on the set of my first feature film, with a swollen nose, a driving phobia and a role with no lines. I had to maneuver someone's brand new Porsche and burn rubber. It took three dozen takes. Damned to let them know my fear, I sucked it up and put the pedal to the metal. It was probably some of the best acting I've ever done.

I knew almost nothing about the rest of the movie when I went to the premiere. Only present for the filming of my scene, I'd never read the whole script.

Frank and I smoked a doobie in the parking lot, ready to settle in for some laughs. For the first ten minutes (in which, thankfully, my part was contained), there was hearty laughter. For the next hour and a half, dead silence filled the theatre, with the exception of a short scene containing the feature film debut of up-and-coming, soon to be very famous shock-jock, Harold Burns. His was the only other scene in the movie to get laughs, and it was a comedy. Not a good sign. The entire cast and crew with their friends and family were in the house and even they weren't laughing. My dad and Roxlyn's scene, as a couple of patrons in a restaurant was lengthy, and they had lines, although, I think everyone wished they hadn't.

The movie opened and closed in a week.

I don't know what hurt more, the fact that once again no one would see my work (blowhard narcissist), or that my father had sabotaged my shot at a bigger role. The pain of that reality never really left. There's been an acceptance in the years since, but the shift it caused could never be completely undone. My perfect father was, alas, human. Who needed to know that?

But I was in a movie and, lame though it was, after it wrapped, Rick invited me to join his improv company.

The Giggle Group was a well-established, popular fixture on the Long Island comedy circuit. Alumni included Wayne Smith, before he became the first African American to command ten million dollars a picture, and Carrie Burns, when being a talk show goddess was only a fantasy she shared with her hairbrush.

It was a well-oiled machine; at least it was until I got there. I'd never done comedic improv except as an exercise in acting class. Completely unprepared for the slick professionalism the troupe displayed, it took a few weeks for me to realize that when they said improv, they meant the audience had never experienced it before, because Lord knows, there was absolutely nothing spontaneous happening on that stage. The order changed and whose mouth the punch line came from varied, but the jokes and the bits of business, were about as fresh as a corpse's breath.

I told Rick at the top I was completely out of my depth.

"I'm an actress. I've done my share of comedies, but I've always had the safety of the playwright's words."

"Don't worry. We'll guide you to the funny."

What I didn't know at the time was they were all stand-up comics, making their living doing sets on the weekends--all, except me.

There was Rick, whose star was quickly rising; Steve, no youngster, who still lived at home and had been around forever, his only claim to fame being that he used to be partners with Sonny; Bobby, a sweet upstart who worshipped Rick and Steve; and Loretta, a rubber faced, sarcastic, funny, aggressive, ambitious Gemini. They welcomed me with hostility and disdain. In rehearsal, they'd work with me and offer encouragement— to an extent. As soon as the audience arrived, all bets were off; it was them against me. They were bored. I gave them new purpose. I could actually see the joy on their faces when they'd refuse to let me in and ignore me onstage. It was stunning.

Eventually I made a little headway. I started to figure out the patterns and where the piece was heading. Sometimes I could even get the punch line out first, but that never felt right. Until the end, I sincerely tried to improv, to think on my feet. I was, therefore, not always very funny. Frankly, I was so uncomfortable that I was rarely funny. I didn't know what the hell I was doing and instead of mentoring me, they were torturing me publicly and enjoying it. Basically, I sucked, but I did have my moments. When I did, Loretta would do everything in her power to make me look stupid. To her, I was a thin, pretty, dumb blond. Everything's relative.

I've never been comfortable with my weight. Even as a kid, I was self-conscious about my thighs. I've got perpetual dark circles under my eyes that only the thickest of cover-up conceals; my teeth are imperfect and far from "movie star white." I hate seeing so many celebrities with the same bright, white, perfect chiclets. And yet, when I see a "Gary Sinise," the first thing I think is, "Why doesn't he fix his teeth?" And then when he does, it's too much. All I can think is, "Bring back the old Gary." Yet, I still covet my own perfect teeth.

What I do have is intense brown eyes and a dimple in my left cheek. My smile is large and honest, no Julia or anything, but it serves me, and my hair is funky and sort of cool.

I was far from perfect, but Loretta was soft and fleshy—sort of Ruth Buzzi-ish, and that was exactly the point. She took what she had and made the most of it. She looked kind of funny and she was funny. She was very funny. Unfortunately, that gave her little joy. She wanted pretty—at that time anyway.

In spite of herself, we became friends—sort of. We could have a good time off stage, away from the guys. She even recommended me for a comedic/music video her boyfriend was producing. We had a ball the day we shot it. But once we hit the stage at The Comedy Shack, all bets were off. Her teeth were bared and I was usually left the brunt of a joke, pretending to be a good sport—until one fateful Thursday.

For some reason I was feeling particularly brave that day. I'd had a few good laughs earlier and I actually had some confidence up there. The guys were picking me more than usual to join them in various sketches. At one point, midway through the show, it was Loretta and me, sisters for this one. As usual, I was the dumb one and she was the funny one. Only this time, when she started giving me shit, I gave it right back.

"Come on, *stupid*," Loretta sneered.

Without thinking, I responded coolly, "Give me a second, slut."

The audience cheered. Loretta started crying. Thinking her tears were part of the act, they cheered more.

She could dish it out, but she sure couldn't take it. She'd done so much worse to me, so many times; I'd fought back tears almost weekly. Every Thursday, I forced myself to put my make-up on, get all dressed up and take the Long Island Railroad out to The Comedy Shack, knowing I was walking into the lion's den and would surely leave mauled. I forced myself to go back, week after week, month after month.

The next night, during my regular, weekly poker game, in the middle of a hand of Fuck Your Buddy, I got a call from Rick.

"Um... hey Andi. We're um, um, making some changes and um, we won't be able to use you any more. Sorry."

Sorry? I think he was. Rick was actually an okay guy. During the shows he really wasn't any kinder than the rest of them, but offstage, he was sort of sweet and respectful. I think he genuinely felt bad.

I hold no ill will towards him. He opened a door for me that I'd probably never have gone through without his invitation. In time, I forgave them all. Not that they cared, but I needed to do it for me, to move on. They were probably just bored, having done the same show for so many years. New blood meant new opportunities for fun and torture.

I decided I had to learn to defend myself. Seasoned at dealing with hecklers and thinking in the moment, they'd each developed their comedic voice and could rely on that. I wanted what they had—a stand-up career.

Frank didn't drink everyday, or even every week, but whenever he did take a swig, he took at least five hundred and fifty of them. Fights, cops and "morning after" apologies were the norm. Soon after my Comedy Shack debacle, which went pretty much unnoticed around the old homestead, after nine years together (eight and a half of them, miserable) we hit a new low.

Late one April night, while he was frantically cooking up a huge batch of Wild Card Chili, Frank downed a couple cases of beer. He looked like Dr. Jekyll madly morphing into Mr. Hyde. Once the cooking was done, he got kind of bored and then grew agitated. Putting on his jacket, he headed towards the door.

"Where're ya going? " I asked, wanting to know, and sort of terrified to hear the answer.

"I'm gonna get those bums."

"What're you talking about?"

"Those squatters across the street. I'll show 'em."

Before I could say another word, he was off in frenzy, slamming the door behind him.

I was paralyzed in bed, imagining the worst.

Or so I thought.

Moments later, he stormed back in.

"I hosed those fuckers down," Frank said, with self-satisfied smugness. "Bet they'll be looking for a new home, now."

His eyes were as wild as his unkempt hair—his lips curled, in a sort of crazy, sardonic grin.

He was scary—really scary.

He left in a huff, his bender ending a short time later with him holed up in his office throwing a chair out of his twentieth story window. I only know that because he called me moments after he pitched it, at about 3:30 a.m. The cops were beating on his door and he wasn't going to let them in. He was yelling, crying—scaring the shit out of me. Neither one of us knew what the hell to do.

Somehow, the police and I talked him into opening his door. And then they arrested him.

I had to go down to the station, but I sure as hell didn't want to. All I wanted was to smoke a joint, pull the covers over my head and make it all go away. But I couldn't. I called Bean, my best friend since college. He picked me up and together we headed to the police station.

Frank was pacing the small holding cell, looking like a caged lion—wild, untamed and dangerous. Still drunk, he wasn't making any sense, but he wouldn't—couldn't—shut the fuck up.

"Those bastards. Rent. They have to PAY. Tell them to stop BANGING, YOU WHORE!"

His bullshit was deafening. I had to get out of there.

Thankfully, the police decided to hold him until he slept it off. I was forced to leave him there. Thank God.

The following afternoon, he called, and asked me to come get him. There was no remorse in his voice. He was angry with me for leaving him there. Of course, it was all my fault. What power men have given me! The things I've been responsible for driving them to do. I bet Napoleon blamed Josephine, Nixon blamed Pat and Clinton blames Hillary.

No doubt, I did plenty to contribute to that night. Love-starved, frustrated and frightened, I had no idea how to get out of that horrific marriage. I stayed, years too long, and dealt Frank my own brand of torture. I was a cold, critical, castrating bitch.

Lord knows, my mom did her share over the years—working her magic on Frank. I'd learned from the best. Nobody could find a flaw like old Cookie, and once she did, she'd chew on it until it was all bloody, swollen and raw.

She questioned Frank incessantly about every detail of his business and personal life, making it clear, with her not-so-subtle sarcasm, that he was doing everything wrong. He defended himself amusedly to her face, and cursed her bitterly behind her back.

She questioned—I nagged. We were a one-two-tag-team, taking him down.

Frank despised these two opinionated Jewish women who were trying to control his life. I'll give him that. He didn't really stand a chance.

I stayed with Frank for months after the chili hose down, but on that April morning, I ended it in my head. It took some time for me to actually move on it. It also took Eddie.

—— Let's have another one, just like the other one ——

Guy was a diminutive, macho, gay Frenchman who ruled the roost at The Café. He charmed the ladies, as I attempted to do the same with the men. One regular customer tipped $100 no matter what he ate or how much he spent. We didn't know what he did for a living, but there was a general assumption that he was "connected." He liked the status quo, so he'd stick with the same waiter for a long time until someone else wooed him away. And, everyone was always trying. I worked on him for quite a while before I won him over. That probably had a lot to do with Guy choosing me to be his partner.

Upon arrival at The Café, we ate the "familia," usually some gloppy concoction of leftovers. It was the perfect incentive to sell the daily special—sautéed sweetbreads, grilled octopus salad, salmon en croute... Whoever sold the most got to eat it for the post shift meal. Guy and I almost always won. It was our mission, both to feed our bellies and our egos.

The night shift began at five. It was slow then, which left plenty of time to gossip, smoke cigarettes and flirt. When six o'clock rolled around, so did the customers; by seven, we were in perpetual motion until around eleven. The only thing we paused for was a drag on a fag, a quick toot in the loo and a bite of whatever we could sneak.

As the years wore on, we became more brazen. The drugs were everywhere and so was the booze. It started at the top with Jan Holland, the manager. He'd enjoy a glass of pricey vintage somewhere around 8:00 and continue throughout the evening. By closing, you could hear him yelling "wanker," from across the street.

Once the liquor started flowing, we druggies made our way to the bathroom for blow—eventually, even daring to sneak down to the electrical room for a few hits of smoke to take the edge off. I had Binaca, gum, Visine and an atomizer of cologne—I'm sure I fooled ~~no one~~ everyone. I was making lots of money for the house, providing way more than competent customer service. Did anyone really care if I had a little fun along the way?

The maître d' was a deadly handsome Iranian named Firouz, who controlled the floor. He begrudged Americans their excess and privileges, yet he was the most cunning, greedy, shamelessly materialistic person I'd ever known. Firouz did not like Jews. And he hated me. He smiled and flirted, but the sneer was always right there. He despised my place in a man's world and was disgusted by my heritage.

Once I began partnering with Guy there was little Firouz could do. He respected Guy and feared him at the same time. Working with Guy was sort of like having the protection of Glenda, when the Wicked Witch of the West was after you. I think Guy was the only one in the world Firouz was actually afraid of. Ironic, that it was a little French fruit who could bring him to his knees.

Firouz was always looking to start some mischief. A slimy snake slithering around the place, he was everywhere. I could usually outmaneuver him, or at least talk my way out of trouble, but he was smart and determined to *get me*.

After seven years, I began captaining in the formal dining room upstairs… it meant no more trays or fighting with the food expeditor. Also recently promoted to waiter-trainer, I held classes once a week for those newly hired, to help them with strategy and finesse. I was now completely full of myself.

Continuing to wait tables in the informal café a couple of times a week, Guy understandably wanted a regular partner. When he found one, I teamed up with Eddie. Eddie was a young, half-bred Italian—the other half was French baguette. (Sorry.) Tall enough, he stood about 5'10". He was fair complected and had beautiful, gleaming, almost black hair that he was constantly swooping out of his impish brown eyes. He had a strong, expressive nose—with a well placed bump—full sensuous lips and the sexiest smirk I'd ever seen. Years later I couldn't look at Noah Wyle without thinking that if he were part Italian and a whole lot cockier, they could've been brothers.

Eddie had been working at The Café for months when Frank's furniture started flying on Broadway and Lafayette. Fresh out of college and new to the city, he was young, cute, funny and extremely attentive. I advised him on restaurants, stores and women. He fed my starving ego, flattering me constantly—respectfully so. It wasn't long before our relationship blossomed into full out lust and denial.

Usually, we'd all go next door to Costello's for a few cocktails, some laughs and a dance or two when we finished our shift. Home was unbearable, so I rarely left the bar before closing. Thankfully, Frank was usually passed out by then. Things had gone from bad to worse since his arrest. In an all-out depression, he rarely got up before noon. He forwarded the calls from his small business to our apartment, only leaving the house when he absolutely had to. We were fighting all the time; I hated his anger, his drinking and his refusal to get the fuck out of bed.

Eddie had taken to making me compilation tapes of music he wanted to turn me on to, and turn me on, he did. Fervent urgings of love and need from Elvis Costello, The Police, Graham Parker and Chrissie Hynde—

each tape more intense than the next. I took my Walkman everywhere, even wore it to bed, convinced that Eddie was speaking to me through those songs. I began to dream of him. I worked hard to play it cool and not show it, but I was flirting more and more, praying he would make a move.

One night, when I got home from Costello's, Frank was sprawled out drunk on the couch, bruised and covered in blood. He'd gotten into a fight in some bar and could barely talk or move. Sick to my stomach I just wanted to run. Instead, I crawled into bed, pulled on my headphones and as Sting crooned, "I burn for you..." I heatedly contemplated my options.

At work the next night, unable to get Eddie, who was off, out of my mind, I raced down to the pay phone at my first opportunity (before Firouz could notice), and dialed Eddie's number, hastily scrawled on my waiter's dupe pad the night before.

"Hey Eddie, it's Andi."

"Hi, what's up?" he asked cheerfully, sounding more than a little surprised to hear from me, but trying hard not to.

"Free to meet me for a drink later?"

"Great. Sure. Costello's?"

"Um...hm...how 'bout someplace... else?"

I guess he got the idea, "East 51st and 2nd, middle of the block. It's an old dive where only the locals hang out. By the time you get there it'll be us and three old drunks."

He did get it.

I could think of nothing else, except what I knew I was about to do to Eddie, and Frank. Torn between horrific guilt and long suppressed need, the latter won.

A couple of hours later, when I entered the bar, there, down at the far end, sat Eddie. It was the first time I'd seen him out of his black and whites. Damn. He looked even better in blue jeans and a t-shirt.

"Hi Eddie. Thanks for meeting me." Fuck, I sounded like his math teacher.

"What'll you have?" he asked, absentmindedly rubbing his nose.

"I'll have a Jack and water, please." The situation definitely called for bourbon.

Repeating my order to the bartender, he lifted his bottle of Bud, signaling for another.

"Have you... um... been here long?" I stammered, trying to think of something—anything—to say.

"Nah, just an hour or two."

We laughed. Our eyes connected. Once they did, we couldn't unhook them. I'm pretty sure it was me who couldn't take it any longer and leaned in. As our lips met, I melted on the spot. His mouth was warm, his lips full, soft and sure. I hadn't been kissed like that in a long time—maybe ever. The months of flirting culminated in that moment.

Now that I'd gotten a taste, I couldn't stop. Wanting to be discreet, but completely unable to be—I didn't come up for air until the bartender gave us a "get a room" smirk. Noticing him staring at my left hand, I realized I'd neglected to remove my wedding band. There was no way that anyone suspected for one moment that Eddie and I were married—to each other. This was illicit; there was no doubt about it.

Disengaging long enough to pay the tab, we grabbed our coats and raced out the door. As soon as we hit the street, Eddie pulled me off a well-lit Second Avenue and into a darkened entryway on 51st Street. Leaning against the building, he pulled me close. Swimming in his kiss, it was one of those moments where I heard a soundtrack playing (Dylan's, *I Want You*) and every inch of me was awakened and on fire. We were one—moving in perfect synchronicity.

After what seemed like seconds, against my will, I forced myself to check my watch. It was close to 4:00. Once the bars closed I could no longer explain my absence.

"I have to go."

Sensing my urgency, Eddie reluctantly hailed a cab. Before I could utter the destination he was kissing me again—on my neck—and I just couldn't think, couldn't speak. How could anything feel that good?

The driver was getting impatient.

I managed to blurt out, "24th and 2nd," before Eddie's mouth was on mine—and I was lost. We couldn't merge deeply enough. We were trying to swallow each other— whole.

All too quickly, the cab stopped and was idling in front of my building. Pulling away, I saw that my doorman was about to look up from his newspaper. Trying to straighten up as best I could, I was sure he'd see me for the slut I was.

Making a quick plan with Eddie to continue first thing in the morning, I tore away, not daring to look back. Flying past José with a quick "hello" I raced to the elevator and out of sight. Taking a moment to compose myself, I couldn't stop touching my face, my mouth, my neck—feeling Eddie still there. I was swimming again, all alone in the hallway. As the elevator arrived, I forced myself to get in and get serious.

Panic set in. What if Frank was still up? Fumbling for my keys, I willed myself not to breathe. Making only the slightest motion and sound, I turned the key in the doorknob as slowly and deliberately as humanly possible. My eyes must have been shut in fear, for as I soundlessly slipped inside, I realized I was in total darkness. Quickly gulping for air, I gingerly removed my coat, slipping into the bathroom to wash the lingering remains of Eddie off my skin. As I splashed the soapy water over my face, I could feel his breath on my cheek.

Starting to swim again, I had to force myself to finish the task at hand. I scrubbed my body furiously, anxiously trying to remove passion's scent. I needn't have been so thorough. As I exited the bathroom, I heard the familiar sound of Frank, sleeping. That deep sleep sound he made when he'd consumed a case or two of beer.

Slipping into bed, I had the Walkman clutched near, headphones on, volume set to "don't wake the husband." As The Pretenders "I Go To Sleep" ran through my ears, I could still feel Eddie all over me.

While willing the sun to come up, I must have drifted off, because the next thing I knew, Frank was closing the door behind him. It was Thursday, my day off, a day when Frank always, somehow, went in to work. Just prior to the weekend, he was busy and he had to go to his office.

I raced out of bed, made a quick cup of coffee, opened the door three times to make sure the coast was clear and dialed Eddie. He lived just over the bridge in Brooklyn Heights. Giving me careful directions, he told me exactly what to tell the cabby.

I still hadn't decided how far I would go. Ideally, I imagined us just kissing and not really cheating. If only I'd had Clinton's definition of sex back then. Calling my friend Marcy, I asked her advice. Totally encouraging me, I got the feeling she was vicariously experiencing the salacious nature of the proposition, not knowing she had recently begun a fling of her own and wanted company in the Cheating Wives Club.

A nervous wreck, I shaved off a layer or two of leg skin. I lotioned my body from head to toe. I perfumed every possible erogenous zone. My skin, flushed with anticipation and raw from the make-out session the night before, made blush unnecessary. I could barely keep my hands steady and had to redo my eyeliner three times. After trying on everything in my closet, I finally settled on a snug white Lycra top (to make certain objects appear larger than they really were) and black jeans (to make others appear smaller).

I snuck out the door half anticipating Frank to be out there with a great big "A-HA!" Walking about three blocks east to get a cab, I was nervous as hell... about *what* exactly? That someone would say they saw me get into a cab, like I did almost every day of my life at that time? I slinked down low in the back seat and whispered the address to the driver. As we headed south on the FDR Drive, I had this vision of being in an accident and having to explain to Frank what the hell I was doing in a cab going over the Brooklyn Bridge. I had called him just before I left the house, trying like hell to sound less incredibly guilty than I felt. Explaining my busy day ahead I told him I'd see him for dinner.

What a skank I was.

As the cab slowed in front of a nicer brownstone than I expected, I was a nervous, anxious mess. Tipping the driver way more than I normally would, I was trying to buy his silence (who the hell did I imagine he'd tell?). Looking both ways, I made a mad dash for the door, reading the address from my crumpled note for the fiftieth time, looking back at the numbers on the entrance to ensure that I wasn't about to make a fool of myself. Well, I was about to do that...

I had no sooner rung the bell than the door opened and there was Eddie, hair still wet from an obviously recent shower, in a blue cotton button-down shirt and jeans. Musky cologne filled the air. He nodded me in as I tentatively crossed the threshold. We stood there awkwardly for a moment, until he offered to take my coat and give me the tour.

The front door opened to a large living room with a very high ceiling. At the back end, there was a short staircase up and an even shorter one down.

Eddie told me that his roommate, Sal, had recently begun an affair with a married woman. He was presently at law school in his ethics class.

He invited me up to check out Sal's loft, which had a busy grad student look. As we began to descend the stairs I could wait no longer. Grabbing Eddie from behind, he turned, and without giving myself time to chicken, my mouth was on his. The urgency of the kiss was beyond any passion I knew I possessed. Enveloping him with my mouth, my arms and my body, we tumbled down the stairs. The next thing I knew we were entwined on the bare wood floor. Somehow, alone there in the safety of that place, my fears and inhibitions were completely out of mind. I was lost in him, living out my fantasy.

For years with Frank I would watch romantic comedies and try to imagine myself in the scene. Staring unabashedly at couples sexily making out on the street, in restaurants and at the airport, I would dream of being "her." With Eddie, I was that girl. "Diamonds, daisies, springtime..."

Suddenly, Eddie stopped. His eyes dove into mine and down to my solar plexus. He stood, helped me up, and guided me down the first flight of stairs. I caught sight of the small kitchen and bathroom and remember thinking it was amazingly clean for a couple of bachelors. Opening a dark wooden door, he led me down a few more steps to his lair.

His was a basement room, which ran the full length and width of the brownstone. There was '70s style, orange, thick, shag carpeting, even on the stairs. A small, full-sized bed, carefully made with brown and beige striped sheets and comforter, occupied one corner. An enormous desk, comprising a couple of file cabinets on either end and an old door slab on top, sat next to it. Stationed at the foot of the bed was a TV/VCR on a rolling stand, loaded with tapes. Against the far wall was an old couch and coffee table. A boom box sat next to a sound-mixing machine, perfect for making those home made compilations. There were books and tapes everywhere. Dark, save for a candle burning on the desk, I noticed there were no windows. It was the perfect hideaway for a nightcrawler and an adulterer. There would never be any way of knowing whether it was day or night, winter or summer.

We'd been disengaged a moment too long. The guilt began to overtake me. I didn't know what to do, what to feel, *where to sit*. I'd had too much time to think. Frank. How could I be considering this?

Coaxing me to sit down on the bed next to him, Eddie had his back up against the rear wall and his legs across the width of the mattress. Noticing a little door behind him, imagining what it was for distracted me just long enough so that when he grabbed my hand and gave a yank, I willingly followed. Now beside him, I was back under his spell. He kissed me so tenderly tears welled in my eyes. There was shame, need, hunger, desire, relief, joy and bliss. He was kissing my cheeks, my ears, my neck, melting my resolve.

When he wedged his hand between our bodies and moved towards my breast, I recoiled. How could I do this? We were certainly heading to the land of no return. Did I not know this was going to happen? Did I really think we were going to just make out? I was almost thirty; how could that kind of desire not lead to the ultimate intimacy?

I was so conflicted. Craving him, yet wanting to be good at the same time. While the left and right side of my brain were duking it out, Eddie swooped me up and turned me lengthwise on the bed. As I put my arms out in protest he clasped my hands in his, outstretching my arms above my head. I struggled—then surrendered—completely and with total abandon. If I was going to hell, I was going down in a blaze of horny.

We made love for hours. Hours. It was better than anything I'd ever fantasized. Eddie, although only in his mid-twenties, was an incredibly skilled lover. It didn't hurt that I hadn't been ravished in years. Years.

It was late afternoon. Realizing I had to high tail it to have time to shower and normalize before Frank got home, I rose to get dressed.

Eddie pulled me back down. "Lay with me for just a few more minutes."

Quickly complying, there was nothing I wanted more. Turning me away from him towards the wall, he spooned me from head to toe. Stroking my cheek, down my shoulder to my thigh, he gently eased me over onto my back, while lightly nibbling my cheek. Pulling out a joint, we lay there, inhaling deeply, exhaling slowly. Losing track of time, we re-engaged.

Glancing at the clock on his desk sometime later, I freaked. It was 4:30, I had less than sixty minutes to get home and it was rush hour. Thankfully, Eddie, realizing the severity of this, immediately called for a car. I was pacing, needing to *go*. Yet, as soon as the horn sounded I was filled with such loneliness at having to leave him. I forced myself out the door.

My skin was burnt red from the friction and my thighs ached. I was exhausted and exhilarated at the same time. We drove against the flow of traffic, which was mercifully light—three blocks from home, I jumped out and ran the rest of the way, not wanting to have to explain why I wasn't in a yellow cab, available everywhere in Manhattan, but rather a big red tank with a Brooklyn area code painted on the side.

Slowing as I got to my corner, I tried to casually stroll into the building. Smiling at Nick, the afternoon guy, I ran to the elevator to try to beat Frank home. As I approached the door of the apartment I listened for a second. When I didn't discern any sound, I quickly unlocked the door, immediately double locking it behind me. Throwing off my clothes, I pushed them low in the hamper, well under the mounds of more recent wear. Jumping in the shower, I scrubbed myself silly, quickly blow-dried my hair *and* the mirror to hide my recent activity. Since when did I shower before dinner?

When I glanced at my reflection I was horrified and overjoyed at the same time. I had that freshly fucked look, no doubt about it. I could barely move, let alone walk. Dragging my sorry ass to the couch, I ordered some Chinese take-out and turned on the TV. Within a minute or two, Frank was unlocking the door.

"Where've you been all day, I called you a dozen times," he said, without much concern.

"I met Marcy for lunch, then went over to the showroom and tried on clothes for hours. You'll be relieved to know, I didn't buy a thing."

Unsure if I sounded convincing, I watched as he walked to the kitchen to get a beer, his back to me. Lighting a bong, I decided the higher I looked the more it would mask my condition. He didn't seem to notice a thing.

The food arrived and Frank kept the beers coming. I didn't feel like moving but needing to talk to Eddie, I decided I *had to have* some vanilla Häagen-Dazs and pretzels. Frank didn't seem to think that was out of line.

"Get me some more beer," he ordered.

Normally that would have started a fight right there. The fact that it didn't made me afraid I might arouse his suspicion—not this night, as luck would have it.

Jogging to a pay phone (ah, the '80s) a few blocks away, I quickly dialed Eddie.

He picked up on the first ring, "I was hoping it'd be you. I miss your face and everything that comes with it. Are you okay?" he asked, sounding genuinely concerned.

"Yeah, he doesn't seem to have noticed anything. I guess that says volumes about our marriage."

"When can I see you?"

"I don't know. I'm on for Sunday, you?"

"I'll get myself on," he said. "Today was the best day of my life."

"Mine too."

Sprinting back to the apartment, just as I was pressing the elevator button, I realized my hands were empty. Racing around the corner, I grabbed some beer and ice cream, opening the door as Frank was finishing his last beer.

"Just in time," he said as he crushed the can in his hands. "That took you awhile."

"They were out of vanilla, I had to go to D'Agostino's and you know the lines there." I'd quickly become quite a proficient liar.

For two weeks while telling Eddie that it had to end, we snuck around stealing kisses. Even though I was endlessly reminding him that I had to protect my marriage, less subconsciously than I wanted to admit, I was planning how I'd leave. No matter what was to become of Eddie and me, now that I was reminded of what was possible, I knew that I could never settle for the loveless life Frank and I had been living for years.

Eddie had delivered a feast for the starving, and I was ravenous for more.

The husband takes the wife

Frank and I had planned a trip to a bed and breakfast, to celebrate our five years of wedded and five more, of unwedded... bliss? Dreading it like a Weight Watchers weigh-in, it meant leaving Eddie.

A new relationship was always all consuming for me. I was one of those move right in kind of girls. Seeing Eddie just a few hours at work, and for an hour or two afterwards, was not cutting it. He was all I was thinking of, all that I wanted.

There was no way out of the trip with Frank. Gratefully, the drive was quiet. I spent most of the time in my head dreaming of Eddie. Arriving at the inn by late afternoon, we had just enough time to shower and get ready for our anniversary dinner.

The bed and breakfast was formal, very old, but beautifully maintained. I prefer new—new bathroom, new sheets, new bed. Not a thrift store shopper, I'd rather spend $100 on a new pair of $100 shoes, than $50 on a pristine pair of $500 used Jimmy Choo's.

Our room was on the second floor of a steep walk-up. As we entered, I noticed that the bed was a double, at best. Even though Eddie had a miniscule 3/4 bed, it was all the room we needed. For Frank and me, this bed was way too close. It was one of those four-poster brass featherbeds. As I sat on the edge, the floorboards creaked. There was a small rug that looked a bit worse for wear. Give me carpeting—quick!

There was an antique desk, a big old club chair and an ancient dresser, with a doily on top, which I wouldn't think of putting my clothes in. How many people had done that in its long wooden life? There was a fireplace at the foot of the bed and I realized that if Eddie were with me, I would have felt completely differently. My intolerance had a lot more to do with my company than with the place. With Frank, I just wanted the Marriott, with cable TV, a king bed and couch on which to be alone.

As I began getting undressed to shower, Frank reached over to kiss me. We hadn't kissed in a long time. It was awkward and unpleasant. I responded with as little as I thought I could get away with, but somehow Frank was encouraged and continued his pursuit.

He'd had little interest in me for the longest time. When we did have sex, which was rarely, it was basically just attending to human need. Scorpio though I am, lustful creature that I can be, I can also become completely asexual as soon as my emotional needs stop being met. I turn off on a dime. In all fairness to Frank, he didn't stand a chance. Not just because of Eddie. I had too much anger and resentment built up, with nowhere for it to go. There was no connection between us to help sort things out; our only communication was argument. We were way too far gone for repair.

"I have to get ready for dinner." I said, not so gently pushing him away.

Frank was having none of it. Did he sense my infidelity and decide to reclaim what was his?

He mounted me, the weight of his body pressing against mine, making any movement impossible. I tried to wiggle free. He laughed as he stared at me in wild, mad defiance, and pressed me further into the old, spongy mattress. Yanking my panties out of his way, there on that little bed, in the middle of nowhere, as far apart as two souls could be, my husband raped me on our fifth wedding anniversary. It was at that moment that I made the completely conscious decision to leave. I now loathed Frank openly, without the slightest need to disguise my contempt.

Pulling my t-shirt down, and my undies up, I grabbed the pipe, pot and matches and locked myself in the bathroom, smoking myself into oblivion. It didn't ease the violation. My tears burst forth with more force than the water trickling out of the ancient showerhead.

We headed downstairs for our celebration dinner, without looking at each other. The dining room was crowded, huge and dimly lit—with lots of private little nooks, ideal for anyone with romance on their mind. Not bad for a couple who wanted to hide, either. Frank ordered a bottle of wine. Drinking a glass down quickly I tried to erase the recent memory. It didn't work. I was filled with rage, pity, fear, disgust and shame. It was my fault, after all. I'd betrayed this man whom I'd vowed to respect. I guess I had it coming.

We got through dinner with minimal conversation. I ate slowly, stalling as much as I could. After Frank paid the bill, I climbed the stairs behind him. As he unlocked the door my heart just stopped. What should I do? *Run?* There was no television; the lighting was dim and awful, which didn't lend itself to reading. It was designed as a high class fuck palace. *Would he dare to do it again?*

I followed him in and went straight to the bathroom, where I smoked myself silly. Ever so slowly, I took off my make-up and attempted to read a magazine. Uncomfortable and sleepy, after almost an hour, I tiptoed into the main room. As I'd hoped, Frank was passed out, his snoring reinforcing my calm.

Slipping into bed as silently and smoothly as possible, barely moving the covers, the floorboards creaked just the same. Holding my breath, I lay motionless for what seemed like forever, to be sure not to awaken him. Staring up at the ceiling, appalled by my circumstance, I tried to figure out how I'd leave.

The next day was sunny and cold. We were off fairly early to sightsee and get to our next destination. A Holiday Inn, praise the Lord. We stopped at a visitor's information center to get some maps and advice on eating, and headed to a recommended restaurant a few miles down the road for lunch. When it was time to pay, Frank reached for his money and panic crossed his face. He didn't have his wallet.

I tried to say something reassuring as I paid the check. "What the fuck?"

Frank, furious and foaming at the mouth, turned to me and said, "You goddamn bitch! Whaddya do with it?"

We drove back to the visitor's center in silence. There was Frank's wallet right on the glass counter where he'd left it. No apology, nothing. I've never hated another human being as much as I did him right then—the memory of the night before crisply fresh. It was no longer a question of how I was going to leave him, just when.

We somehow got through the next day and a half. I smoked round the clock and lived in my head, with the knowledge that someone was going to love me—soon.

Getting back to New York late Sunday afternoon, I ordered in some food and slowly began unpacking. Without my even trying, we started to fight. When Frank reminded me of my every error of judgment since childhood, I grabbed my uniform for the next day, my half-packed suitcases and, without looking back, I walked out on ten years of hell.

Ran is more like it.

Timing the lights and the traffic, I never stopped for a second, all the way to Cookie and Si's. My mother and stepfather lived thirteen blocks away. Completely out of breath when I got there, I held my finger on the bell until they answered. As soon as they buzzed me in, I raced up the four flights of stairs, rather than wait for the elevator, fearing Frank was chasing me and would force me to go back home with him. I was gasping for air when Si opened the door to their apartment. Noticing the suitcase in my hand, he reached for it and nodded me in. The phone was already ringing.

"Don't answer that, please," I pleaded.

Cookie was in her nightgown, drinking a cup of tea. She had the *Sunday New York Times* strewn around her on the couch and living room floor. Setting down the Arts and Leisure section, half read, she came into the foyer.

"Why shouldn't we answer the phone? Who is it? What's wrong?" she asked, scrutinizing me.

At that moment, she noticed the suitcase in Si's hand.

"What's going on, Andi?"

"I left Frank."

"*What*? Why?"

"Because I'm miserable."

"How long has that been going on?"

"Years."

"Really? I had no idea," my mother sort of mumbled.

I'd become so good at putting on my show, that they had no way to know how unhappy I was. They'd come to like Frank, despite their earlier objections.

My mother had witnessed Frank's benders more than once. She and Si knew about his drunken night in the slammer. They'd even gotten him a lawyer and invited us to their place in California for a couple of weeks afterwards, as we tried to piece our life back together. *How could she be so surprised?*

"Is he drinking again?" She asked, in a whisper.

"Again? When did he stop?" I was shocked that she thought otherwise, then realized that wasn't fair. Frank was never an everyday drinker. He could go days, weeks even, without touching a drop. It was just that when he did indulge, he couldn't stop until he passed out.

"It's so much more than just the booze. He's abusive and scary."

"Did he hit you?" Si asked, getting red in the face, his fists clenching.

"No. Never. But he's punched his share of walls. Peek behind the pictures, sometime."

"Why now? Did something happen on your trip?"

I didn't have the heart to tell them about my night on the four-poster.

After some more questions and my somewhat honest attempt to at last be straight with them, I decided to fess up.

"There's also someone else."

"Aha!" said Si. "Now I get it."

"It's not because of that."

"Of course not, " Si said, with a knowing smile.

As much as I tried to explain that Eddie wasn't the reason, Si just kept shaking his head. He was smart, that Si. The truth was, one day, Eddie or no Eddie, that marriage had to end. That doesn't, in any way, excuse my inexcusable behavior.

The phone started ringing again. I nodded and Cookie picked it up.

"Um... yes Frank... we understand... we're sorry, too." She looked at me and motioned toward the extension. I shook my head firmly. "NO."

"Frank, she doesn't want to talk right now."

Cookie was being patient and compassionate. It made me crazy. *If only she knew.*

I kept my mouth shut, went into the den and dialed Eddie. We hadn't spoken for days. It was before cell phones, when lovers couldn't so easily steal a chat.

"I left him," I said, feeling scared for a whole new set of reasons. Was I ready for this? For him?

"Where are you? What happened? Are you alright?"

"I'm at my mom's. It got really ugly. I'm okay."

"Please get in a cab, right now. Hurry. Andi, I love you, I'll take care of you."

Bingo, the magic words.

"I have to go," I said, returning to the kitchen.

"It's late. Where're you going? What'll we tell Frank?" Cookie asked, frantically.

Si gave me a wink, a $100 bill and a shove out the door. "Don't worry about a thing. I'll handle Frank. Go!"

Running down the stairs, I was in a cab within seconds. The trip to The Heights seemed interminable, even though it was Sunday night and there was no traffic. As I pulled up in front of Eddie's, the door swung open and he raced towards me. I jumped out of the cab and leapt into his arms. We stood in that spot tightly intertwined for ages. Well, until the driver reminded me that I owed him $13.25.

Eddie and I went down to his dungeon, and didn't emerge until 3:00 p.m. the next day. Sated and starving.

One toke over the line

Over the next few months, Eddie and I were inseparable, only getting out of bed to work and eat. Finally out of hiding, we were a strange looking couple. Eddie appeared younger than his twenty-four years and in those days, I was working hard to look older than my twenty-nine. *Why exactly?* The older woman/younger guy thing was far from cool back then. Coupled with my recent promotion to captain, I gave the staff at The Café an arsenal of ammo. They were merciless. Whenever we worked together, Eddie compensated by showing me and everyone else, who was boss. My sweet little boy had suddenly become an expert at service and a big old bully. Now that I'd left my husband, my apartment and my stuff, I was at his mercy. Why couldn't we've just stayed in bed?

It was karma, I guess. Falling in love with Eddie, before leaving Frank, was just wrong—even if Frank was an abusive, controlling, alcoholic pothead.

Or was that Eddie?

One night, about midway through our shift, Tom, an old-timer, gave me the nod to meet him in the basement. Taking my usual precautions, I didn't see Firouz anywhere and slipped downstairs. At the last moment, before disappearing out of sight, I caught a glimpse of Firouz standing on the balcony above and thought perhaps he'd seen me, as well. Deciding I was just being paranoid, I entered the electrical room, pulling the door closed behind me. There was no light, save for the match Tom was using on the *smokeless* pipe—smokeless, except for the exhalation. After a few tokes, we began to freshen up for the journey back to restaurantville. Without warning, the door swung open, the light switch flipped on, and there was Firouz with the biggest *I got you* grin I've ever seen.

I went back to my station sick to my stomach, awaiting the inevitable message that I knew would come, telling me that I was wanted upstairs. It came very quickly.

Slowly ascending the back staircase, I sensed it might be the last time I would do so. Eight years up in smoke. Poof.

Jan Holland tried hard to look stern, but hurt was all I saw. And disappointment. Even though he was an alcoholic, drinking nightly on the job, that was sort of acceptable. Pot was not.

Firouz had immediately and gleefully told everyone in the place that he'd busted me. I'd given Jan no choice.

"I'm regretfully terminating your employment," he said quietly, without looking up.

The shame was almost unbearable. Tom received the same news. He too, was devastated. Eddie was less than sympathetic. He gave me this, "You should've been more careful," look.

Sneaking out of there as quickly as I could, I headed to Cookie's, where I was going to have to face the music.

"Sit down, would you?" I said to Cookie and Si.

They knew I smoked pot. Although, I know they had no idea how much or how often.

"I got caught smoking marijuana downstairs at The Café tonight. Jan fired me. He had to. Everyone knew."

"It's time you got out of there anyway," Si said, amazingly cool, instantly setting me at ease. He'd been encouraging me for ages to figure out what I wanted to be when I grew up. "Now you get to find out," he said.

Without skipping a beat, he added, "Go to law school. I'll pay." His generosity and support floored me, but I didn't really give it serious consideration.

I argue for sport, not profit.

Once the dust had settled and I'd had time to think, I started getting angry. Deciding I had been unjustly treated, I went to see Jan Holland to fight for my job.

Looking pained, Jan agreed to talk to me. We'd been more than employer/employee, we'd been friends for years. Jan had been to my wedding and I'd attended his holiday parties. Under his tutelage, I'd risen through The Café ranks at warp speed. This was a personal disappointment. I'd let him down. Not that he thought smoking pot was such a bad thing, but it was illegal. I was stupid enough to get caught. I forced his hand.

Without looking at him, before I had a chance to chicken, I was off and running.

"Jan, how many waiters have been caught drunk on the floor while their customers were left unattended? Even when they were too loaded to continue working, the only punishment they incurred was a night or two off."

I could tell that Jan was genuinely considering my words. Encouraged, I continued.

"At least I imbibed out of sight of the customers and no one was left wanting. I came back on the floor totally capable of carrying out my shift. I've never behaved inappropriately before—well, you know what I mean," I said, with a wink.

Jan smiled.

"After almost ten years, don't I deserve a second chance?"

"Yes" he said, to my amazement.

I'd never considered convincing him, it was just something I thought I should try to do.

Recalculating quickly, I decided to push the envelope.

"Jan, thank you—*really*. But, isn't this gonna be weird for everyone? You fire me and then here I am again? What would you say to agreeing that I quit, and approving my unemployment? Then, I disappear and life goes on as usual around here."

Quickly considering, Jan stuck out his hand and said, "Deal."

Not that unemployment was going to save me. Most of my earnings were gratuities. The percentage I'd receive from unemployment would be based on my miniscule salary and a tiny bit of my reported tips. Nonetheless, I was officially living with Cookie and Si, unofficially with

Eddie, who was very generous and too macho to allow me to contribute. I wouldn't need much money.

Leaving the meeting with Jan exhilarated, it was the first time since college I was free to pursue my acting career full time. The focus had just shifted a bit.

Ever since my days with The Giggle Group, I'd dreamt of redeeming myself. I figured being a hysterically funny stand-up comedian would be my best revenge. *How the fuck was I gonna do that?*

I began incessantly scribbling notes. I had no clue how to construct an act and knew I needed help. But, I also needed time to decompress, acclimate, and map out a plan.

When my mom and Si invited me to head to California with them on their yearly pilgrimage, it seemed like the perfect idea. *Only, how was I gonna leave Eddie?*

Even though he could be tough and opinionated, he was also the most romantic, sexy boy I'd ever known. The trade-off seemed worth it. But, I needed time to think and focus on my future. Maybe the solitude would do me good.

———— Go west young (?) girl ————

Cookie and Si wintered in California. When a season is used as a verb, it tends to imply money. Si wasn't one of those showy types with a twenty-something second wife and a Corvette. Cookie was of a certain age, and he drove a Jeep.

On my first morning in town, while nibbling on a corn rye bagel and sipping a cup of joe, Scotty Fitzgerald smiled out at me from the front page of the local newspaper. The coffee dribbled down my chin. Due to injuries and his advancing age, I hadn't seen him in almost two years.

The main attraction in a local tournament beginning that day, I convinced my not–into-sports-mother, to let me treat her, to see him play. A relatively small event, it lent itself to a certain intimacy. Scotty was at his charismatic best. Even Cookie was enjoying herself.

He quickly and handily won. As he toweled down at the end of play, I stood, silently daring him to see me. Within a few interminable moments, facing into the sunlight, he squinted towards the stands. His eyes swept past me. He slowly moved his gaze backwards and then sped it up, until it fell directly upon me. Did he recognize me? Did he know who I was without The Café backdrop? It was daytime. In nine years he'd never laid eyes on me in natural light.

Seeming to know me, he smiled. Or, was he just doing the Scotty thing? He sort of motioned a "come 'ere" with his head and I immediately obeyed, with a quick "Be right back" to Cookie, who was busy freshening up and in no rush to leave. Trying to act cool and not hurdle my way down to him, I sauntered as seductively as I could manage. My cheeks, flushed from the sun and his smirk, surely gave me away.

Smooth, Andi, be smooth.

"Do you know who I am?" I asked, demurely, like a challenging idiot. *What if he didn't, what was he going to say then?*

"Of course I do. What're you doing here?"

At least he knew that he knew me—I think. But, did he know from where? After nine years of flirting, was it possible that he didn't put it together?

Can someone forget a person they've rubbed up against, been fed by and kissed? Who knows about famous people anyway? Are they mortal? Do they remember people, places and things? In my experience, they often act as if they don't.

What if Scotty really didn't have a clue who I was?

After explaining that I was visiting my parents, I motioned over to Cookie. He waved to her. I liked him so much at that moment. Or was he just playing with me? His smile appeared genuine. Unless it was wishful thinking, he seemed to be blushing a bit too. He wasn't making much eye contact, but he was grinning. *He knew me, right?*

"Would you and your mom like to come to my press conference?"

Would we like to come? I'd been living for this invitation for nine frikkin' years.

Trying to act nonplussed, I smiled and said, "Let me check."

Attempting to walk away provocatively, I fell off my Dr. Scholl's. I could feel him laughing, watching behind me. I laughed too.

Leaning over to Cookie, trying to control my mounting excitement, I attempted to whisper.

"Scotty invited us to his press conference, okay?"

As if Cookie needed encouragement to do something so cool. I am my mother's daughter.

We walked over to Scotty as he and Don were packing up his gear. There were introductions all around. I came to find out Don was Scotty's "West Coast Wally." An old friend and trusted confidant, he looked after him and saw to his needs.

Scotty was so attentive and charming, even Cookie was self-conscious. Fans were trying to get his attention and he only had eyes for us. What a fucking rush!

Leading the way to the press tent, there were dozens of reporters and photographers waiting for him. Still the old comeback kid, there wasn't a more popular player on the circuit. He'd changed the face of tennis, almost single-handedly. Now in his mid-thirties, he was pushing retirement. Everyone loves an underdog and that certainly was Scotty in those days.

As he made his way to the table down front, each person on the aisle reached out to touch him. He shook hands and had words and winks for all of them. No wonder they loved him.

Standing with Don I tried to remain invisible in the rear, Cookie was alongside me, taking it all in. Flashbulbs were popping like crazy. After a few minutes of good-natured question and answer, Scotty stood, smiled and said, "Thanks everyone. See you tomorrow. That is, if I win."

To the cheers and encouragement of the crowd, Scotty made his way back to Don, Cookie and me, signaling for us to follow. Walking briskly and with purpose through the mess tent, he led us out to a lawn where the players and their families were milling about. Don knew the drill and began flirtatiously chatting up Cookie, while Scotty led me to an empty spot on the lawn.

I can't recall anything we said. I just remember catching his gaze, both of us too shy to hold it for more than a moment. He seemed like he didn't want to leave and yet was clearly uncomfortable being on display. The biggest star by far, everyone was looking at him.

"What are you doing the next couple of days?"

Shrugging, I smiled, as he added, "Would you like to go to dinner?"

Would I like to go to dinner?

"Sure."

He took a pen and pad out of his duffel bag and handed it to me. I jotted down my mother's phone number.

Hanging out for a while, being shyly suggestive, yet discreet, we were drawing prolonged stares from the passers by. It started getting really uncomfortable.

"I'm sorry, would you mind if we put this on hold until dinner?"

Disappointed, but understanding, I followed, as he escorted me over to my mom. Giving her a peck on the cheek and a wink, he bade us adieu.

For the rest of the day, I sat around staring into space, reliving every moment. Even Si, usually unimpressed by celebrity, was taken by this turn of events.

He couldn't help but tease, "What about your little Eddie boy? What's he gonna say about this?"

Oh my God, Eddie. What was I gonna tell Eddie? Surely this didn't count as cheating. I hadn't done anything. I'd probably never see Scotty again. Besides, this was different. This was my nine-year obsession. I was crazy about Eddie, but this was bigger than Eddie. This was Scotty Fitzgerald. I'd have forgiven Eddie such an indiscretion, wouldn't I? No friggin' way. I'd have cut off his balls and made the front page of the *New York Post*. Lorena Bobbitt would've been a lot less famous.

I decided to just keep it to myself, for Eddie's sake. After all, nothing happened. Who the hell tells their boyfriend when they flirt with someone else, for Christ's sake?

The next day, I was eating breakfast after an early morning speed-walk, the most effortless of my life, still sort of floating. The phone rang. Si motioned that it was for me.

"Who is it?" I whispered.

He gave me an unknowing shrug.

A vaguely familiar voice said, "Andi?"

"Hi, this is she."

"Whaddya doing?"

My mind was racing trying to figure out who the hell it was. Wanting to buy time, I stammered, "Um, nothing, what are you doing?"

"I'm sitting here with our friend, who'd like to know if you want to have dinner with him tonight."

Ohmigod, ohmigod, ohmigod—it was *him*! I could hear Scotty in the background, playfully giving instructions to Don. It was so Cyrano—very romantic, but, why?

Don continued to broker the deal. "Can you meet us at *Las Casuellas*?"

"Um, sure. I um, don't have a car out here. I can catch a ride there, but I'll need a way home."

I wasn't about to tell them I was a phobic driver and therefore couldn't borrow my mother's wheels. Mumbled discussion on their end, then I heard Scotty say, "Of course we'll drive her home."

Don came back, "No problem. We'll meet you there at 6:45."

What was I going to wear? Trying on every single thing I'd brought with me, I settled on a pair of pink Garibaldi jeans, because they were a size 5 and I could get into them. I kept those jeans for almost twenty years, trying them on periodically and never coming close to getting them over my hips, let alone closed. Funny, all I could think of that afternoon was how fat I was compared to all the female athletes he was used to. Even though I speed-walked daily and did *Jane Fonda*, I was still completely insecure about my thirty-year-old body. What I wouldn't give...

I wore a snug, striped, short-sleeved red and white top that emphasized my boobs, put on bronzer to fake a tan, and a ton of make-up to help create the "natural look." Even though I'd begun getting ready hours in advance I still had to rush to be out the door by 6:15. I insisted on leaving early, much to Cookie's chagrin. What if we got stuck? Lost? So what if it was just one straight road for fifteen miles? You never know.

We arrived at *Las Casuellas* at 6:30. I wanted Cookie to just go and leave me there. But, what if it was a cruel joke and he never showed up? By 6:41 I was so nervous, I couldn't take it any longer.

"I'll be fine. Really. Go!"

Reluctantly, after much coaxing, Cookie left me standing in the driveway, obviously uncomfortable with her decision.

Not so sure about fathers, but mothers really do know best.

— To do it or not to do it? Is *that* the question? —

At exactly 6:45 a van pulled up. I could see Don was driving, but the passenger seat was empty. *Where was Scotty?*

Don motioned for me to enter. When I reached for the handle he motioned to the side back door. As I struggled to get it open, it was suddenly released from within. I looked up and there he was. I was sure Scotty could hear my heart beating, pounding, in my chest. It was so loud it was echoing in my head. I couldn't hear anything else, so when Don began speaking, I looked up and articulately replied, "Huh?"

Scotty and I were alone for the first time—well, sort of. We were in the back of a very large van, pretty far from Don, our designated driver. We were both looking down, sneaking glances, until we'd catch each other. Then we'd smile and quickly look away. Much of what happened next is lost; I was too nervous to retain anything. So not in the moment, I was trying to read his thoughts, trying to be witty, intelligent and desirable— mostly, desirable. Failing miserably at all three. I sounded simple, boring and fat.

"There's this great chicken place I know, do you mind doing take-out?"

I realized he didn't want to be seen out with a young woman, married man that he was. Suspecting he and Cathy were on another break, I wasn't sure if I'd read it, or dreamt it. Although involved, no longer married myself, I was a little disappointed that he didn't want to show me off (or allow me to show him off). I was, at the same time, relieved, that I wouldn't have to move from that spot (I wasn't exactly sure that I could remember how to put one foot in front of the other).

"That's fine."

It was impossible to relax while eating greasy finger food with someone I was trying hard to impress—and hoping would devour me. I ended up eating basically nothing, the usual "girl on a first date" thing.

Once Don had finished eating, Scotty asked him to drive. Somewhere between the wet nap and the highway, we kissed. It was a nervous, anxious, trying too hard kiss—rigid and dry. Not at all the kiss I'd imagined. Things improved over the course of the next few minutes as we practiced, kind of like warming up for a match.

Nuzzling my ear, he whispered, "Let's do it."

"HERE? NOW? With *him*?" I gestured with my eyes towards Don, less than ten feet away, slyly watching in the rear view mirror.

Scotty seemed to know there was something wrong with asking a nice girl to do it, right there in the van—with his pal in attendance. He didn't press.

There was nowhere to go from there, not that night.

All those years of wanting and I turned him down. I knew without question that I'd done the right thing. He'd given me no choice. I hoped he wanted me more for it. I was sick just the same.

Somehow, we were suddenly parked right outside his hotel cottage and it hit me. He didn't talk to me himself on the phone, because he was afraid to be taped. He couldn't invite me into his room fearing to be seen with a woman other than his wife. It was all too dangerous. He was just too famous.

He was staring at me, touching my hair.

"I have a big day tomorrow. I really should turn in early."

He took my face in his hands; "I'd love for you to be at the finals tomorrow."

Calling out to Don, he said, "Be sure there are two tickets at the Will Call for Andi."

Turning to me, he added, "Don't forget to give Don your last name."

"Make sure you see this lady safely home," he said to Don, not taking his eyes or his hands off me.

With one last kiss, he was gone.

I was so conflicted. I knew I'd done the right thing, but damn!

There was still tomorrow. Maybe he'd figure out a way to be alone with me.

Moving up to the front passenger seat at Don's suggestion, I noted he wasn't driving anywhere. Taking out an old receipt, I jotted down my name. He still didn't move.

"I can see why you're so special to Scott..."

The next thing I knew, he jumped me.

"Are you kidding me?"

This guy actually thought I was going to do him after turning down Scotty Fitzgerald? *Was he nuts?*

Apparently so.

When he finally got that it wasn't going to happen, he just sat there silently. Making no move to drive me home.

It dawned on me that I was about thirty miles from Cookie's, in the middle of the California desert. I wasn't about to call her to come get me and have to explain the events of the night. She'd never have brought me back for the finals the next day.

"Would you call me a cab, please?" I finally asked, furious that I had to do so.

We sat around in silence for about twenty minutes waiting for the car to arrive. When it did, I handed Don the paper with my name spelled out.

"What's this for?"

"The Will Call."

He took the paper without looking at it, and stuffed it in his back pocket.

Thankfully, I had enough money to cover the cab, almost fifty dollars worth.

Once back at my mother's I smoked a bowl and cried myself to sleep, comforted by the thought that the next day I could tell Scotty what Don had done and he would, of course, right the whole thing and let Don have it.

At breakfast the next morning, I told Cookie we'd had a lovely time, basically leaving out the entire sordid story. Attempting to duck further questioning, I told her to hurry up and get ready, Scotty had invited us to the finals.

Arriving at the Will Call, I discovered that Don had not taken care of it at all. You'd think I would've anticipated it. It made perfect sense that he wouldn't want me around, discussing his behavior with Scotty.

Embarrassed and angry, fortunately, or unfortunately, there were still tickets available. Purchasing two, I was now into this little rendezvous for a bundle. *Had I no shame?*

Cookie was giving me the old, "I told you so look," but she was merciful enough to not press. I blamed Scotty for not making sure it was done. In retrospect, why wouldn't he have assumed that Don had carried out his wishes? When I was a no show, Don could simply say that I never picked up the tickets, figuring, that would piss off Scotty enough to never call me again. On the other hand, Scotty was a married man and, to that point, had not betrayed his vows, in a Clintonesque sort of way. Maybe it was his idea for me to just disappear and forget the whole thing ever happened.

Finally coming to my senses, I was furious that Scotty had even tried to get me in the back of that van—livid that I was left at the mercy of his friend—crazed that the whole mess cost me a fortune—and humiliated that I had to buy tickets in front of Cookie. I hated Scotty. I prayed for him to lose. And lose he did. After the match, I didn't try to see him, but I did send him a note.

"Scotty,

Just wondering if Don filled you in on what happened last night. Did he tell you that he tried to shove his tongue down my throat moments after you left? Did he mention that his idea of seeing me home safely was calling a cab and having me, not only find it myself, but pay for it, as well? Did he happen to say that he conveniently forgot to leave my name at the Will Call—shaming me senseless in front of my mother?

What a pity you lost.

Andi"

My tone, vile and accusatory, felt appropriate. Was it really possible that Scotty was just some selfish, sadistic, motherfucker and had told Don not to leave the tickets to just get rid of me?

I couldn't go there. I could not believe that after all those years, all of those gentlemanly gestures—except the van request— that he could be so mean. Ultimately, I chose to blame Don.

I never did find out if Scotty got that note, or, if he knew the truth about Don. It's been years; I haven't seen him since, but every time I read his name in the paper or catch him on TV, my heart beats a little faster and I can't help but wonder...

THREE

FAITH

—————— Looked like an angel, that devil ——————

In spite of my lapse, I was crazy about Eddie.

Back home, we picked up right where we'd left off. I didn't tell him about my Scotty escapade and he didn't fess up about the little pot of moisturizer I found under his bed.

We were having incredible sex, lots of it, filled with long, wet, soul kisses—a sure sign of early love. Why I had risked the most passionate relationship I'd ever known with a married, unavailable celebrity, is scarily ridiculous. I took solace in the fact that I hadn't actually gone through with it. I had kissed Scotty. I'd wanted him. But, maybe I would've resisted him even in the best of circumstances.

It's possible.

Allowing myself little remorse, I rationalized that Scotty was an exception. Not because he was famous—because of the years of longing. But, did I long for him because he was famous?

When the guilt surfaced, I smoked it away. Pot was the great eraser. Of thoughts, feelings and accountability.

I'd justified cheating on Frank and, now, I'd more than contemplated doing the same to Eddie. Pass the bong.

Eddie had someone cover his shifts my first few days back in town, enabling us to spend every moment together. Once he returned to work, I undertook my new career with verve, except I knew even less about stand-up than I did about improv. My act was pathetic. I didn't actually do it anywhere, didn't even recite it out loud; I just wrote about everything and anything. Occasionally, I made myself laugh. I knew the only way I'd make any real headway was to get help. I hate that shit.

The first two stand-up classes I audited were lackluster and boring. Feeling pretty hopeless later that week, I ran down 42nd Street, up two flights of stairs, arriving late and out of breath for yet another class. Flinging myself into the room, the instructor was the first thing I saw. As I turned my back to close the door, I smiled as I thought the first of my three hundred and sixty-seven first thoughts.

Manly and handsome, in a sort of waspy, Middle American way, he looked kind, evolved and stable. I glanced at my notes. Lenny Blakeman. Even his name was friendly. As I sat there listening to the clear, confident, sense he was making, I thought, *this is the kind of guy you can bring home to meet the folks.* Clearly not my type.

I was usually attracted to the swarthy types, not only in appearance, but in demeanor as well, but Lenny was blond and affable. Blue eyes have never done it for me, yet Lenny's were soft and inviting—his gaze, gentle and mischievous. From the looks of him, I'd have sworn he wasn't one of the tribe, but his name left little doubt. Lenny Blakeman was a Jewish mother's wet dream.

There was a relaxed and easy way about him. He smiled often and was very funny, but he wasn't "on." I hate "on"—the type that's always talking, needing to be the center of attention. Right. That would be me.

Thank goodness I loved Eddie. The last thing I needed was a distraction.

I wish someone would've told that to the woman I suddenly noticed sitting off to Lenny's left, apart from the rest of the class.

He sure was cute.

Could she be getting that? She was staring, more like glaring at me, with a look of someone staking ownership. She was making it clear, in no uncertain terms, that he was hers. I know that look well. I've employed it many times myself.

Fairly nondescript, in retrospect, she was sort of a poor man's Jennifer Aniston, except she had big boobs—really big. Lenny was obviously a tit man. I was fairly ample, but nothing like my friend Rachel, over there. There were a lot of things about myself that caused me a lot more insecurity.

When Lenny asked us to introduce ourselves and give a little background as to why we were taking the class, I decided to impress the shit out of him and make sure he knew that I wasn't a novice like the rest of those losers.

"Hi, my name is Andi Stone. I've been an actress all my life. I've got a BFA in drama education, been on *After Midnight Live* a bunch of times and did a year of improv with The Giggle Group."

I could hear my classmates nervously shifting in their chairs.

I didn't think ahead to how ridiculous that would seem to them once they heard my act.

Mona (I came to find out was the name of his girl) was not digging me. The looks she was shooting my way just fueled my fire. I knew Lenny was going to pay. Not that he was doing anything other than his job, but he did seem to be enjoying the attention. There were two other women in the room also giving him the eye. One was a sexy Greek Goddess with an unflinching gaze. The other was a genuinely funny, zaftig ex-hooker.

When I began the class I had pages and pages of bullshit, a few decent premises, and maybe a punch line or two, at best. I thought I was hysterical, brilliant and original, until I had to stand up for the first time in front of the class.

What I had was passion. Like a lioness roaming back and forth protecting her young, intense and focused, I was in perpetual motion. Unfortunately, I was not particularly funny. I wasn't boring either; I was *interesting*. It wasn't exactly what I was going for, but it was a start.

All week we'd write, then come to class and perform our material, hoping to end up with five minutes we could use in a club at the end of the three-month class. The greatest accomplishment was getting a rise out of Lenny. He had a hearty, infectious laugh. You could see the envy register around the room when one of us made that happen.

As if being green wasn't enough of a handicap, people weren't used to laughing at women who didn't look the part. You were doubly fucked. Sarah Silverman, a crazily attractive, funny girl, worked her ass off for more than a dozen years before she became an overnight sensation.

I was a kind of smart, very enthusiastic girl with potential and no patience. I wanted it all, *now*. Lenny tried to tell us that it would take at least a few years to find ourselves up there, perhaps longer. He warned us not to expect too many rewards (such as laughter) for quite a while, strongly suggesting we write daily and work out our material as much as possible, without giving thought to auditioning for a regular slot at the clubs.

Lenny and I became fast friends. The son of a philosophy professor, he'd begun teaching the definitive stand-up comedy class in New York to supplement his stand-up. It also gave him something to do in the late afternoon. Mainly, I think it was a way for him to hook up with chicks— young, over eager women, anxious to get on stage, vent their rage and become a star.

There's nothing sexier than a funny man. A lot of comics capitalize on that advantage. Lenny was the slow, non-aggressive type. Teaching gave him the forum to earn a woman's respect and afforded him the time for them to throw themselves at him.

Teaching gave him something else, too. Unparalleled, he was the best. His classes were packed and in high demand. His students were an eclectic mix of actors, lawyers, businessmen, college students and housewives— all looking to change their lives and score.

Still shell-shocked from my improv debacle, feeling very vulnerable, Lenny inspired and encouraged me. He laughed in all the right places, giving me the confidence to try to find my place on the stand-up stage.

Before Eminem was out of diapers, previous to Marky Mark taking down his pants, before it was a category at the Grammys, I did a rap—a *JAP Rap*—before every comic ended with one. *No, really*. I had music, props and attitude out the wazoo. It sort of carried me. At least I had a closer that I could depend on. It was self-deprecating, but not seriously enough to be painful. It left people laughing, which was more than I can say for most of my act.

Then there was the ongoing battle at home. Eddie did not like this comedy thing, he did not like it one bit. Being the brunt of much of my material did not sit well with his ego.

A writer himself, Eddie was a sort of modern day Marquis De Sade, with legions of fans for his dirty little ditties of depraved poetry. Written in old English, they were silly misogynistic yarns, where the women were all whores, only good for pleasuring men. The boys ate it up, reciting the poems aloud as if they were sacred text. It was before the Internet, when sharing took effort. They'd Xerox copies, get as high as humanly possible and have candlelit readings in Eddie's dungeon.

Eddie's redeemable talent was as a songwriter. Both musically and lyrically he could fashion a hit. He had passion, guts and confidence, but his voice was sort of punky, and a little bit off. His ego did not allow for any recognition of that, so no correction was ever attempted or made. Success eluded him.

I volunteered to manage his career. Since it was all about Eddie, he was all for it. Not exactly *all* for it. He had this macho thing about taking advice from anyone, let alone a woman. Now that I was his woman, I had even less credibility.

My first order of business was to put a band behind him. Once the trio was in place, I took some photos and assembled press kits. I had no experience, no plan and no idea what the hell I was doing. I didn't think, I just kept moving. Nurturing someone else's talent came far more naturally to me. For the first time, I was truly fearless. I put together a press pack of hype and bullshit. Is there any other kind?

Simultaneously, I was nearing the end of my three-month stand-up class. Lenny had been preparing us for our final: a five-minute set at The Comedy House on the west side of Manhattan. A pre-show, the only audience would be the one we provided. Lenny had warned us that it was in our best interest to debut for strangers, so I invited casual acquaintances, as did most of the class. Combined, we managed to fill the house.

I sat in the green room, desperately trying to remember my opening joke, as my stomach flipped. Lenny came in moments before curtain to assign us show placement.

"Andi, you'll close," he said, with a smile.

A sign of confidence, it scared me shitless.

As the evening wore on, the laughter increased with each comic. The three Lenny groupies—the Greek Goddess, the hooker and me, were bringing up the rear, in that order. Just before The Goddess went on, Mona (who was sitting in the back with Lenny) decided that she didn't want the packed house to go to waste. She'd taken the class—and Lenny—the session before us. Out doing short sets in the real world, she considered herself a seasoned performer. Therefore, Mona decided she should close the show, and pestered Lenny until he agreed. Coming up to me rather sheepishly, just as Greek Girl was about to go on, I could tell he was embarrassed.

"Hey Andi, there's been a slight change in plans. When you finish your set, bring Mona up, okay?" He seemed to be almost pleading for my understanding.

I was disappointed, but I had a new sense of purpose. Who did she think she was intruding on our one night? She was doing it every night. Why did she have to have this, too?

Greek Girl killed. S&M woman slayed. The pressure was on. I was a wreck.

I was also pissed. Getting up there, I unleashed every ounce of my competitive spirit, determined to do my best, connect with the audience, and make it really hard for Mona to follow me. While making eye contact with everyone in the house, I spent my five minutes exposing my foibles and taking the heat for my failed life. I ended my JAP Rap to thunderous applause (it *was* an invited audience and they'd had plenty of booze by then).

I graciously and enthusiastically brought up Mona, secretly praying for her to fail. In retrospect, I'd like to think that's not something I'd do today. *I'd like to think*.

Just as I'd hoped, Mona was completely anticlimactic. She spent her five minutes railing on every man in her life, doing a bad Joan Rivers rant. She came off angry and resentful. It lay there like a lox.

Eddie had walked in just in time to catch the last four sets. As much as he hated what I was doing, he despised the other girls even more. After conceding that I did a pretty good job, he guilted me into leaving. Embarrassed that we weren't staying to celebrate with the class, I started to inch towards the door. Lenny caught up with us just before we reached the exit.

"You did great Andi. You really commanded the stage. I'm proud of you." Lenny's praise meant more to me than all the laughter in the room. I left on top of the world, envisioning my future, doing panel with Johnny.

Mona was in the back, watching and seething, unbeknownst to Lenny. Boy, was he going to get it this time. Eddie sneered, dragging me out of there while muttering under his breath, "Buncha whores..."

The Greek Goddess, the hooker and I began roaming the comedy clubs on a nightly basis. For the most part we observed, but every once in awhile one of us found the balls and got on. It was usually the Goddess or me. Hooker-woman, the most naturally funny of the three of us, had the most fear. She could give blowjobs to strangers, but she couldn't tell jokes to a couple of tourists.

The sets were short, so we usually did okay. With our confidence growing, the three of us soon arranged another showcase at a downtown club. The deal was that if we brought the audience, they'd give us the stage time. Defying Lenny's advice, I called everyone I knew.

We packed the house. Since I'd brought in the most people, I got to close the show. Everyone I called, came: my mother, ex-co-workers and every friend I could think of—even my gynecologist was there, front and center. (His usual spot.)

The show went great. The crowd wanted us to do well, and they couldn't have been more demonstrative. It was such a high and, like most highs, it provided a false reality. It allowed me to believe the misconception that I was ready to perform in front of people I knew. Hell, I wasn't really ready to perform in front of people, period. I still only had a handful of jokes that worked—my rap and, at best, an earnest attitude.

Going to the B-list clubs on a nightly basis, I quickly learned where I could get on if I hung out long enough. I ran into Mona quite a bit. We pretended to like and support each other.

I also went to the A-list clubs, just to watch. There you had to audition before you could get on at all. Lenny had warned us not to even think about auditioning until we'd put in our time.

After a couple of months, I got a call out of the blue from Mona asking if I'd like to do my first paid gig.

"You'll only have to do five minutes," she said, as if it were nothing. "You'll open, piece a cake."

Shocked to be getting this gift from Mona, I was pretty sure it was a set-up. "Come on Andi. Lenny and I know you can do it. You're ready."

Lenny knew I could do it?

Well, if Lenny knew…

I nervously agreed. This time, I invited no one. Who knew that was why promotion-conscious Mona had asked me to be on the bill?

Rock Bar was a brand new, small, albeit groovy deco club, down a few stairs and a few steps away from The Bitter End on Bleecker Street. When I got there the place was empty, save for the bartender, a waitress, the two middle-aged owners, and a guy having a beer. Mona, anxiously pacing back and forth, was cracking wise as Lenny sat at a table reading the paper, trying to ignore her. The other comics began arriving and, thankfully, a couple of tables of patrons—not caring about comedy, just burgers.

Realizing it was what it was, and this was all it was going to be, Mona took the stage. After a few jokes that went nowhere, she brought me up. It was too weird for me to be nervous. I was a late night fill-in at best, and used to performing in front of small crowds. This was my comfort zone. Eyeballing every person in the place, I gave it my all.

My rap was a little high energy for the occasion, but it seemed to wake everyone up. I felt okay when I was done—even better when I saw how the rest of the comics were doing. With the exception of Lenny, I had the best set. Not because I was the funniest. Like Avis, I tried harder.

After the show, John, the bartender, who was also the manager, bought me a drink. I was already buzzing pretty good from the stage high, but grateful to have a beer to take the edge off.

Lana, a sexy Nordic blond, came to the service bar to fill an order. "You kicked ass," she said, as she filled a glass with coke. "You were definitely the best."

I loved her immediately.

The owners—Dale, a forty-something, handsome, yuppie type, and Marvin, about fifty, short, bald and fiery—were good-naturedly chatting up the small crowd.

As they approached the bar, I ballsed it up and said, "What a great place you have here. It deserves to be more crowded." Without taking time to think I added, "I manage a rock band. We could pack the place."

"Okay toots, you're on," said Marvin, as he gestured for John (the bartender/manager/booker) to bring over the upcoming schedule.

Settling on a Thursday night, four weeks down the road, I figured it gave me enough time to call everyone I knew, and prayed it would give Eddie time to learn to sing on key.

Throwing it against the wall

Five minutes of stand-up can fly by in a nanosecond when it's going well, and drag like a junkie jonesing for a fix, when it's not. My five was getting fairly decent. It'd only taken me six months of twelve-hour days to get inconsistently mediocre.

On some nights it worked. In one particular venue, it always worked—an east side diner that morphed into a comedy club in the evening. The owner, a gruff gangster type named Tony, quickly took me under his wing, always putting me on in the sweet spot—not too late, not too early, right when everyone was primed. It was the only club where I was a regular, which meant I could just show up and get on. Within a couple of months, Tony had me MCing, which boosted my confidence and freed me to try new stuff.

I'd waited on a big time comedy manager while still at The Café. With my cockiness soaring, I decided to give Mr. Lane a call. Inviting me to his office, he graciously listened to my bravado and was cynically encouraging.

On my behalf, he called the booker of The Club—a hotbed for upcoming talent, requesting that he set up an audition for me. Lenny must have been rolling over in his non-marital bed.

Lawrence, the booker of The Club, was a tough, no-nonsense guy who prided himself on being a hard-ass. My set went okay, I guess. I got some laughs, but I could tell Lawrence wasn't overly impressed.

"Keep getting up and come back in a few months. I'm not sure there's anything special about you, but anyone Mr. Lane recommends gets a second shot."

All right, sir.

Undeterred by rejection number one, I strode confidently into Punch, the most prestigious celebrity-hang in New York. Those auditioning went up late night, after the regular show, having had the misfortune to sit around all night watching the pros perform—an ego deflator, extraordinaire.

On my audition night, Barry Sobel—running very hot then—got up, followed by Steven Wright, at the height of his fame. Joy Behar was hanging out, having already performed. In 1986, she was known, but not famous. I sat on a stool beside her at the bar. Very forthcoming about her own rise to then semi-stardom, she was kind and empathetic, temporarily distracting me from my terror.

Just as they were about to turn the evening over to the auditioners, Ian McFadden showed up, long before he hit his stride doing the weekend update on *After Midnight Live*. He was still a late night act and more than a bit tipsy. When he took the stage there were about thirty people in the room. Forty minutes later, he was still up there with only three tired, wasted, customers remaining.

I wanted to run screaming from the place. I should have. Time stood still as the two drunken businessmen ignored me and tried to seduce their slumped over, nearly sleeping, secretary. My five minutes felt like fifty.

It was pass/fail. If only they graded on a curve.

I raced back to the Heights, longing for Eddie.

"I can't believe that drunken bastard knew there were a bunch of us waiting to audition and still stayed on stage until he'd driven every conscious person from the room. I didn't stand a chance."

"Sure, blame him," Eddie said, laughing.

The first story I'd told that evening that landed. I got stoned and cried myself to sleep.

The next morning, I called Lenny and arranged a writing session. I'd been humbled, at least for the moment.

Lenny gave me directions to his place on the upper-upper west side. One block from Harlem, he insisted it was "Columbialand" and I had nothing to fear. I sucked it up and hopped the 1 train uptown.

As I exited the subway at West 116th Street, I discovered Lenny had been straight up in his description. Columbia stood before me, in all its majesty. The tree-lined streets were pristine and filled with mothers pushing strollers.

Entering Lenny's studio apartment I could barely get past the still-opened convertible sofa in the middle of the room. Mona was near the window applying the finishing touches to her lipstick. I prayed she wouldn't notice the "Screw" t-shirt I was wearing inside out. Why exactly was I wearing it to a writing session with Lenny, anyway? If I were Mona, I sure would've closed the damn bed.

Once she was gone, Lenny and I sat down on the Castro Convertible with all feet planted firmly on the floor. As I was paying by the hour and his time did not come cheap, we got right to it. Completely focused on the business at hand – *damn he's cute*—we stretched out and got comfortable. Lying in bed with a sexy guy, and compensating him for his services. This was a first.

He knew my act well, having helped me sculpt it. Almost immediately he came up with a joke worth every cent of the session.

"My boyfriend's so young, his pajamas have feet... he's so young, when I went to work he was in the bathroom; when I got home, he was still in there, yelling, 'I'm finished...!'"

We batted ideas back and forth and had a lot of laughs as we shyly and respectfully did not flirt.

Was he thinking what I was thinking?

What was I thinking?

Furious with my new career, Eddie did everything he could to beat me down and destroy whatever confidence I had.

"Listen to this joke Lenny and I wrote..." Before I'd even gotten to the punch line, Eddie spat, "You paid for that?"

He never laughed; he didn't even smile when I ran stuff by him.

"Andi, face it. You have many gifts. Comedy isn't one of them."

Once, a laugh escaped him. He literally covered his mouth with his hand.

A few nights later he came to pick me up at Tony's place. He walked in just in time to hear the "I'm finished" joke, and finished he was. As soon as I got offstage, without giving me a moment to savor the applause, he gave me "the look" and headed for the exit. I furiously, albeit obediently, followed.

A guy patted Eddie on the back and said, "You're one lucky son of a b."

With a look that could maim, Eddie sneered, "Oh, I'm lucky, all right."

With that, he sort of pushed me out the door. That was the last time he ever acknowledged my stand-up, let alone came to witness it.

It was all about him and his impending gig. Hard Line was rehearsing like crazy. Making calls every waking moment, I had lists for my lists. Since it was Eddie's first official show in the city, everyone we knew was coming.

On the big night, as promised, there wasn't an empty seat in the house. It was the first time in its short history that Rock Bar was packed on a weeknight. Dale and Marvin were beside themselves, until the band played their first lick. It was loud, way too loud. The mix was mud—the vocals were unintelligible over the screaming guitar, thrashing drums and thumping bass. A new wave, punk, pop, garage band was not what Dale and Marvin had in mind. Marvin looked like he was being personally assaulted. He and Dale were trying to be good sports for a song or two, but they were soon at wit's end, and pleaded with me to have them turn it down.

Approaching Eddie from the side, he completely ignored me. There was no denying the material was solid, catchy and danceable. It was also clear that the sound was way out of whack and there was something a little off. With the promise to get the volume under control, Marvin and Dale scheduled a follow-up gig in a month from the day. I had no clue how I was going to pack the place again.

Heeding my instincts, we made up flyers and passed them out everywhere there were club-going types: record stores, bars, music clubs and street corners. Eddie and I worked it, taking opposite ends of Bleecker Street and chatting up every person we could. I'd smile at the guys and he'd flatter the girls. The day before the gig, I called every friend in both of our phone books and invited them out to "play."

The music was a bonus. I enticed them with the notion of a night with friends in a great little club where everybody would know their name.

Once again, the room was packed. Marvin and Dale were nervous wrecks about the volume and the music, but I just kept pointing to the ringing cash register.

When the set ended, Marvin waved me over to the bar.

"So, when're we doing this again, honey?"

I took a Thursday, four weeks hence, and crossed my fingers.

We papered the city, worked the clubs and the streets and, again, on the day of the gig, I called everyone we knew—plus the fifty or so new numbers I'd collected of people that had wandered in during the last two shows. One time lucky, twice charmed—three times…

More than a little bit cocky and a lot full of myself, I started giving Dale and Marty all kinds of suggestions on how they could score on a nightly basis. Making it up as I went along, I suspected regular listings in the newspapers and on the radio would help. I had just started sending Eddie's promo stuff around and figured a press release for the club could follow the same made-up format I was using for the band. My approach was to spin the info as hot as possible, lay it out in a unique and funky fashion and, wherever possible, do it funny.

Dale was desperate for success. Marvin got straight to the point.

"Hey kid, why don't you come work for us?"

"What about my stand-up?"

"How much time does that take? We'll give you $200 bucks a week—cash. Put in a few hours and get us some business. If it works, we'll talk again soon."

With my unemployment and no rent it would afford me a little spending money. I hated being broke.

"I'll do it—with the understanding that we talk again in a month. Okay?"

"Okay," Marvin said, sticking out his hand.

I put in way more than the agreed upon few hours to set up contact with every newspaper, magazine and radio station that did free listings. Sending personal notes, I included Rock Bar's cool t-shirt. Within a couple of weeks the mentions started. I began going to clubs every night, checking out bands, and made suggestions to John, who was doing the booking. Any group that had their own following and appealed to my ear, I fought to get on the schedule.

John had done a good job putting quality music on the Rock Bar stage, but on a street full of partying kids, the Rock-a-Billy just wasn't cutting it—even if the players were first rate. Original bands were out of the question. Marvin and Dale had had it with Hard Line. They made them the one exception, on a semi-regular basis, to please me—and their pocketbooks. I tried to convince Marvin we could do that kind of business every night with the right acts. But they wanted cover bands—to attract the bridge and tunnel crowd that spent the big money. It was Marvin and Dale's club--their call. Thanks to John, I met a lot of great players who were sidemen for stadium-filling rockers. For fun and ego they fronted their own cover bands. We booked them nightly.

Robert Wiener had just started his own late night talk show. A consistently funny, very successful stand-up, he'd been around since he was a regular on Ed Sullivan. But, he was untested as a late night host. In a highly competitive market, his opening hook was to wear one of the t-shirts sent in by his fans. It was a good tactic, great PR for those chosen, and a way to ensure that people were at least watching the first ten minutes of his show. Everyone seemed to have something to promote, and a shirt to do it with.

Robert had been a regular customer at The Café. He was always really nice, accessible, and a great tipper. I guaranteed Dale and Marvin that I could get him to wear the Rock Bar shirt on his show one night. Marvin countered that if I did, they'd double my salary. That was a dare I wasn't about to let pass.

A happening t-shirt in its own right, it was black with a hot pink Chevy emblazed in the center, and Rock Bar in white deco lettering underneath. It sold itself. I figured I'd send the package return receipt directly to Mr. Weiner, with a personal note about waiting on him at The Café—noting how nice he'd always been—and that if he wore this shirt it would double my salary in my struggling new profession as a promoter… yada, yada, yada. I figured, even if his assistant opened it, it was personal enough to get shown to him, or at least get talked about. It had to be one of the cooler shirts he was getting—plus, it had worked before. I'd done it with Sonny Gold. Return receipt seemed to get to them. I had nothing to lose.

I began watching the show immediately, as if the very next day he not only would've received the shirt, but would be wearing it, too. Night after night, I watched. With each passing evening, Marvin would give me that cynical, "What's the matter, Andi, can't get it done?" look.

I got a bit shaky after ten days or so, but I wasn't about to let Marvin see me sweat. Each night I strutted around, completely certain in my uncertainty. On the thirteenth night, at 11:30, as I had every night, I turned one of the bar TVs to *The Robert Weiner Show*. During his opening monologue, as always, he turned to the bandleader while undoing his button-down shirt. I was barely paying attention—there was a really cute guy, soulfully singing onstage—when out of the corner of my eye, I glimpsed some black and hot pink. I needed a witness quick, and screamed for John and Lana. Robert peeled off his man-tailored shirt, turned around and revealed the Rock Bar tee! I screamed. I jumped. I hugged. Then, I ran to call Marvin.

Achieving that minor success was huge for me. It gave me a confidence I'd seldom had in myself professionally. It was such a little thing, but it was a test. The whole process of having an idea, thinking it through and making it happen. Now earning $400 a week, living rent-free and still collecting unemployment, I was back in Clarins.

I'd recently done Howie Lowe's radio show, which was no big deal for a somebody, but for a young, two-bit comic like myself, it was thrilling. Howie's wife, Amy, wrote New York's definitive gossip column. I thought if I worded it just so, I could probably get a mention from her, if I connected myself to Howie. Still caught up in the momentum of my recent Weiner score, I again approached Marvin and Dale.

"What if I can get a mention in Amy Lowe's column about Robert Weiner wearing our shirt?"

Caught up in the crush for t-shirts selling at the bar, Marvin countered, "You get this in Amy Lowe and we'll double your salary again."

It was too much to ask for. How could Amy refuse me, knowing the impact she could have on my life—a struggling comic, whom Howie had already deemed fit to assist?

Again I did the return receipt thing and waited. And waited. I'd noticed that Amy's column was a little slow in its timeliness. This would require patience.

In the meantime, I was doing more of the bookings, spending much of my day listening to tapes and reading press kits. There seemed to be a lot less time to do standup. While I struggled to make the slightest headway in the comedy clubs, with rock 'n' roll, I was moving swiftly—caught up in the scene and loving the attention of all the gig-seeking musicians.

Eddie was not liking my new career one little bit. At first he'd encouraged me, because he saw the potential for it to help him. Once the reality of my proximity to all those rock boys sunk in, he got kind of crazy. Suddenly, comedy with the nerdy Jew boys wasn't looking so bad.

Now doing all of the booking, publicity and promotion, with John's help, and connections, Rock Bar was getting hot. After a few weeks, Amy Lowe did indeed give us a mention, a whole paragraph. Business was booming. Hello $800 a week—goodbye unemployment.

Crazee glue

The stage was tiny, but the talent that appeared on it nightly was enormous. The majority of the bands were fronted by A-list sidemen. Pretty quickly the rock stars themselves were making guest appearances. We were getting street cred and a lot of press.

After a few months the *Daily News* called requesting an interview. The article ran that Sunday on the front page of the entertainment section, with an enormous picture of me on a good hair day. I'd barely even gotten my name in the paper as a comic.

Now that success had come to Rock Bar, John and I figured we'd see less of Marvin and Dale. Au contraire. They were more visible and opinionated than ever—criticizing the music, the performers and the volume—seemingly less happy now than when their club stood empty. Becoming increasingly agitated and impossible to please, they seemed to derive zero joy from the place.

Things were getting tenser by the moment with Eddie. The age difference, had everyone making fun of us—especially Marvin and Dale—who were about as subtle as Jim Carrey on crack.

Eddie was in a constant state of sarcastic. Because I was the one doling out the gigs, the players were attentive and a bit flirtatious. Everyone knew I didn't fool around—everyone, except Eddie. It wasn't me so much that he worried about. It was them—the rock guys, their success, talent and availability. I'm not sure what made him crazier—their proximity to me, or to the main stage at Madison Square Garden.

He began staying out almost every night, without explanation. His silence made me obsessed with the girl at his new real estate gig, his old friend from college and his visiting ex. The jealousy thing didn't hurt our sex life, but it was wreaking havoc with my serenity. At the club, I was confident and in control; at home—insecure and anxious. The contrast was stunning.

We started spending more and more nights apart. I enjoyed my independence when I wasn't consumed with where Eddie was, and with whom.

Cookie and I were having our share of mother/daughter issues. She had no tolerance for my affection for Eddie. To her, I was a thirty-one-year-old, unmarried, childless, underachiever—cavorting with an infantile rock boy waiter with no future. She could barely contain her disdain, which unleashed my fury. She thought I was an overly sensitive pushover and I thought she was a callously insensitive bully. Neither of us were ever wrong, or budged from our position.

I began keeping my distance. Even though Cookie wasn't crazy about my choices, she still wanted my company. At her insistence, we started seeing a therapist together.

After a few sessions, Arlene, in her early sixties, suggested I see a colleague who was closer to my age, and with whom she thought I might feel more comfortable and connected.

That's how I met Fay. She was animated, energetic and proactive. A lot of shrinks are in it for the long haul and play their patients to keep them around. Not Fay. She's in the business of get better, get out—until the next crisis.

We began with Cookie.

"If you're looking to be loved and supported, look somewhere else. It's a lousy hand, but it's the one you've been dealt. Minimize your contact with her." Period.

From there we moved on to Marvin and Dale. "Either learn to let them roll off your back, or quit." Period.

Eventually we made our way to Eddie.

"You need out of that."

I didn't want out, but I knew I had no choice. He was working on me daily, trying to chip away at my newfound confidence, but I held fast, certain that I was onto something. With stand-up, I was all too aware of my weaknesses. In promotion, I had no fear. Something was driving me and for once, I was not to be deterred.

Yet, I was so drawn to Eddie and his way of loving me. It was like trying to pry a magnet off the refrigerator. He was, without a doubt, the most passionate and romantic guy I'd ever known.

One Valentine's Day, I awoke to him sitting naked in bed, his guitar strategically placed. Just as I opened my eyes, without a word, he began to play "My Funny Valentine." Fueled with emotion, he gave Elvis Costello a run for his money. I have no memory if he gave me flowers or a card, or anything else, but for this Jewish Princess, the queen of expectations, he'd exceeded all of mine.

He wrote me a slew of incredible love songs, pledging eternal devotion. We could never be in the same room without him touching me, kissing me, loving me—except of course when he was making fun of me. And therein lay the rub—as there always is with bad boys.

Why did he have to be such an asshole?

— I'm a comic, a promoter, a joker, a toker,
I'm your mother, I'm your sister… Jack! —

In my early days at Rock Bar, I hit the comedy clubs a few nights a week. As my commitment to rock 'n' roll grew, I had less time for stand-up. Eventually, I was lucky if I got up once a week and, before long, that dwindled to once a month, at best.

Eddie and I were fighting constantly, so when Marvin okayed a week long vacation, about nine months into my tenure at Rock Bar, I jumped at the chance to join Cookie and Si in Vegas. My brother had gotten a job at the newly opened Mirage, and arranged adjoining rooms on the top floor.

As I was unpacking, the blinking Caesar's Palace marquee next door caught my eye. Donald Ranger, the weekend headliner, appeared in huge letters. Below, in smaller print, it read: "Featuring: Rick Weston." I hadn't been in touch with Rick since he'd fired me from The Giggle Group. I called Caesar's and asked for his room.

"Hi. This is Andi Stone, an old friend of Rick's," I said, almost apologetically.

A vaguely familiar voice, sounding pleasantly surprised, responded, "Andi, hi—it's Mark,"

The one friendly constant during my Giggle Group days, I'd always liked Mark. Often the lone laugher when I struggled to hold my own, he managed The Comedy Shack and doled out the weekly paychecks. He seemed to always be watching, finding the good in my work, when no one else did—including myself.

"Mark! Whaddya doing here?"

"I've been managing Rick for about a year." After a pause, he added, "Did you say, 'here'?"

"Look out your window. That's me waving from the top floor of the Mirage."

"Excellent! Can you come to the show tonight?"

"If it's okay to bring the familia I can."

"No problem. Wait for me at the table after the show. I'll come get you."

When we entered the showroom later that night, the maître d' escorted us ringside, to the choicest booth, front and center. I suppose celebrities get accustomed to VIP treatment but, for me, it's always thrilling.

Moments after the show ended, Mark came out to greet us, inviting me to join him and Rick for a late supper. We headed over to Caesar's Coffee Shop and caught each other up. I amped up my career, regaling Mark and

Rick with tales of my act, as if it were current information. I was MCing at Tony's club when I was able to steal away from Rock Bar, but that was happening very infrequently. In spite of that, I'd managed to amass about thirty minutes of material. It worked at Tony's for the most part because I felt so comfortable there. Attitude counts for a lot. If you boiled it down to the actual jokes, I probably had a decent ten.

On the spot, Mark offered me a slot, middling for Rick at The Comedy Shack. I'd dreamt of returning to the scene of my crime—killing, my revenge. But, I was in no way a middle act.

Not dealt the patience card in this life, I was rushing things, a lot. It hadn't really backfired yet, so I took that as a sign that I was doing the right thing.

The natural order was to do short spots for a couple of years, graduate to MC, eventually be a middle act (which, more often than not, took years) and, if one was truly gifted and/or lucky, it led to headlining. I was skipping ahead—two to three years at least.

Fearlessly, with reckless abandon, I accepted the challenge. We agreed on a Thursday night, a month away.

Twenty minutes.

I'd agreed to do twenty minutes.

How the fuck was I going to do twenty minutes?

I could do it. I had a whole month to prepare.

The hard way

After vacation, I returned to Rock Bar to discover Dale and Marvin frantic—barking orders and demanding all my attention. Business was better than ever, but they couldn't relax and enjoy it. More controlling than usual about the bands, the volume and my time, they kept me jumping.

Eddie was, as always, evasive, refusing to account for his whereabouts. *What was he hiding?*

I figured if I did stand up a few times a week for the next month and had a writing session or two with Lenny, I'd be set. The only problem was that between Dale, Marvin and Eddie there wasn't a minute.

With two weeks to go before my gig at The Comedy Shack, I called Lenny and arranged a writing session for the next afternoon. If he was cynical about my middling so early in my career, particularly after not even standing up regularly for so long, he didn't let on. We had a relaxed, fun time. *Damn, he's cute.* He helped me with a few new punch lines and tightened a couple of bits. I was ready.

The weekend before the gig, I managed to get one twenty-minute set in at Tony's. Despite the time lapse I still felt at home there. It was thrilling to be back on stage. My set went really well. I was definitely ready.

In the eleven months I'd been doing stand-up, my dad and his wife, Roxlyn, had yet to see my show and were resentful as hell that Cookie and Si had. The Comedy Shack was less than a mile from their house. In spite of my nagging gut, I invited them.

Of all the rules Lenny had taught in his class—stand-up nightly, or as often as is possible; don't rush the process, or your act; don't invite friends and relatives—at least not until you're well established and, spend the first year perfecting your five to ten minutes—there wasn't one I'd honored.

The night of the show, I got to the club an hour early. Mark was already there, waiting for me. Rick arrived a few minutes later. I was anxious and distracted, but did my best to hide it. I was also straight, which wasn't helping anything.

Tom Pepper was MCing, which was a huge relief. I'd worked with Tom in the city a number of times. He was easygoing, funny, fairly green, and black—which made us both minorities. In the stand-up world—in those days anyway—being a woman was definitely a handicap.

My dad and Roxlyn arrived about fifteen minutes before show time. As soon as I saw their faces, I knew I'd made a terrible mistake. As if their furrowed brows weren't enough, their six friends that followed sealed the deal. They looked like the Jewish extended family of American Gothic—serious, unsmiling, and freakin' scary.

They sat towards the back, on the side. I was grateful they'd be in the dark abyss. The room was thinly seated. A couple here, another there—perhaps twenty people in all. I'd worked to smaller houses in the city, always enjoying the challenge. There, however, they knew how to seat for maximum benefit. Close.

Here, the few customers were sprinkled throughout the cavernous room, which could easily have held a couple of hundred people. There was one young couple seated fairly close and center. The girl had that over-teased, over-sprayed, over-made-up thing. The guy, clearly bored and checking his Rolex for the hundredth time, was as slick as a rain-soaked highway.

Another couple, a bit further back and way off to the side, was busy talking, laughing and kissing, oblivious to the fact that they were in a public place. There was a group of three girls, in the center of the house, celebrating a birthday, and two other couples who were so far back I couldn't make them out.

No pressure. Small crowd. I'll just do my thing.

Tom opened the show with a strong, smart joke that barely got a chuckle. He continued with his best stuff. If not for the appreciation of Mark, Rick, and me, it would've been pretty quiet. Quickly reassessing, he moved to plan B, pulling out the filthy stuff. Not surprisingly, that won over most of the crowd. At the end of his ten, he closed with a few "nigger" jokes. They killed.

Bringing me up with, "And now, for a young lady making her Comedy Shack debut..." I faced almost certain death. As soon as you tell a comedy crowd that someone is new to stand-up, it's like telling a room full of ninth graders that they'll be having a substitute teacher that day. I could almost hear the "let's get 'er."

Shit! Fuck!

I silently reminded myself to calm down. It's only twenty minutes.

Smiling and doing my best to exude poise and confidence, I strode across the stage, thanked my friend Tom and set out to relax the crowd. *Who the fuck was gonna relax me?*

I figured it'd help to let them know that I had indeed worked the club before and, in fact, was a long time member of their beloved Giggle Group.

The half comatose crowd was completely unimpressed.

Nineteen minutes to go.

I decided to engage the couple down front in a little friendly chitchat, knowing that once I got them, the rest of the room would surely follow. It always worked at Tony's.

The girl wouldn't even look at me, let alone answer my questions. She was glaring at her boyfriend, daring him to so much as glance at me. He obliged her by giving me his back.

"Thanks for the love," I said, which got a titter of laughter. Encouraged, I turned my attention to the couple on the side.

They were talking to each other so intently, they didn't even notice that I was addressing them.

Eighteen minutes.

The three celebrants, a bit on the homely, chubby side, were staring at me with disdain.

"Who's our birthday girl?" I asked, cheerfully.

"She is," said the homeliest of the bunch, pointing to prettiest.

"Happy Birthday. How old are you today?" I asked, encouraged to be getting a response.

"Twenty-one," answered the birthday girl, flatly.

"Congratulations. Are you enjoying your first-ever cocktail? Wink-wink!"

"I was until now."

Zap! Right between the eyes. My cheeks flushed.

Seventeen minutes.

I knew I had to act quickly, so I stayed with the bitch, knowing it was risky.

"Do you have a boyfriend?" I asked, praying she did.

"Yup," was all that came back, but it was enough. It enabled me to move to material. I dove in with my ever dependable, "My boyfriend's so young" hunk.

Beginning with the "I'm finished" joke, I didn't even wait for laughs. I moved right into, "My boyfriend's so young, my negligees have feet."

Nothing.

Not a sound, except for the guffaws of Mark, Rick and Tom.

I forged on.

"My boyfriend's so young, his Harley has training wheels."

Silence.

Shit!

Looking over at my dad and Roxlyn, I noticed they both had their arms folded in front of them. I didn't need to be Sigmund Freud to read that body language.

Shaken, I continued, "He hates grocery shopping with me. Especially when I won't let him sit in the cart."

The only laughter—from my three compadres in the rear.

Holy shit! Fifteen minutes to go.

I was sweating now.

I segued into my family hunk, strong and dependable, not realizing in that moment, that it was almost all about Cookie and Si—not a mention of Jerry or Roxlyn.

Stony silence came back.

Inspired by the dire urgency to save myself, I offered, "My dad's here tonight. If things don't pick up pronto, I'm getting shipped off to nursing school."

I could hear Mark, Rick and Tom scream approval—the rest of the room, still as a morgue. Dad and Roxlyn, blank as a clean sheet of paper.

It continued on pretty much the same way for the duration of my set, through my political hunk and my pop culture exposé.

With five agonizing minutes to go, I noticed Rick and Tom shake their heads and escape to the green room. If only I could've joined them. Sweet Mark, my sole supporter, still laughing, was holding up the rear. He looked pained. Was he embarrassed for me or for them? I wanted to give him a hall pass and excuse him from my execution, but there was a modicum of comfort in his presence.

Abandoning any hope of reversal, my closer, my JAP Rap, always a surefire, ace-in-the-hole, loomed before me like another lead balloon. Fulfilling my expectations, it crashed and burned.

To a smattering of applause, and rousing cheers from Tom and Rick, who had rejoined the hooting Mark, I took a quick bow. As I exited the stage I noticed my dad and Roxlyn gazing south and barely managing to look at each other. My year of stand-up flashed before my eyes like a "best of" reel played for the latest *American Idol* loser.

If dying is easy and comedy is hard, dying while doing comedy is unmerciful.

I never did stand-up again.

FOUR

COURAGE

Rock, my world

Resigned that I was not meant to be a comedienne, I threw myself into the Rock Bar gig as if I were the CEO of a Fortune 500 company. Dale and Marvin could not have been happier. Eddie, thrilled that I would no longer be humiliating him on stage, supported me completely, until the next day, when Dead Drunk played the club. They were four talented, successful, hard partying, slutty, bad boys. Eddie again considered that the comedy thing might not have been so bad after all.

Oops, too late.

It was ironic that Lenny, Mona and a stand-up set had led me to rock 'n' roll. I never really looked back. After spending most of my life on stage, it was hard to fathom that I could drop it without regret. But this was still high profile—in a way more so, because I had some success with it. So often when I've moved on, I've left half my heart and one foot behind. Not this time. Segueing into my new life, I planted two feet firmly in it.

A couple of Rock Bar regulars, Maryann and Melanie always seemed to arrive à deux. Many a late night was spent commiserating with them and Lana, now a bartender, about our non-productive, sexual obsessions. Bonding quickly, the four of us began hitting the clubs regularly.

It was part of my job to promote Rock Bar events whenever and wherever possible, especially to the young, hip and moneyed. I was also trying to distance myself from Eddie, whom I was seeing less and less. Needy and neurotic, I always had to have a man in my life, and they usually overlapped just enough so that I didn't have to spend a night alone—until now.

I'd never been part of an estrogen posse before. There we were, four happening chicks, and not one of us ever got hit on. I guess we were pretty intimidating en masse. As I got more ambitious in my career and more daring in my social independence, Maryann mentored me on how to go clubbing by myself. It was terrifying the first time, less so the next and, within a couple of weeks, I was doing it nightly after work. I always found at least someone I knew and, as time wore on, I knew just about everyone at my regular haunts. Interestingly, no one hit on me then, either.

In my quest to grow as an independent woman, along with seeing Fay, my therapist, I was reading every self-help book I could get my hands on. My favorite at the time was, *Women Who Love Too Much.* However, my copy read, *Women Who Love Themselves Too Much,* thanks to Eddie and a big black marker.

The book suggested forming support groups and gave careful details on the protocol to follow. Eddie loved this idea.

Maryann, Melanie, Lana and I met once a week and followed the book's guidelines. Immediately breaking rules two and six, we ate during the meetings and drank a little wine as well. I was also always stoned. That didn't even come up in the rules. I assumed that made it acceptable behavior.

We shared dark secrets and gained strength from our mutual struggles. All their fingers were pointing to me ending it with Eddie. I sought further confirmation and made an appointment to see a famous psychic.

Yolanda was known for having helped the police solve crimes. I was instructed to bring photos, a blank tape and $100. Seemed a reasonable enough price for the answers to all my questions.

A couple of months later, on the night before my appointment, The Women Who Love Too Much, as we came to be known, hooked up at B-Bar. There was a long line behind the velvet ropes vying to get in, but we were regulars and friends with the doorman. It didn't hurt that we were four, single women, head to toe in black leather.

We got there as usual, just after midnight. We made our way through the crowd to the circular bar where Smitty had the Jack Daniels ready. Our friend Veronica was chatting up some tall, dark, handsome guy. As we approached, he turned, and our eyes met.

BINGGGGGGG!

He looked so familiar.

It took just a moment for me to connect that it was Vincent Santerini— Pandora Amora's pizza guy.

Much cuter in person than in magazines, he had "it" and he knew it. His smile was thrilling. Especially when directed at me.

I had one of those instant attractions I seem to have so many of. But this, was different.

After a little playful small talk, I forced myself to go find Maryann and Melanie. Veronica joined us and filled me in.

"Tim and I have double dated with him and Pandora a few times. They're madly in love, but Vincent has a hard time being her boy-toy. He hates the mocking he takes in the press."

I'd recently read that he'd punched out a photographer.

He was cocky, confident and smooth. He was also almost famous.

Watching him from across the bar while chatting with Veronica, I noticed him glancing over at us, more than once, flashing that devil grin. That boy spelled TROUBLE with a capital T that rhymed with ME, and boy, was I in TROUBLE.

There's this sort of unspoken code among girlfriends. When one of us gets interested in someone, it's hands off for the rest. He's yours, whether you end up with him or not. There are times when it's really hard honoring the code, but honor it we do, because we know that guys (even husbands, sometimes) will come and go, but our women are ours, forever.

I sensed the girls were toughing out the code. I'd done nothing more than chat with Vincent, but a connection had been made. Without a word of claim, he was mine. Veronica kept fueling the fire, while Maryann was winking at me with glee. It was already an assumption to them and, more importantly, to Vincent, who was circling the bar, brushing up close to me each time around with an innocent, "Oh, excuse me."

He was leading the flirt dance. I wasn't quite sure how to follow.

He had Pandora. I had Eddie—even though he hadn't spent the night in a while. We were definitely winding down. I was, for all intents and purposes, free, yet I felt like such a slut wanting yet another man. But, all told, in the prior thirteen years, I'd only been with two. Okay, three—sort of.

We circled 'round the bar for hours it seemed, occasionally stopping for a moment and a word or two. On one such spin, I spun right into Tim, who gave me a hug, just as Vincent was sashaying by.

"Hey, come meet my gal Andi," Tim yelled, over the din of house music.

"Meet?" Vincent mocked. "We go waaay back. We went to high school together!"

I was nine years older than him, obviously not classmate material. I laughed uproariously. Vincent, like most men, loved being appreciated for his wit. His chest swelled a foot.

A few Jacks later and a whole lot looser, my friend Bruce wandered by. As we chatted, Vincent circled. Bruce began introducing us. Vincent cut him off, repeating his earlier claim…"We go waaaaay back, we went to high school together." This was to become "our line." Either he was good, or I was an idiot.

For the rest of the evening we continued circling in opposite directions, but there was an invisible thread connecting us—it's pulled me for years.

Destiny calling. Destiny who?

The next morning, still groggy, I quickly assembled a collection of relevant photos, pulled a cassette out of the "dead band" pile and gussied myself up for my date with destiny. I thought I should look my best for my visit to Yolanda, a legendary psychic with a solid reputation for getting it right. I was chomping at the bit for insight and clarity.

Yolanda worked out of a luxury hotel in midtown, on a high floor with lots of glass and incredible views. It was a sparkling clear day—which I took as a sure sign that her vision would be unobstructed, as well. Her assistant escorted me into the main room of the suite. Yolanda, in a very bright colored caftan—middle-aged, overweight and bleached blond—swept into the room, smiling warmly. She pointed me over to a small round table and said, "Please sit. Do you have a tape?"

I handed her my cassette, which she slipped into a small boom box and said, "Let's begin."

"Let me start by saying that oftentimes names come to me quickly. The sounds sweep past my ears so fast that it's almost a blur. The exact name might be off, but the sound will be close, very close."

"Who's Cookie?"

Can't get much closer than that.

She asked for her picture and then said enough about my mom and Si to gain my trust.

"Who's Maryann?"

I handed her a photo of the two of us. Without taking a beat, she said, "She's a lifelong friend, someone you can trust. A gentleman will enter her life. He'll have children. I hear," and she said something like... Mah... Meh... (I couldn't remember the exact name she settled on, but no problem, it was all being recorded.)

I smiled. Maryann had been waiting a long time for Mah, Meh, whatever his name is.

Glancing at a photo of Eddie, she dropped it quickly and said, "He's history, absolutely no good for you."

With his snarly grin, she didn't need to be psychic to figure that out. She nailed Frank, and my old friend Bean (although she called him Dean. Must have been that sound whooshing thing), who'd been through everything with me since college.

"He's a keeper," she said.

No shit, Sherlock.

Then she got to the good part.

"Who's Vinny?"

My still hazy mind raced. Vinny, oh my God, *Vincent*. Why is she asking about him? I just met the guy.

Testing her, I asked, "I know a couple Vinnys, which one?"

"I think you know, " she said, challenging me back, and creeping me out, more than just a bit.

"Um... I don't have a picture of him. Do you have any magazines?"

"Why?"

"Vinny's a celebrity of sorts."

She shook her head knowingly. "Yes, yes, I think I know of whom you speak." "I wish I had a picture, but I'm sure. You will marry him."

"*WHAT?* You're kidding, right?"

"I'm not kidding, my dear."

"I just met him last night. Does he make it as an actor?"

"I see him behind the scenes, producing or directing, something, like that. Whatever it is, you'll like it."

I didn't hear another word she said. Thank goodness for the tape. When my session was up, I ran down to a pay phone and dialed Maryann.

"You're not gonna believe this! Yolanda said I'm gonna MARRY VINCENT!"

Silence on the other end, and then howling laughter.

I told her about Meh or Mah, or whatever her Prince Charming's name was going to be. Just the fact that there was a Prince Charming was all she needed to hear just then.

"I can't remember much more. But I have a tape. Interested?"

"Are you kidding?"

"I'll be right over."

I raced down to Thompson Street and up the four flights of stairs as if it were nothing. Maryann had the boom box all ready to go. I popped the tape in.

"TTTTTSSSSSSSSSSSSSSSSSSSSSSSSSSSSSSSSSSSSSSSSSSSSSSSS"

"That's weird, it must be on the other side," I said, as I turned the tape over, fast-forwarded, and hit play.

"TTSSSSSSSSSSSSSSSSSSSSSSSS"

We rewound, we fast-forwarded, we turned it over and over again and no matter when we hit play, all we heard was, "TTTTSSSSSSSSSSSSSSSSSSSSS."

"Ohmigod, ohmigod, ohmigod..." I mumbled, over and over. "That's what I get for trying to tape over a no-talent, yet erstwhile, struggling band."

Maryann ever the optimist, said, "Don't panic, it's fresh in your mind, we can reconstruct it. Tell me everything you recall and I'll write it down."

I did remember more than I thought I would, but it wasn't the same. I was freaked.

I never could remember Meh or Mah's full name. We've joked about it for years. Especially when Maryann's Prince Charming did arrive and his name was Bill.

Trying to comfort me and get me back to my earlier joy, Maryann reminded me that I'd heard the words. I didn't need a tape to verify it.

Vincent was to be my man.

———— Reefer, RockBoys and Cheetos... oh my ————

I was elated by Yolanda's news. But, what the fuck? Vincent was having a very high profile romance with Pandora Amora. Photos of them snuggling were in magazines everywhere. It was 1989 and Pandora was at the height of her fame, getting the respect she'd always craved and looking better than ever—thanks to the glow of love and some very extensive cosmetic surgery.

The Women Who Loved Too Much were having our weekly meeting at Maryann's a few days later. As always, before we officially began, we sat around eating crap and talking shit. I was silently debating whether to share my psychic news with Lana and Melanie. My inner voice was screaming, "DON'T."

When will I learn that when my inner voice speaks, I need to shut the fuck up and listen? Not this day. I told them everything, about Vinny, the marriage, everything.

Lana, cross-legged on the floor, fell backwards, laughing. "That is the greatest thing I've ever heard! Ever! I bet Vinny has a lot of really cute little friends. I believe. Hallelujah!"

"Amen," said Maryann.

The three of us carried on like eight year olds.

Melanie just sat there. I knew she wasn't into the psychic stuff but she seemed angry. It made me uncomfortable. It made us all uncomfortable. I smoked a bowl and started the meeting.

At midnight we met up at B-Bar. Like vampires thirsting for blood, that's when we came alive.

The club was buzzing. Quickly scanning the room I caught sight of Vinny leaning seductively at the far end of the bar, looking not unlike John Travolta *in Urban Cowboy* when Debra Winger notices him for the first time. I wiped my mouth before the drool could dribble down my chin. It wasn't just me. Pandora had been quoted as saying that he was the most beautiful man she'd ever seen. And she'd seen quite a few.

Sensing my presence, he turned in my direction and shot me a smile. As if in quicksand, I couldn't move. Fortunately, Lana approached at just that moment. Unaware of the spell I was under, she dragged me into reality and up to the bar for a shooter.

While downing my third shot, I got bumped from behind, almost knocking the glass out of my hand. Slightly perturbed, I turned around ready to display a nice sarcastic smirk and looked right into pizza boy's big brown eyes. They were laughing, those eyes, and in an instant, so was I. I tried to maintain my huff, but neither of us was buying it.

Re-introducing him to the girls, he reminded them and me, that we went waaay back, to high school. We batted our eyes and laughed too loudly at his jokes. When he'd gotten the sufficient boost he was craving, he swaggered off with a self-satisfied smirk. We giggled and toasted my future groom.

For the next four nights, at the stroke of midnight, as I made my entrance to the lower levels of B-Bar, each night afraid to hope, there he'd be. It was always the same. Stolen glances from across the crowded room—pretending not to notice, not to stare—looking away, avoiding eye contact and yet, somehow, always ending up within inches of each other, getting embarrassed, saying a few words and moving on.

On the fifth night, he was nowhere to be found. I immediately began jonesing for him. An hour or so later, distracted and flirting with Tad (a tall, good looking rock 'n' roller I'd recently started booking), I got rear-ended so hard that I had to grab the bar to stop my momentum. Furious, I whipped around and there was Vinny, shaking his head and wagging his finger. Without explanation he walked away and started sort of dancing with himself. I couldn't take my eyes off him and he damn well knew it. Tad did not like the interruption and was talking very close, staring into my eyes, working hard to maintain my total attention. Next thing I knew, he was sort of dancing and leading me into his moves.

Why is it that for months, single and looking, not one guy expressed interest in me—not the slightest—and now, here were two gorgeous boys making dancing fools out of themselves?

Why? Who gives a fuck why?

The next night Maryann and I were having a combined birthday party at Rock Bar. I casually mentioned it to Vinny, after spending three hours planning my one sentence invitation. He nodded and didn't commit, giving me a teeny taste of the fun that was yet to come.

Tad was nudging me to leave and have a nightcap elsewhere. As much as I wanted to stay, I suspected my leaving with Tad would potentially do more good than harm.

Oh, what a tangled web I weave.

As Tad and I headed for the exit, I caught a glimpse of Vinny, chatting up a young lovely. Checkmate.

It wasn't until we hit the street that I noticed how intoxicated Tad was. Watching pizza boy had taken its toll. He insisted we go around the corner to his place.

He was acting kind of scary. So, naturally, I agreed.

Within moments of smoking a bowl, he was sloppy, stoned and all over me. Trying to push him off with all of my strength, the more I resisted, the more he persisted. I was sweating, my mind racing to memories of Frank and that awful night. The cocky cocktease was scared. Really scared.

Just as I was beginning to panic, Tad's roommate bounded through the door. Figuring we were engaging in an intimate act, he turned to leave. I grabbed his arm and insisted he join us. As he sat down, I excused myself to go to the bathroom and ran out the front door like an escaping POW.

Oh, the glamorous life of a single girl.

The next day, still pretty shook, I barely gave thought to my impending birthday party. Thankfully, John and Lana saw to everything. By nightfall, Rock Bar's VIP room almost looked like one. In no time, the place began filling up. Maryann and I were both working the room, relaxed and joyful—last night's nightmare on hold.

Lenny stopped by for a quick scotch and a peck on the cheek before his set. *He sure was cute.*

I was chatting with Rick—a big, adorable, bad boy drummer Maryann had a thing for. We were both admiring her from across the room, when the air suddenly became electric. Without turning around, I knew. Pizza boy was in the house.

All eyes were fixed in his direction, although only peripherally. No one would look directly at him; they had to continue what they were doing and pretend not to look. But they just couldn't help it. Despite being a boy-toy pizza-boy, he was "the shit," with a measure of fame (or infamy, if you asked him).

I could feel my cheeks flush and my heart race. Marvin and Dale were freaking in the corner. Before I had a chance to welcome Vinny, they were in my face excitedly congratulating me on my new friend, shocked that I had actually gotten him to Bleecker Street. To them, this was a golden publicity opportunity. Like '50s cartoon characters, they might as well have had dollar signs etched on their eyeballs.

Vinny was slowly making his way around the room, chatting with Lana, Melanie and Maryann. I casually moved towards him. Almost simultaneously, we both turned our backs to the other, just in time to bump tush to tush—accidentally on purpose.

Vinny flashed that grin and said, "Well, if it isn't my old high school bud."

I laughed.

Yes, I'd laughed at the same joke thirty damn times already, but I would've bought a bridge from that boy.

The room was packed and we were standing very close. I silently mouthed, "Thanks for coming."

"This is *your* party?" I was just in the neighborhood and got thirsty."

Rock Bar was so not his scene. This was definitely personal.

He leaned in, gently kissed my cheek and whispered, "Happy Birthday."

He then took Maryann's face in his hands and kissed her cheek as well. Unseen by anyone, she grabbed my hand and gave me a tight squeeze. Maryann, true friend, was genuinely happy for me.

Life was good.

Rock Bar's stock was on the rise. I was working round the clock, determined to put us on the map and myself along with it.

B-Bar became like my second home. I was comfortable there and required no accompaniment to enter. From the moment I hit the velvet ropes, I was welcomed like family. The bouncer, Bobby V, always made me feel like rock royalty by unhooking the chain divider as soon as my toe hit the curb, exiting a cab. Once down in the bowels of coolness, I could assess the room from the entrance platform, sight friends and make my move through the crowd to my destination. The bar was my usual hang. Smitty always had the bourbon waiting.

Most weeknights were busy, but not hectic, with the exception of "Model Mondays," which I never attended. My self-esteem couldn't have handled it. It was B-Bar's biggest scene. The club was loaded with athletes, rock stars, actors, middle-aged gangsters and wannabes—all trying to score with the beautiful, young, skinny-as-shit, very tall women.

Wednesday nights were devoted to live music. It was all about the jam. I lived for Wednesdays and the chance to hear Bowie, Jon Bon Jovi, Richie Sambora, Peter Frampton, even Mick, get up and do covers with the house band. The best part was that when they weren't playing, they were "playing," just like the rest of us—and totally accessible.

The room was filled with musicians eagerly waiting their turn to take the stage. There were also plenty of women—rock chicks, groupies, and I was certainly one of them. Even though I didn't sleep around, I flirted my way through.

I envisioned myself promoting there one day—queen of the Wednesday Night Jam.

My reality at Rock Bar wasn't so bad.

Rick Derringer, "Rock and Roll, Hoochie Koo'd," on a regular basis. (When I was barely a teenager, I'd snuck in to see him play at the Fillmore East just before it closed.) Carole King, Elliot Easton, Eddie Ojeda, Taylor

Dayne, Badfinger and Davy friggin' Jones all graced our tiny stage. They were my heroes.

A couple of sexy, swarthy, Italian types, The Moretti Brothers, were playing this night. They were working with Ursula Rain on her comeback album. She'd been promising for weeks to stop by. I worshipped her, knew every word to every song on her debut album, "Lyrical Lad." I'd performed them nightly in my bedroom for years.

I'd had a little crush on Sal Moretti for a while. Nothing big, just a very subtle flirt that made working on the nights he was playing more fun. He was shy. His brother James, the front man, was the outgoing one—the one who chatted up the ladies and got most of them, I suspect.

James waved me over, introducing me to Ursula. Fawning over her, I declared my lifelong adulation and devotion. I showered her in french fries. Ursula loved to eat and we had the best fries short of Nathan's. She hung out for hours, singing and eating.

It was amazing to have this icon performing an almost private concert on this quiet Tuesday evening.

At 2 am, we turned the house lights full up, not so subtly suggesting that everyone get the fuck out. It was our time to play. James and Ursula were chatting in the corner,

"Want to join us for a bite?" she asked.

Are you kidding me???

I'd been living at Cookie's for months while I half-heartedly apartment searched. But, Eddie had invited me to spend the night. We both had an itch that needed scratching. Knowing he was out drinking every night until the bars closed, never saying where, or with whom, I figured—fuck it. Hanging out with Ursula, my angst-ridden, teen years chanteuse, was a once in a lifetime opportunity. I'd get to Eddie's when I got there.

Sal went home to bed.

Damn.

James, Ursula and I headed off to The Empire Diner. Thanks to her easy manner and the joint I had smoked in the back room before leaving, I was pretty relaxed. She invited me to share a Caesar salad with her. It was outrageously delicious and loaded with garlic. Eddie despised the scent of garlic and chastised me for such eating. It'd been years since I'd enjoyed a garlic laden Caesar.

Screw him.

I ate with gusto.

If he could get plastered, I could eat whatever the hell I wanted. We weren't kissing anymore anyway. Sadly, that's one of the first things to go when time and contempt creep in.

I had no way to know at the time, but there would be a far more relevant consequence for my frivolous gastronomy.

James and Ursula drove me back to The Heights. The three of us strolled arm in arm down the Promenade as if we'd done it a million times before. Sandwiched tightly between them, arms intertwined a la "Off To See The Wizard," we giggled our way from one end to the other.

Ursula whispered, "I engineered this evening at James' request. He seems to have a bit of a crush on you."

"James? Really?"

I was shocked. I seemed to be the only woman he didn't flirt with. Besides, I'd had my eye on his unassuming, younger brother.

Quickly reassessing, I deduced that for all intents and purposes, I was single. Eddie and I barely spoke. Vinny hadn't made a move of any significance. *Why not?*

I gave Ursula the go-ahead. She must have given James the high sign, for in the next moment he was snuggling against me as we walked. Glancing at my watch, I realized that I might not beat Eddie to his place. I disentangled and requested a ride. Before exiting the car, James asked me out for the following evening. Really anxious now, I scribbled my mother's number and raced to the door.

Creeping down to Eddie's lair, I sighed with relief when I realized I was alone. In the next instant fury began to overtake me. Where was he, anyhow? It was almost 4:00 a.m. He hadn't even called. The answering machine light was steady. *Where the fuck was he?*

Almost immediately, I realized the absurdity of my anger, and let go a laugh.

By the time Eddie stumbled down the stairs a few moments later, I couldn't have cared less. This change in my behavior did not sit well with the boy, who was used to my histrionics. He tried hard to engage me in battle. I was having none of it. My last waking thoughts were of where I'd begin my apartment search. I was a grown-up, I was single, and I needed to face it, once and for all.

The next day, while I was putting a few miles on Cookie's treadmill, Si came walking through, inhaled deeply and smiled broadly.

"Heard you have a date tonight?"

"Uh huh."

"Does Eddie know?"

"How do you know it's not with Eddie?"

"Easy," he said, inhaling deeply.

With that, he laughed heartily and kept moving.

Shit! I reeked.

Si knew well of the moratorium I had placed on garlic since my affair with the Eddie had begun. The entire room was under a haze emitting from my every pore.

No amount of toothpaste, mouthwash or gum could mask the smell of that day old Caesar salad. Of all days to end my garlic abstinence, this was not a savvy choice.

James was waiting for me at a little watering hole across the street from his apartment. He expeditiously began the seduction by speaking very softly, directly into my ear—as if the low muted jukebox was overpowering us with its sound.

All I could think of was my stench. I knew my perfume and six sticks of gum could not help me up close. His lips were brushing my hair and skin with each word. I could feel his warm breath with every syllable, romancing my entirety—all except my brain, which was screaming for me to run. I was nodding appropriately, not uttering a word, lest I should have to open my mouth and let that foulness out.

After a couple of drinks, I turned around and—whoops—there we were at his place, on his futon. *What now, smarty pants?* I slinked out of his grasp, rolled a big fat joint and sat across from him, smoking long and hard.

Maybe if he got high enough he wouldn't notice the odor. Maybe if I got high enough, I wouldn't care. There wasn't enough grass in Manhattan for either.

We kissed a little, but it was awkward. Maybe the garlic wasn't the only thing stinking up the joint. Perhaps we just lacked chemistry.

I was spending the night at Cookie's and it was late. I used that as my exit excuse.

James was due to play Rock Bar the following week. With each passing day that he didn't call, my ardor rose. Despite my feminist outer shell, my interior was pure 1950s. Even though James was not what I wanted, I wanted him to want me, damn it!

A few days later, Maryann and I were hanging at B-Bar when Vinny sauntered in. He did his little dance, sucked me in and then split—leaving me wanting.

Always left wanting.

Rick the shit was playing Maryann too. While commiserating about the pathetic state of our love lives, Maryann snarled, "Dick-dogs. They're all dick-dogs." And offered this definition:

\'**dik-dog**\ n **1** *slang* **commitment phobic charmer;**
2 *slang* **manipulative bad boy 3** *truth* **self-absorbed prick.**

It so perfectly described the rock boys we were forever falling in lust with, who we welcomed into our lives to play, only to break our hearts. We were so needy, hungry and desperate for love, yet, ultimately, so unapproachable. Even those brave enough to try were exhausted by the effort—almost forced to take shelter and comfort elsewhere.

Smart women are a pain in the ass.

I was obsessing about two men now. Damn that Vinny. Screw that James. I hadn't even given him a thought until he rushed me. "Rushing" is an old dick–dog technique of blinding a woman with attention, hanging on her on every word and admiring her beauty with each unblinking stare. And then, hurry up and wait—for the calls that stop coming, the dates that don't happen and the burning desire that's left to smolder and die a gruesome, torturously slow death.

Here we were, two horny women in our prime, ready to rock and no guys willing to roll—left high and dry (in every sense of the word). Maryann said she knew the cure, some herbal oil guaranteed to do the trick. A few little sips and the obsession would lift. We raced to the all-night health food store.

Bach Remedy to the rescue. A few Cheetos wouldn't hurt, neither.

Is it live or is it Memorex?

I soon found the perfect L-shaped studio, imperfectly located two buildings away from my ex-husband, Frank. A child of divorce, I had a habit of seeking the familiar. I'd lived on this same street, in four different apartments, over a twenty-year period. When I began my latest quest, I was immediately drawn to listings in the area, already familiar with the local restaurants, shops and pot dealers. I didn't really need to know the dealers—that's what boyfriends were for.

Within weeks, the papers were signed and I was moving into my first owned home of my own, thanks to a generous gift from Cookie and a hefty, interest-free loan from Si. Cookie gifted me with a few furniture treasures she'd saved for me and helped me scour the city for the rest. Few things gave Cookie greater pleasure than shopping, so for the most part, we were saved from our usual contentious bickering. Soon the place was looking chic and inviting—black, white and wood—ultra modern, accented with antiques. Somehow it worked.

For the first time, I was living on my own, without a man in my life, and I wasn't lonely.

Unfazed by the lack of square footage, I created my ideal environment without any interference or contrary opinion. To separate the kitchen from the living room, I had a Formica island built with a large overhung lip that allowed for tall, comfortable, armed stools. It served as prep-station and storage unit for the kitchen, a divider from the living room, an eating table, a workspace and my favorite place to hang. The rounded end was partially in the kitchen, jutted a bit into the hallway and began the living room. Placing one of my comfy, black leather, high backed stools in that spot, it immediately became my sacred space. From that vantage point I could see most of the apartment, and, if I bent down just a bit and caught just the perfect angle, I could glimpse the tip of the Empire State building. I felt safe in my cozy little dwelling, especially right there in that spot. At long last, I felt viable on my own.

At first, Eddie had a key and would come by mostly to enrich his vast porn collection. He didn't have all the cool Manhattan public access channels in Brooklyn Heights and had become very fond of *The Robin Byrd Show*. I'd come home at 4:00 a.m. to find him happily taping away. Sleeping with me was merely icing on the cake, certainly not his raison d'etre.

We'd become more like brother and sister, squabbling constantly, our mutual resentments simmering. Kissing seemed yucky, almost incestuous, yet there was still a mutual fascination and attraction. I made an effort to physically detach, hoping it would help me to do so emotionally as well.

While hugging the outside corner of my double bed, trying hard to not have any part of me touch any part of him, I drifted off to sleep.

I was in a closet—walk-in would not begin to describe it. It was more like a drive-through—for a city bus. There was an entire wall of shoes and another of purses, hats, scarves and belts. Clothes were hanging at various levels with a sort of runway down the middle.

The colors were vibrant. Did I usually dream in color? I could see clearly, but felt like I was hiding underneath the low hanging slacks. I remember feeling afraid of being found. Was someone nearby?

We were lying on plush, red, carpeting. He was kissing me. I could smell Rise shaving cream on his freshly groomed skin and feel his lips as they made their way all over my face—brushing my cheeks, eyes and forehead. I could taste his mouth, with the faintest hint of Coffee Time soda vaguely lingering. I opened my eyes and looked into his. It was Vinny. VINNY? It was Vinny!

I had the unmistakable feeling that this was Pandora's closet and she was close at hand. We were quiet, very quiet, which fueled the fire. I shut my eyes, losing myself in his kiss.

Opening them again, something was different. I could feel the firm mattress under my back. I was now in my bed with Eddie, who was fast asleep.

I was exhilarated and exhausted. I felt jet-lagged as if I had just flown across the country. I could still smell Vinny's shaving cream on my skin, still taste the Coffee Time on my lips. *How could that be?*

I wasn't one to remember my dreams, thanks to my daily pot consumption. Occasionally, an image or feeling would be with me first thing in the morning, but that was unusual. I could rarely hold on to the thought. This particular morning was different.

I was on the treadmill when Eddie got up and had a cup of coffee. I couldn't look him in the eye; I was sure he knew—that he could tell. I felt like I was wearing it all over me—the scent of Vinny's cologne still on my skin. Eddie was talking; I was a million miles away, responding in one-word answers.

"What's up with you, woman? You're not yourself this morning."

"Dunno."

"What you thinking on, Dee?"

Eddie hadn't called me Dee in a long time. He must have sensed something. He only called me that when he was scared.

The more thought I gave the dream, the more I could recall. That was certainly new for me. Dream details always quickly faded, unless I was swift enough to immediately write them down. I was rarely that on top of it.

Digging a bit deeper, I recalled a black leather vest with silver beaded fringe hanging on a hook, like it had been worn that day, or would be the next. A black leather cowboy hat was on the hook just above it and boots were off to the side. Damn.

As the day worn on, the surer I became that this was like no dream I'd ever experienced before.

Maryann stopped into Rock Bar shortly after I arrived. Standing near the entrance, I was reliving the kiss for the zillionth time that day. When she snapped her fingers in front of my glazed eyes, I shook myself out of it.

"Where were you?" she asked.

"That's a very good question."

I proceeded to tell her the story in minute detail. Maryann didn't blink. When I got to smelling the shaving cream after I woke, her eyes lit up.

"During astral projection, the physical body remains in one place, while the spiritual body travels to another, unperceived. I, myself, have experienced this phenomenon, and know of others who have as well."

Maryann was a very smart, keenly intuitive person; I wanted to believe her. Hell, I did believe her. It was the only answer that made any sense, even if it meant to stop making sense. How else did I get there? That was not my beautiful closet.

So, if I actually was there, was Vinny really there, too?

Did he awaken that morning confused?

Would there be any indicators the next time I saw him?

Or was Maryann just a whack?

Maybe this was just the best dream ever.

I couldn't shake it. As if the possibility of Vinny being my future husband weren't enough—that kiss certainly was.

Pizza boy was taking up way too much room in my head; I was itching to see him. Desperate is more like it. We had the same hang, so I knew if I weren't running into him he must not be around. I still searched for him each night at B-Bar, hoping he'd surface. I rummaged the gossip columns, frantically seeking information that might indicate his return.

A new downtown club on West 23rd Street, I-dee-o, was trying to give B-Bar a run for its money. They already owned Thursdays. It was their jam night and anyone who was anyone was showing up to play: Axl Rose, in his heyday, Ace Frehley, Greg Allman, Stanley Jordan and Cyndi Lauper, among many others. Then there were those who just came to check out the hang: Eddie Murphy, Nick Nolte, Mets pitcher Ron Darling—and on and on.

Entering into a grand old barroom, it emptied into a big dance space with a stage at the far end. There was a small, guarded, side door, stage left, which led to the kitchen and was the not-so-secret entrance to the VIP room above.

The upstairs was divided into four rooms. One housed the performers and celebrities seeking privacy. Holding eight people at most, it was set off from a larger room, which was empty except for a solitary couch, rarely used. That led into the main VIP bar. It was grungy and sparse with the perfect rock vibe. At the far end of the room was a small door, always closed, with a huge unsmiling bouncer protecting it. This led to the coveted VIPP room. (Which stood for: Very Important Person. Period.) Quite a few C-listers spent considerable effort trying to scratch their way in there.

A few weeks after my dream, there was a blurb on Page Six that Vincent and Pandora had split. I'd read that garbage too many times to believe a word.

It was a Thursday. I was at I-dee-o, as were hundreds of others. Making my way up the jammed back stairs to the VIP room, as I neared the top, I looked up and there he was, a few stairs ahead, staring at me. I smiled. He responded, albeit dimly, looking distraught. Jostled by the throngs coming and going, I finally reached him.

"I need a hug," he said, as he rested his head on my shoulder.

Holding him tightly, I knew instantly the newspaper had gotten it right this time. He was in pain. There was never any doubt that he was madly in love with Pandora and had been for years. The fact that he mildly flirted with me was moot. Right then, I was his friend. The fact that he had sought comfort from me was enough—for the moment, anyway.

We didn't talk about her. I don't think Vincent ever even said her name in my presence (although I'm sure she was never far from either of our minds).

He took my hand, leading me downstairs. Standing in the back, listening to the music, there were no words. A couple of times he squeezed my hand.

After a bit, he sighed. "I think I'm gonna take off."

I smiled wanly, "Sure, I... uh..."

He interrupted my awkwardness. "I know. Thank you," he said, his eyes momentarily locking with mine. Leaning over, he kissed my forehead, allowing his lips to linger there a moment, gave my hand a last squeeze and disappeared into the crowd.

I felt sick. I had long imagined him being free, but not like that. I knew I must really care about him, because all that mattered was his happiness, and the fact that right then, he had none.

Vinny was around a lot after that. I ran into him most nights at one club or other. It was always the same. We flirted. I swooned. He left.

Why was it that with almost everyone else I was sharp and capable, but around him I was a blithering idiot?

One night, when The Women Who Love Too Much were in full swing. Maryann, Melanie and Lana were strewn about in various niches of B-Bar chatting up an old friend or two. I was shamelessly ogling Richie Sambora, who had just come off the stage, hot and sweaty. Hot, indeed.

From the corner of my eye I could see Melanie throwing her head back in laughter. Her reaction seemed exaggerated and unnatural. Following her gaze, I wasn't surprised to see that Vinny was the source of her joy.

Hey, wait a minute, that's my gig.

I tried to read their lips, while at the same time appear focused on Richie, who was moving on. Now alone, attempting to act cool, I was anything but.

Quickly making my way over to Maryann, I was determined not to watch Melanie and Vinny. I lost track of them just as I was getting bumped from behind. Before I had even turned around, Vinny's now familiar voice from behind me spat, "Oh yeah?"

"What?"

"Husband, huh?"

I felt like I'd been kicked in the solar plexus. That bitch! I couldn't believe Melanie had betrayed me. This was not how he was supposed to find out. After the "I dos," was my plan. How fucking humiliating.

He wanted to know exactly what Yolanda had said—not that he believed any of it.

I explained the name whooshing thing that she had described and her asking, "Who's Vinny," clear as a bell, right off the bat.

"It took me a moment, having just met you. I was sure she must have meant someone else. I then sort of explained who you were and she said, 'That's the one.'"

I left out the marriage part, but clearly Melanie hadn't.

At his probing, I continued, "I asked if your future was as an actor, and she said, "He'll do something else, behind the scenes—producing, directing—whatever it is, you'll like it."

Vinny rolled it around in his brain a while, smiled, then added, "Yeah, well, you're not my type."

Ouch!

Things were weird after that. He still flirted with me, but it wasn't the same. He always stopped himself. A couple of times he reminded me, again, that I was not his type, but there were mixed signals all over the place.

Once, in the midst of a tease, he said, "You know I love you."

I do? *You do?*

A few days later, while giving me a hello hug, he said, "I don't like your perfume." It seemed so hurtful and random. I was wearing Magie Noire and had been for a while, always receiving compliments on it. Did my scent really offend him, or was he just trying to push me away? He seemed to always be putting a negative spin on me. But that didn't diminish my ardor. Not one little bit.

I resented the hell out of Melanie. This was all her fault.

Months earlier, a cute young rocker had invited me to the Bottom Line to hear his friend's band. I hardly knew the guy. Feeling shy, I invited Melanie along as a buffer. As soon as she caught sight of my little friend she crossed her legs provocatively, played with her hair and batted her eyes. *People really do that?* Turning her chair to face him, she spoke only to him, giving me her back for the rest of the show. This continued at the bar later. She literally picked up her stool to face him. I ended up being the odd man out. She knew the circumstance—that it was a sort of a first date. But, the boy didn't matter to me—she did, so I let it slide.

Vinny was different and she knew it. Soon after meeting him, she'd let slip that she'd cut out a magazine photo of him and put it on her desk. Thinking it strange at the time, I paid no attention to my nagging gut. Reflecting back to my retelling of Yolanda's prophecy and Melanie's self-righteous indignation, I realized all the signs were there. She wanted him, too. Code or no code, she was going for it.

A short time later, without taking pause, I blurted out, "I can't forgive you for telling Vinny my secret—not that you're asking." Somehow, I likened her to Joel Steinberg, the wife-beating baby killer. I apologized for that ridiculousness, but I certainly made clear my hurt and disappointment. I'd confided my secret in the sanctity of our support group. Melanie had betrayed that. She was not a woman to trust. Therefore, she was not a woman to love. It broke my heart and The Women Who Love Too Much.

I check in on her through Maryann from time to time, still suffering the loss. I wished I'd have handled it differently. Melanie wasn't trying to hurt me. She wasn't thinking about me. She was thinking about Melanie. With a guy like Vinny, can I really blame her?

Fuck, yeah!

The skinny on my fat

I've spent almost my entire adult life trying to lose the same ten pounds. At times I've been successful, but not for long. My body seems to always drift back to its comfort zone, at least five pounds more than I'd like, and closer to twenty pounds more than any actress my height. I've been on every diet, worked out doing every conceivable kind of exercise, and still can't look at my naked body in the mirror without getting queasy—except for a couple of days in the summer of '89.

Comparing myself to Pandora was a friggin' nightmare. With personal trainers, cooks—all the resources known to womankind at her fingertips, she had a killer body. I knew she worked hard for it, but despite the workouts and plastic surgery, there was no denying she'd been blessed.

I was determined to not be the chunky one. I wasn't fat per se, not for the real world, but in the land of rock boys and girls, I was enormous. At least that was my perception. I had hips, boobs, thighs and a butt—a big old butt. Although I'd been working out for years, I often ate more than any treadmill could compensate for.

One night at Rock Bar, while being rushed by yet another, unavailable, dick-dog musician, I overheard him calling me "the face." The implication being that I was attractive—from the neck-up.

I was crushed.

Snacking was my downfall. I could show some restraint at meals, but that hour right before bed, my defenses were nonexistent. Actually, I could eat way too much at any given time and often did.

When I wasn't eating, I was thinking about what I wanted to eat next. I've spent more than half my life planning meals, eating and then feeling guilty about it. I'd make rules and plans and never stick to them. Dieting constantly, and failing, if not for my daily workouts, I can't imagine what size I'd be. Usually within ten pounds of my target weight, I fluctuated day-by-day, hour-by-hour, and weighed myself incessantly.

I read an article years ago about an eating disorder where the primary symptom is an obsession with food. It described my disease to a T. No bingeing or purging, simply constant thought around food. It has a name, although I can't remember it—probably because I'm too focused on the leftover pizza in my fridge.

There was no deterrent powerful enough to rid me of my single-minded, all-consuming passion for eating.

Except Vinny.

There was also, always, the ever-present reminder of Pandora—sleek, fit and chicer than shit. I saw her only in magazines and movies; she didn't know I existed—yet, I still imagined her mocking me.

"You think you're gonna get Vincent? You? You, with the chunky thighs and big ass? Ha! Be gone. You have no power here."

Real or imagined, it was a lot to live up to for anyone, let alone a Jewish girl with big hips.

How the hell could I compete with her?

Signing up for Nutrisystem, I was determined to stick to it—no matter what. That was just prior to the discovery that it could potentially eat one's liver. Hey, that's a pound or two, right there!

For the first time in my life, I didn't cheat. I ate exactly what was allowed and that was it. Not a single french fry passed my lips for weeks. Consuming so little fat, coupled with my insane workouts—exceeding two hours daily—within two months I'd lost twelve pounds and my period. Prioritizing, I continued, not realizing at the time that I was risking a vital organ and my ability to spawn.

It was worth it. For a few days, in July of 1989, I was happy with my body.

Once my daily workout was complete, I rewarded myself with the day's first buzz. The business at hand, followed. Usually I had press releases to write, tapes to listen to and phone calls to return. All better done stoned.

I was a very functional pothead, an ambitious workaholic. I never missed deadlines and was usually adding responsibilities, rather than avoiding them. There was basically nothing in my life that I did in moderation. I still find it a challenge to seek that balance.

Following the deskwork, I refreshed my buzz, showered and headed to Rock Bar by five—in time for my daily battle with Dale and Marvin about the bands I was booking, money and the volume.

We had a small dinner crowd. Working hard to find just the right music to develop a regular early scene, I had my eye on Pete Donner. Pete was an attractive, charming, southern rock boy with long, wavy, blond hair. Perfectly tanned, with a well-toned physique, he had huge dimples and a wacky, winning way. He looked very much like David Lee Roth, only better—less weathered. He dressed in short-shorts and midriff tops, no matter what the season, and usually had at least a nail or two, painted red. There was never any question as to his sexual orientation; he loved women—all women—and they began to line up to support him.

Dale and Marvin insisted he sing only cover songs. Performing the gamut from Elvis to Hendrix, he quickly became frustrated by the limitation and formed a side band with five adorable girls, to showcase his crazy, catchy originals. I began managing them and getting them gigs elsewhere.

While handling the booking, PR and publicity at Rock Bar, I juggled Eddie's band and "Pastor Pete," while courting a solo artist who'd had a successful soap opera career and wanted to pursue his songwriting and performing. In the best interests of everything I was doing, I'd hit the clubs once Rock Bar closed for the night. I could network for Rock Bar and shop my small roster. On Sundays, I'd often head over to I-dee-o after work to chat up Billy, one of the owners, in hopes of romancing him into giving me a gig.

Unlike Rock Bar, most clubs hired promoters to run a night. I dreamt of owning one, as Pat the Fat did Thursdays at I-dee-o and Tim did Wednesdays at B-Bar. I had some cred running a little hip club in the village, but it wasn't the same.

One Sunday, a few weeks into my Nutrisystem plan, I celebrated by buying some tight black jeans and a midriff top that exposed a few inches of my now flat, muscled tummy. Heading over to I-dee-o (which was empty), I sat down on an overstuffed couch by the stage, decided to finish my Bud Lite and head home.

Through the blackness approached a dark-haired, leather-clad male with a familiar gait. As he neared the overhead bulb, there was no mistaking that it was *him*. There were no buffers. It was just us. Trying to downplay my terror, I took a sip of beer, missing my mouth almost completely. *Smooth.* Distracted, he didn't seem to notice. Plopping down on the coach, sitting very close, he whispered, "This place is dead, let's get outta here."

You mean with me? My brain screamed inside my head. Out of my mouth, came other verbiage. "Sure, let's go. Um, where to? I live straight east of here."

"Let's go to my place," Vinny said decisively, jumping up with new energy. Grabbing my hand, he pulled me up with him, leading me to the door.

Blindsided, the crazy thoughts wouldn't stay at bay. *He doesn't find me attractive, yet he flirts with me all the time. Never making a move, he's always coming towards me. He's never asked me out, but now he's taking me home. What does he want with me?*

I really didn't care. I'd have gone anywhere, done just about anything with him. I had mad passion for the boy and there was no logic in it.

We hopped in a cab and sat close. I was self-conscious and feeling fat. I had no idea what was in store. Was this a date? Were we just going to hang out? *What's on his mind?*

It was late Sunday night. The traffic was light. Within minutes we were at his place. The apartment was sparsely furnished—very bachelor looking. Some clothes and dishes were strewn about, and there was no rhyme or reason to the basic brown wood furnishings and worn green carpeting. The lighting was dim and yellow, with not much thought given to mood.

It was actually Frankie's place. Frankie owned a west side dance club where Vinny bartended when he was in town. Older and soft-spoken, there were rumors that he was connected. There was something enticing, yet terrifying, about him. That night, thankfully, he was nowhere to be found.

Vinny led me over to the couch on the far side of the room, near the window. Playing host, he asked, "What can I get you to drink?"

Could he hear my empty stomach growling? Asking for a glass of water, then another, I drank about five refills quickly, hoping the quantity would fill me up and quiet me down. It did, but it also made me have to pee. I was too shy to ask where the bathroom was and too scared to leave the room and risk breaking the spell (lest he'd have time to think, come to his senses and remember that he didn't like me *that* way.)

Vinny began rinsing dishes on the other side of the room in the small kitchenette. I had no idea what he was talking about. I was nodding, at I think appropriate intervals, but my mind was screaming, *holy shit!*

After drying his hands, he picked up an expensive looking camera (a gift from Pandora?) and aimed it squarely at me. Putting my hands up reflexively, I blocked my face.

"Hey, stop that, you," he scolded. "Come on, let me take a few."

As he began rearranging the lights, he filled me in on his new passion for photography. I barely heard a word he said. I couldn't have felt more self-conscious. I'd put my make-up on eons before, hadn't checked it in hours and was sure that by now my mascara was smeared, my nose was shiny and my lipstick gone. I turned away from him. Undaunted, he began snapping. Over my protests, he continued.

Finally relenting, I realized that photos of me from the rear were a far worse idea. Trying to position myself on the couch, to minimize the roll of flab I imagined was peeking out from over my too-tight jeans, I tousled my hair with my fingers hoping to create that just out of bed, Bardot look—yet somehow knowing I was simply creating a mess. Stretching my legs out in front of me, I tried to make them appear longer and leaner. Attempting to look "sexy," I felt insecure and stupid. He snapped away, moving around me, taking shots from above, on one knee, from the right and the left. I was not easing into it. Remaining petrified, I squirmed uncomfortably, needing desperately to visit the john.

After what seemed like forever, he ran out of film and set the camera down. Refilling my water (my eyeballs, now floating), he sat down next to me. In high spirits, he was enjoying playing host. Without warning, he moved in close.

Reminiscent of Scotty Fitzgerald, the kiss was years in the wanting. Once again, it was not the kiss I'd imagined. It was certainly not the kiss of my dream. His lips were tight and dry. *Jeez, he was nervous too.* He stood, pulling me up to join him. Running his hands down my body, he kissed my face and neck. As magnificent as it should have felt, I was too distracted, trying to compare the feel of me, to that of Pandora. *Was he thinking that too?* In my favor, I was younger, perhaps softer? I was one hundred percent natural—*did that feel better or worse?*

As I considered, he put his hands on my waist and lifted me up. I was sure that I felt as heavy as an elephant. Ignoring my protests, he was unrelenting. I could see the bulge in his biceps and couldn't help admiring them. Somehow, my legs wrapped around his waist. Like a scene right out of one of Pandora's films, we were spinning, lips locked. The next thing I knew, he was carrying me into the other room, guiding me down on the unmade bed. Without ever detaching his lips from mine, he slid in next to me. Slowly working his way down my body, touching me, kissing me, I wanted to watch, but felt shy. Closing my eyes, I prayed he did the same. On his return trip north, he took a pit stop at my suddenly exposed breast.

Where was this going?

Even though we'd known each other for a couple of years, regardless of the fact that he was going to be my husband (maybe even because of that fact), I was not about to give it up on our first date—if you could call this, that.

The more I pushed his hand away from my pants zipper the more firmly he persisted, whispering, "Yes, Vinny. Yes, Vinny…" *Was he trying to convince me, or him?*

I was determined not to sleep with him. Not this night. But, I'd wanted him for so long and for the first time, I was sure he wanted me too.

The spell was abruptly halted when we heard keys turning in the lock. Jumping out of bed, I raced for the bathroom, finally relieving the pressure in my bladder. I tried in vain to quiet the flow that was pouring out of me. Willing it to be silent, I prayed they were deep in conversation and not listening to Niagara Falls! I hated going to the bathroom at anyone's house when there was even a chance of being heard. When I cared about a guy, that fear was multiplied tenfold.

When I finally emerged from the bathroom, after futilely trying to put myself back together, Vinny was standing in the dining room, chatting quietly with Frankie.

As I approached, Vinny began the now familiar introduction. "Frankie, I'd like you to meet Andi. She and I go waaaay back. We went to high school together."

I smiled wanly, too focused on whether or not they had heard me pee, to care.

I felt so caught, so shamed. I was sure Frankie was thinking, "Who's the slut?" Instead, he said, "Sure, I know Andi. Whatcha been up to?"

I was flattered that he'd heard of me. After a bit of shoptalk, even more so, because he knew so much about my work. Vinny offered to walk me down to get a cab. Relieved and saddened, I didn't want the night to end. I feared it might never happen again, but I wanted to get away from Frankie and the feeling that I was wearing a big, scarlet "A." I tried to silently convey that nothing had happened and that I'd pushed Vinny away, but my appearance suggested otherwise.

Once Vinny and I got in the elevator, our mutual discomfort cranked up to "11."

Finally, he said, "Sorry 'bout this. I'll call you."

In all the time we'd known each other, we'd never talked on the phone.

"Let me give you my number," I said, perhaps a little too eagerly.

Pulling a pen and paper from my purse, I jotted down my digits. When we got to the corner, Vinny hailed a cab, opened the curbside door, kissed me quickly on the cheek and, without another word, off I sped into the early morning light.

I left unsettled for a number of reasons—not the least of which was that he'd put me in the cab, leaving me to pay. He'd suggested his place (I use the term loosely), even though we were less than a mile from mine to begin with. At my place—which truly was my place—we would not have come to such an embarrassing end. I suspect he wanted to feel in control. As much as he scared the hell out of me, the fact that I was eight years older was perhaps a bit daunting to him—Pandora, or no Pandora.

The cost of the cab wasn't a big deal. Yet, it was. It said something about him, about what he thought of me. Or didn't think of me. Maybe he was just on "Pandora pilot," where money was never a thought, let alone a concern.

Despite the awkward first kiss and the unfortunate conclusion, I envisioned the relationship we were about to embark upon and the eventual wedding we were destined to have. Wondering how long it would take him to call me—or if he would call at all. *What if he never called?*

I didn't sleep. As soon as it was a reasonable enough hour, I called Mark. Mark dated a lot. He'd know the rules, expectations and hidden meanings.

"If it were me, I'd wait three days before calling. The day after is far too needy, the second day, still too eager, the third day, perfect. It displays control—with interest. If he hasn't called by the fourth day, forgetaboutit."

I got through the waiting by reliving the memory—actually, rewriting it. The one part of the story I couldn't improve upon was Vincent literally sweeping me off my feet. I shared that and other details with Maryann, dreamily recounting my excitement, downplaying the disappointing kiss. She was in total agreement. I should chalk that up to nerves.

On Monday, knowing Vinny would be at B-Bar, I stayed home, deciding it was better to be missed.

At 4:00 p.m. singing with the radio while finishing my make-up, the phone rang.

"Hello," I said, distracted by my half made-up, lips.

"Hey." The voice was unfamiliar.

"Hey."

"What're you doing?" The strange male voice continued.

"Getting ready for work. You?"

With that, something clicked. It was Tuesday. Day two. It had to mean, HE LOVES ME!

We talked for a long time. I knew I was going to be late for work, but I didn't care. I was never late. John could handle Dale and Marvin until I got there.

As I got more comfortable, I started with the, "When we go to…" and "When we do…" I can't remember what the hell I was referring to, I just knew I was getting ahead of myself and realizing it a few moments too late.

For most of the conversation, Vinny had been talkative and enthusiastic. Once I started with *the plans*, although still polite, he said little. I hung up thrilled, with an underlying sense of dread.

I floated around work that night, rewriting recent memory.

But then the days turned into weeks without another word.

I heard he'd gone back to LA.

About a month later, hanging out in the VIP room at I-dee-o, Frankie joined me. I willed myself to not begin the frantic look-see for his roommate—a search I'd conducted unsuccessfully on a nightly basis for weeks.

"Hey Andi, what's up?"

"I've just begun talks with Billy to take over Mondays here."

Suddenly focused behind my left shoulder, he said, "Hey Vin, don't you think that's a fine idea?"

My heart started racing. I didn't see him, but felt a hand rest on my shoulder.

"What's a fine idea, Frankie?"

"Andi's thinking of doing a night here. Don't you think she'd do great?"

"No doubt," he said more to himself, while surveying the room. "Good to be back."

"Oh, were you away?" I asked, feigning a yawn.

"I haven't even been home yet," he said, giving me a playful shove. "Came straight from the airport."

Someone called out to him from across the room and off he went. Frankie and I sat there a while, finally running out of things to say. I blushed, wondering if he knew that Vincent had blown me off.

Of course he knew. They were best friends.

Embarrassed, I excused myself and set out determined to look like I knew where the hell I was heading. Ducking into the other room, I started chatting up the first guy I saw. Luckily for me, it was Eddie Ojeda from Twisted Sister, a sweetheart I'd known for years. I relaxed in his comfortable presence—until I got broadsided from the left. Hip to hip.

"Hey, Frankie and I are gonna go get somethin' to eat. Wanna come?"

Nothing like a little rocker action to get Vinny's attention.

"Um, sure. Would you excuse me Eddie?"

"Of course, doll," he said with a wink, kissing me goodbye, smack on the lips. Gotta love him.

Vinny, taking me by the hand, nodded over to Frankie and off we went.

Frankie had a sweet little Jaguar with seating for two. Just as I started to protest, Vinny slid in and pulled me down on his lap. Even though I was well into Nutrisystem and below my goal weight, I was sure I'd break his legs. Pushing them apart, I sat in between them.

Frankie was driving fast. With every turn, gravity pulled me right into Vinny's groin. I could hear a murmur of delight as I adjusted my bum after one particularly sharp curve. His hands were resting on my legs. There was no way around how sexy it was.

Getting to Little Italy in no time, Frankie parked in the red zone without a care. The Umberto's doorman greeted us like we were family. *Maybe some of us were?* Everyone inside knew them and welcomed us warmly.

There was no better deterrent for cheating on my diet than Vinny. I decided a dozen raw oysters could do me no harm and might actually come in handy. Vinny ordered some clams and the linguini with hot sauce, as did Frankie. They both asked for a Coffee Time soda.

"Coffee Time?" I repeated, almost choking on my words.

"Have ya ever tried it?"

"I did, sort of, once," I said, silently freaking out.

I'll be damned if he didn't look at me knowingly for a moment.

What if I did astral project myself into Pandora's closet that night?

Eating with great relish, he reached over and helped himself to one of my oysters. He winked. I grinned like an idiot and turned my attention to Frankie.

They ate quickly, hugged the maitre'd and off we went.

The Jag was still parked right outside in the red zone. No ticket. No surprise.

Vinny opened the door, got in and pulled me on top of him. As I tried to recreate my earlier position, he clamped his legs shut, forcing me to sit on his lap. His arms circled around me.

As Frankie drove uptown, music blaring, I relaxed enough to be playful. Grooving to *Pump Up the Jam*, I could feel Vinny's appreciation.

"Where da'ya live?" Frankie asked.

As soon as I uttered the street, we seemed to be there. I couldn't invite them up. Three's an awkward number.

"Thanks Frankie. It was fun," I said, giving him a quick peck on the cheek.

As I turned to do the same with Vinny, he put his hand up to stop me. Hurt, I reached for the door. Guiding me out of the car with his hands, he jumped out too. Closing the car door behind him, he leaned against it, pulling me close.

And then he kissed me.

Really kissed me.

It was amazing—and familiar—the taste of Coffee Time, the smell of his after-shave, the excitement of someone else close by.

Damn! My dream was a premonition.

Frankie was singing loudly to the radio, trying hard to ignore us. My doorman, Sal, was pretending to read the newspaper, but he was definitely enjoying the show.

No longer able to ignore the audience, I turned to go. Vinny pulled me back for one long, last, kiss.

When he released me, I sort of stumbled backwards and waved goodbye. As much as I wanted to, I didn't turn around to see if he was watching me as I entered my building.

Besides, I was busy.

Mick was blaring in my brain.

You can't always get what you want,
But if you try sometimes,
You just might find
You get what you need,
Ah yeah...

I did, finally, get the kiss of my dream—and confirmation that there was some magic between us.

Maybe Yolanda the visionary wasn't so crazy after all.

Do you know the way to San Jose?

Still unsure of my future with men and music, I wanted guaranfuckin-tees, so I decided to visit another psychic to get a second opinion. Theresa, whom I'd heard was John Lennon's former live-in clairvoyant, came highly recommended. I was told her gift was unparalleled, as long as the moon wasn't in Libra—she lost her sight then. I made an appointment—having no idea where the fuck the moon would be, figuring I had an eleven out of twelve shot at clarity.

Theresa looked pretty much as I imagined she would: oldish, with grey frizzy hair, and a long flowery print dress, belted at the waist, covering her almost emaciated frame.

She lived on the Upper East Side of Manhattan in an apartment she'd obviously occupied for years. The paint was dirty and peeling. There were cats everywhere. At least one always seemed to occupy her lap.

She invited me to sit at the table and pick cards from a regular playing deck.

"I see a couple of men that will take you far in your career," she said. "You'll be successful, but not in a Page Six sort of way."

Oh yeah?

"Always work and stay focused on your career. Stocks and bonds are sexy. If you abandon your dreams, it will cost you in love," she warned.

As if!

"There will be five men at the same time."

FIVE? I can't even keep one man's interest.

"One will be very blond and really want you, but I don't think he'll get you. There'll be a medium dark one, a very dark and sexy one, and an older man with salt-and-pepper hair. One will have hair like yours. He'll be the one. They'll all be on the scene soon, vying for your attention. You'll have a lot of fun sorting it out."

No shit!

"Here's something interesting. I've only seen this a few times. Something BIG and important is going to happen to you. A once in a lifetime dream come true. Not like winning the lottery. Something else. You'll know when it happens."

Are you sure?

Thrilled but skeptical, I decided to get yet another opinion. After all, Yolanda said I'd marry Vinny and he was definitely the dark, sexy one.

I made an appointment with Josephine, the antithesis of Theresa. She lived in a Midtown brownstone, which reeked of money and sophistication. She was well dressed in a black designer pants suit, with a crisp, white, button-down shirt beneath. She escorted me to her finished basement, which served as her office. It was a wonderful room with a large working fireplace, huge mahogany desk and two very elegant comfortable leather chairs.

She had done my astrological chart in advance of the visit.

"You already know your future husband, you just don't know who he is yet."

Maybe it was *Vinny!*

"He's an Aries, or an Aries type. He'll support you and really be there for you. It'll be a good relationship that will last for a long time."

Not forever?

"He'll make a lot of money," she said, laughing now. "A lot of money." Her demeanor suddenly grew serious. "You'll be moving soon."

"There must be some mistake. I just bought an apartment and I love it. There's no way I'm moving," I responded defiantly.

"It'll be a step up, something even better," she continued, ignoring me.

I began to protest; but quickly decided it wasn't worth it. She was clearly a quack!

"Will I be successful?" I asked, petrified to hear her answer.

"To a degree, but not a big success, not now. It's not meant to be, it's not in the cards."

Great, another one projecting my mediocrity.

"You have a strong later-in-life chart," she added, smiling, as if delivering good news. "I see a writing project."

"Great." That was not what I wanted to hear.

"What about performing—being an actress or comedienne?"

"It's just not your time now. You could audition until you're blue in the face; it's not going to happen now. But later, in your middle years, you'll be everybody's darling. Yes, you can be an actress, a comedienne— whatever you want—and do quite well with it."

I didn't even want to be an actress anymore, but I'll be damned if anyone was going to tell me that I couldn't!

The kicker was when I asked, "Will I be happy?"

"Happy? Not in the traditional white picket fence sort of way. You're meant to be challenged in this life. You'll have a lot, accomplish a lot, but as soon as you do, you'll be on to the next."

I left that townhouse PISSED.

"I'll be happy, goddamnit. I'll show you, Miss Josephine!"

Here, there and everyfrigginwhere

After spending three years at Rock Bar, I finally left, largely because Marvin and Dale had gotten insane with their complaints. Nothing was ever enough for them. They were constantly whining to the point of exhaustion. My stepfather, Si, kept encouraging me to move on. So, when Billy and Terry offered me Monday nights at I-dee-o, I grabbed the opportunity and didn't look back.

Guest lists were the not-so-secret secret to success. They served everyone. Promoters were compensated by the number of attendees— whether they paid to get in or not. The regular customers felt like big shots bypassing the cover charge and the velvet ropes, and the club owners made their real money at the bar—so it was win, win, win.

Much like in my Rock Bar days, I called everyone personally, thank you very much. Pat the Fat was too busy for that. Every Wednesday I got a call from his girls inviting me to his Thursday nights at I-dee-o. They didn't ask if I was coming, they asked how many people I was bringing. I guess that tactic worked on some but it just pissed me off. I didn't even know those girls. And I worked there! How friggin' presumptuous!

At first I was making about a hundred calls every Monday. Eventually, it was more like three hundred. I preferred calling home numbers when I knew people were at work. It sped things up. I could leave my spiel on their machines and not get caught up in conversation. It also allowed me to avoid my cranky friends who complained that they only heard from me on Mondays.

"At least I call," I'd respond.

A lot of my friends were happy to get the call. Some were VIPs for the first time. I quickly developed a large and loyal following that showed up each week—no matter who was playing—just to hang out and mingle. My Mondays were warm and magical with a really cool vibe.

Terry, the owner of the club, was a visionary. He was exciting. He was difficult. He was also insane. Fueled by massive amounts of blow, he and Billy became increasingly rude to me, my guests and to the musicians. After about six months of Mondays, it had gotten unbearable.

Frankie, Vinny's roommate, had charted my progress and at that exact, perfect moment, offered me Thursdays at his Midtown club, going head to head with Pat the Fat. It was a challenge I couldn't refuse. Frankie and his exuberant, extravagant, possibly connected partner, Ralph, put their money where their mouth was. They hired an artist to create a logo with my name and likeness and put it on thousands of posters, flyers and invites, made on glossy card stock, in full color.

Frankie called Vinny in LA and offered to fly him in to DJ. Pandora was on tour, about to appear in New York City, which would give Vinny another welcomed excuse to come home. There were rumors that he and Pandora were back together, which would explain his prolonged absence since that night at Umberto's. My tummy still ached when I thought of him. Nothing an ounce or two of pot didn't obscure.

I'd been consistent, timely and respectful with my press releases over the years, and the journalists, in response, were very kind to me. My opening night press blurb made it into all the New York papers.

I'd become fast friends with Dan, Harold Burns' producer. I got him into the VIP rooms; he got me an occasional plug on the air. Harold, my once, virtually unknown co-star, was now the most famous shock jock in America. He'd made fun of Vinny for years—his age, his temper, mostly his elevated status due to his love life. Vinny, elusive and media shy, was a "get." Harold was more than eager to have him on his show—so much so, that he was willing to let Vincent promote my night and promised not to give him a hard time about Pandora, just to score the interview. To my amazement, Vinny was willing. That, I assumed, was for Frankie, but I hoped I played some small part in his decision.

While on the rounds to promote my opening at Stone House, I stopped by Buddy's to work the crowd. Buddy's was a new, downtown club, supposedly owned by Eric Bud, one of rock 'n' roll's royalty. In reality, I heard they just paid to use his name to add street cred. Jim Fellows actually owned and ran the place. Jim was almost famous for being married to Leona Johns at the height of her heyday, and for fathering two of her legitimate children. Controversy always seemed to surround her, never more than her years with Jim. Leona was the first black singer to become an international sex symbol and epitomize glamour. She was also the first to cross over and garner an Oscar nomination, on her first film.

Many years after her first child was born, the rumors swirled that Jim was not the father. The scuttlebutt was that Leona had had a long, secret affair with her very famous, married, record producer.

An art gallery upstairs, Buddy's enjoyed hip status, but business was for the most part, dismal. When Maryann and I hit the place, save for a few musicians drinking at the bar and the bartenders serving them, the room was empty. After dispensing invites to all of them, we were about to leave when I noticed a silver-and-black haired, handsome, mature gentleman. I say gentleman because he was wearing a button down instead of the usual ripped t-shirt. He was walking behind the bar, taking cash from the registers. I figured he was Jim Fellows—he was the only one in the place who looked old enough to be.

It was dark—the pink lighting created a sensual hue. Perhaps that's why he looked so damned attractive. Silverish black hair—now wait a minute.

I knew who the dark and sexy one was. Vinny had that base covered. The blond could well be Pastor Pete. He'd recently proclaimed his love, but I suspect I was, at minimum, the third woman to whom he had made the proclamation to that day. The one with the same color hair as mine was still a mystery, as was the other brunette. Theresa the psychic was clearly crazy.

Surreptitiously following Jim upstairs to his gallery, so that I could get a closer look, as if on cue, he came up and introduced himself to me. He was charming, as only a man of a certain age knows how to be.

Despite the salt-and-pepper hair, he had a very young and playful way about him.

"What's cooking, ladies?" he asked Maryann and me, obviously pleased with himself.

"Just promoting my opening. Sorry, if that's not cool."

Smiling back broadly, he reached out for an invitation. "Let me see what you've got there."

Handing him a glossy invite, I watched as he examined it.

"May I keep this? In fact, mind if I come?" He asked with a wink.

"I'd be honored," I responded, now blushing.

Jim introduced us to his partner, Steve, and invited us to have a glass of wine with them. After a couple of drinks, they began acting really silly. No matter what age, a rock boy is a rock boy.

"How come you're leaving I-dee-o? Jim asked.

"It's just time to move on."

"You've come a long way from Bleecker Street."

He sure seemed to know a lot about me.

After a bit, we bade them goodnight.

Jim called out after us, "See you Thursday."

The next morning Jim called me at home. I have no idea how he found me. As if old friends, we chatted effortlessly for almost an hour.

"How 'bout lunch?" he asked.

Fifteen minutes later, he picked me up and took me to a chic vegetarian bistro in the Village. Definitely making his interest clear, he romanced me with food, wine and laughter. As attracted as I was to him, I played it down. I wasn't used to being pursued; there hadn't been many times in my life when I had been. I seemed to always want the unattainable and relished the challenge of my pursuit—to the point of obsession. I was unprepared for the tables being turned.

In the car, stopped at a light, he turned to kiss me. The closer he moved towards me, the further away I went. When I'm doing the chasing I can't get enough. When I'm being pursued, I become a total prude. I guess I'm only comfortable when I'm "driving."

My last Monday at I-dee-o, I considered keeping the gig and doing both clubs simultaneously, but figured I'd probably sabotage myself in both venues.

I-dee-o was a boys' club anyway. Billy and Terry never treated me as an equal. It was, nonetheless, a hip, cozy scene. I was going to miss hosting nights there. It was the beginning of the "big time" for me, where I developed my promoting chops. As cool as Rock Bar had been, it was a Bleecker Street club and, like Rodney, got no respect.

On that last Monday, I arrived eager to enjoy my farewell. Standing at the ropes with Bobby V, who was working the door for me, was usual early arrival, Lenny. He came every Monday to share an early drink with me before I got crazy busy and he had to run off to a comedy club for his set. We'd remained casual friends over the past few years, supporting each other's careers. He came to my nights and I went to see him perform.

Atypical, he was not alone this night. He and his friend David joined Maryann and me at the downstairs bar. Considering my impending club move, and sensing this might be the last intimate cocktail that Lenny and I were to share, I got daring.

"Dating anyone?"

"Not really," he said, looking at his shoes.

"What about Mona?"

"We broke up about a year ago," he said.

"You're kidding. I had no idea."

"How's Eddie?" he asked.

"Old news. We've been breaking up for at least a year or more."

"Breaking up?" Lenny looked puzzled.

"We hang out once in awhile out of habit, but it's over and we both know it. I'm completely available but my love life's crap. Where are all the nice single guys—like you?"

Maryann, overhearing, chimed in, "I'll drink to that."

Clinking glasses, we both laughed. David and Lenny, exchanging a raised eyebrow, joined in our toast. The four of us chatted some more until the bar began filling up.

Time to do my thing. I introduced this guy to that girl, that player to this star and so on... and so on... and so on.

· The crowd was soon packed on the dance floor and fixed on a young fiddle player's impassioned performance.

During a short break, I made my way upstairs. Lenny and David were sitting on the couch in the large room with Maryann resting on the arm, laughing.

She came up behind me and whispered, "He likes you. He definitely does."

"Why hasn't he ever asked me out?"

"He's shy. I think this is your move."

Taking a deep breath, I headed over to the couch.

"Lenny, with my nights here winding down and the new place so enormous, who knows the next time we'll get to have a quiet drink. Maybe we should take it outside. Whaddya think?"

Lenny smiled, looking relieved. *Was Maryann right?*

"That'd be great. Why don't I call you?"

"I'll be at my mom's for the weekend. Maryann and I are Hamptons bound."

"Lucky you," he said, handing me a pen.

Quickly jotting down the number, I handed the pen, paper and some high hopes back to Lenny.

FIVE

INTEGRITY

Last first date(s)

Cookie had suggested I spend a couple of days with her and Si at the beach to help me get centered prior to my opening night. I decided to bring Maryann along as a buffer. It helped Cookie and me to have a diversion. With someone else around, Cookie was slightly less likely to offer unsolicited advice and I was slightly less likely to get pissed off.

Hopping the Jitney on the East Side of Manhattan, two hours later, Maryann and I were drenched in sun and affluence. Soon after, enjoying a light lunch in Cookie's condo kitchen, the phone rang.

"Pick it up, Andi," Cookie yelled from her bedroom,

"Hello?"

"Hi, Andi. It's Lenny."

"Hi," eyes wide, putting my hand over the mouthpiece, I stage whispered, "It's Lenny," to Maryann, who gave me a wink.

After making small talk for a while, I ventured, "So, should we have dinner?" He'd made the call, so I felt okay ballsing the next move.

"Great."

"I'll be back in town on Monday." I said, giving Maryanne a thumbs up.

"How's Tuesday?" He asked.

"Sounds good. Should we talk that morning?"

"Perfect, I'll give you a call. Have a nice weekend."

"You, too, Lenny. Bye."

"Goodbye, Andi."

"Did Lenny and I just make a date, or is it just dinner?" I asked Maryann, genuinely unsure of the answer.

"Sounds like a date to me," Cookie, now right behind me, said with a grin and a mother's knowing nod of the head.

She'd only met Lenny once, at my first stand-up gig, but he was Jewish, nice-looking and employed.

Did I mention he was Jewish?

Even after Maryann concurred, I was still unsure but shook it off, deciding I'd have more information soon enough.

I was anticipating the opening night of JamGirl (as Frankie's club was to be renamed on Thursdays). The Stone House marquee would come down and up my likeness and new moniker would go. The logo incorporated a caricature of me between the "m" and the "G" in JamGirl. It was the closest

I'd ever gotten to having my name in lights on Broadway—right there in the midst of the most historic theatres in New York. It was such a huge night for me. I decided to forgo just my usual "day of" calls, and started on Monday.

On Tuesday, up to the Ls, my call waiting beeped in. I clicked over to "Hey Andi, we still on for tonight?" Lenny's friendly voice offered a welcome reprieve from the stress of self-promotion.

"Yeah. Great. Where? When?"

"How about I pick you up around 7:00, and we can decide then?"

"Perfect. Let me give you my address."

Continuing with my calls, I still wondered, *Is this a date, or what?*

At exactly 7:00 p.m., my downstairs buzzer rang.

Running to the full-length mirror on the back of the bathroom door for a last-minute check, I wondered why I was so nervous. I'd known Lenny for years; he'd never made me sweat before. *Was this a date, or what?*

A few moments later, there was a light knock on the door. Waiting a respectable ten seconds before answering, I swung the door open as nonchalantly as possible. Lenny, smiling nervously at me, seemed as unsure as I was.

"Welcome to my humble chapeau." It was a weak *My Favorite Year* reference. Lenny got it, smiled, and took a few tentative steps inside as we exchanged an awkward embrace.

"Let me show you around," I said, taking his hand and one step to the right. "This is the kitchen."

"Nice. I love the black and white, especially the tile," he said, as he perused the details of the small, but visually stimulating and completely coordinated, area.

Taking his hand again, we took two steps forward and to the left. "This is the dining room and my office," I announced, as I pointed to the island counter and high-legged chairs.

"Give me a second to adjust to the altitude shift," he said.

Giggling, I led him another two steps forward, stepping on the faux zebra skin rug. "This would be the living room."

"Great couch," he said, indicating the cushy black leather centerpiece of the room. "Great everything; I love it."

"Thanks. I do too."

Leading him another six steps forward, I turned to the left. "The boudoir," I said, as I swept my arm, Carol Merrill style.

My bedroom—I use the term loosely—was a bed, a lamp and a telephone. Period. No door, no walls, just an alcove.

"I have the same sheets," he added, glad to have something—anything—to say.

Exchanging a smile, we moved on. I led him into the small bathroom, also black and white, with barely enough space for us both to stand. Lenny started to laugh.

"What's so funny?"

"I have the same towels."

"Get out!" I said, giving him a playful shove. He moved about a foot, which put him out of the room altogether.

Leading the way back to the dining room, I motioned for him to sit.

"What can I get you? Wine, beer, diet soda..."

"I'll have a glass of wine, if you will."

I opened a bottle, pulling a couple of glasses down from the cabinet. I turned to see Lenny, staring in stunned disbelief.

"Have you been following me, having my place photographed or something?"

"What're you talking about?"

"I have the same glasses," Lenny said quietly, almost guiltily.

We both burst out laughing while giving each other a somewhat suspicious look.

"This calls for the heavy artillery. Where the hell's my bong?"

Lenny left the choice of restaurant to me. I suggested a little Japanese place a few blocks away. It was small, quiet and reasonable. Still unsure if it was a date, I wondered if I should offer to pay. I was the one who suggested we get together. Does Lenny pay because he's the guy and made the call? Do we split it because we're friends and we're modern?

The waitress came.

"I'll have a sake, please."

"Make that two, please," Lenny added.

Nothing unusual there. Who doesn't order sake in a Japanese restaurant?

Chatting as we perused the menu, when the waitress returned with the drinks I had to decide what to do—order sushi, costly and nervy if Lenny was paying, or play it safe and order something less pricey?

"I'll have the chicken teriyaki please,"

"Soup or salad?" she asked.

"Salad, please."

"I'll have the exact same thing," Lenny said, with smile.

As the waitress made her way to the kitchen, I looked him square in the eye, "Okay, this is getting weird."

"Getting weird? I feel like I've been in an alternate universe since I entered your apartment."

Talking about our failed relationships through the sake and salad, we discovered that Mona and Eddie had entered and exited our lives at approximately the same time. *Of course they did.*

While picking at our chicken (it must be a date; neither of us is really eating), I shared my anxiety about my impending opening night, then realized I was rambling.

"What are you up to these days, Lenny?"

"I'm working on a screenplay."

"How exciting!"

"My writing partner and I…"

Cutting Lenny off, as is my wont, I asked, "Who're you writing with?"

"His name's Barry Schoenbaum."

"Barry Schoenbaum? I went to grade school with a Barry Schoenbaum."

Lenny looked at me cynically. "Do you realize how many Barry Schoenbaums there are in New York? It can't possibly be the same one."

"Is he short, blond and from the Bronx?"

"No." he said, obviously relieved. "Average height, dark hair and from Brooklyn, I believe."

Not to be deterred, I continued, "It's so weird. Barry was my best friend in sixth through ninth grades. He lived around the corner from me. We hung out everyday—took acting classes together, performed in a bunch of community theatre shows; we even took over school plays, directing each other and co-starring in everything. I think he sort of had a crush on me, but he was really short and I had a thing for Ray Santo. But I really liked him. Then I moved away and never saw him again. Just happens. We were kids."

"Funny—definitely a different Barry. I'm sure he told me Brooklyn and he's not short or blond."

"I know this is crazy Lenny, but this whole evening's been insane. The sheets, the towels, the glasses—dontcha think?"

"I'll call him."

"Thank you. Oh, by the way, he'd know me as Andi Schwartz, it was pre-Stone."

Getting up, he pulled out some change and headed for the pay phone in the back. It was 1990, pre-cell phones—at least to the world at large.

I was psyched. Barry Schoenbaum.

A moment later Lenny returned to the table, sat down and sighed, "Wasn't home, I left a message."

The check came. Moment of truth. Drum roll please. Before I could utter a syllable, move a muscle, let alone blink, he'd snatched it up and was peeling bills out of his wallet.

"Thanks Lenny."

So this was a date.

Right?

I had to go hear a new band, which was recording nearby. Lenny was game to join me. He had a car, most unusual for a Manhattan guy. He opened the door for me, waited for me to get comfortable, and then closed it behind me, before rounding to his side. It was a big old car with a bench seat in front—before the days of required seat belt wearing. Feeling bolder now that he had paid and made things clearer, I slid towards the middle. We both relaxed a bit, accepting that our relationship had shifted.

I knew in the first minute the band could never play one of my nights. They were way too out there. Wanting to be polite, we stayed through three painful songs.

Next stop was B-Bar, where I had some last minute promoting to do.

We got a parking spot less than a block from the club, shocking for the Upper West Side. Coming around to open the door for me, Lenny took me by the arm and escorted me across the street. As we neared the velvet ropes, Bobby V unhooked them and welcomed me with a bear hug.

"Bobby, this is Lenny, an old friend of mine."

"Yeah, I remember you from I-dee-o. Any friend of Andi's... you're always welcome."

"Thanks, man."

As we walked down the stairs, I filled Lenny in on some of the better B-Bar gossip. Entering the main room, which was fairly sparse, I looked at my watch. It was only 11:30, a little too early for my crowd. Smitty had my Jack and water ready before we hit the bar. After introductions, he brought Lenny his requested scotch. Thank heavens—something we didn't have in common. House music was pumping. Within moments, the club began filling up.

Glancing across the bar, I think I audibly gasped.

Vincent.

I hadn't seen him in awhile. He was here in town, for me—or Frankie—or both of us. *Whatever.*

I waved. He grinned. My stomach flipped. For a moment, I forgot where I was, who I was with—everything. Snapping out of it, I turned to Lenny who'd been watching a little barroom drama to his right. Leaning in, I whispered in his ear. It *was* loud in there. Employing the James Moretti technique, I made sure that my lips brushed his ear. It was a bold move, made easier by the bourbon and the proximity of Vinny. As I suspected, he was watching intently.

Lenny, startled by my overt contact, responded immediately. Was it his scotch talking? He leaned in closer.

In less than a nanosecond, I could feel Vinny behind me. Not only was I not alone as I usually was, but I was in the company of one fine looking gentleman.

"Hey Andi, long time no see," he said, as he pulled me close and gave me an uncharacteristically warm hug.

"Vinny, this is my old friend, Lenny," I said, instantly foiling his high school routine. What fun.

As they shook hands, I could tell that Lenny recognized Vinny. They began silently sizing each other up.

Thankfully, we were almost immediately interrupted by Lana. Lenny knew her from Rock Bar and all of those I-dee-o Mondays. Her presence definitely helped him feel more comfortable. He ordered her a drink and the three of us chatted about old times. Vinny, clearly annoyed, moved on.

"I know you have to work. I'll be off and leave you to it," Lenny said, as he finished his drink.

"Let me walk you out."

As I suspected, Vinny was watching without respite. Lenny grasped my elbow, leading me out. I could feel Vinny's eyes following us.

As we neared the car, I wondered what to do.

We kind of did what we'd always done. We hugged and quickly kissed on the cheek but, this time, we held each other's gaze.

Was this a new beginning?

As he drove off, I pondered my fate. There was Vinny, who only wanted me very, very, very occasionally, if at all, and Lenny, who was interested (I think), available, stable and sane.

As I passed Bobby V, he smiled. "Nice guy. I approve."

"Me too."

Back downstairs, I quickly found Lana. Vinny, fortunately, had his back to me. Making my way around the bar, I bumped him lightly from behind. Turning in disgust, when he saw it was me, his eyes darted around. I acted as if I had no idea what, or should I say whom, he was looking for.

"Where's your friend?" he asked, sarcastically.

"Lenny? He's so sweet! He knew I had work to do and took off."

"Sweet, huh?"

I sighed.

There's something so cute about young guys and their inability to temper their feelings. Well, sometimes.

Like a couple of cats in heat, Vinny circled close and growled at me for the rest of the night, while I preened and purred.

Meow.

─────── **Prophetic realization** ───────

I had pre-grand opening night jitters with visions of no one showing up. I barely slept.

Finally giving up, I got out of bed around 6:00, unsure of when Vinny would be on the air. At 8:30, Harold Burns introduced him. Gingerly, he asked Vinny if he and Pandora were back together. When Vinny didn't respond, Harold didn't press. Shocking. So was the fact that Vinny seemed surprisingly relaxed as he touted the opening night of JamGirl, "I flew in to DJ and support my good friends Andi and Frankie." *No shit!*

I spent the rest of the day on the phone, followed by an evening of making the rounds at B-Bar and I-dee-o. The buzz was strong. Everyone I ran into seemed almost as excited as I was.

My last stop was to check in at The Stone House. Entering, I was overcome by the smell of stale beer. It was nauseating. I'd assumed when Frankie promised to shampoo the carpets that that would take care of it. It barely made a difference at all. Years of spilled beer had taken their toll.

As it was, The Stone House had an awful reputation. The club drew a bridge and tunnel crowd of young, overeager unwanteds from the outer boroughs, who couldn't get into the chicer places Downtown. If you had the green, you were welcomed with open arms into the un-hip scene. What the hell were my people going to think about this place? The stench was surely not going to help.

There was nothing I could do. It was too late. I'd walked away from I-dee-o Mondays. Now that I'd moved on to Thursdays, there was no turning back. Maybe Jim Fellows would show up and offer me Thursdays at Buddy's. The club was too new to have a following, but it was hip. That's me all over—barely starting one thing, already thinking about the next.

At around 9:30 the following morning, I finally gave up the pretense that perhaps I might be able to fall asleep.

Maryann called excitedly.

"Have you seen today's *Post*?"

"No, I haven't been out yet. Why?"

"So much for the psychic!"

"What are you talking about?"

"Page Six. Headline: 'Sacrifice.' Text: *'Vincent Santerini swallowed his pride and went on the Harold Burns show yesterday even though the host had ridiculed him and infuriated Pandora Amora with his song parodies and mimicry during the heady days of their romance. Vincent subjected himself to Burns' unique inquisitorial technique to promote Andi Stone's JamGirl Thursdays. Santerini is the special guest DJ tonight. He might even get a visit from Pandora after her gig at the Garden.'"*

"Holy shit! Holy shit, HOLY SHIT!!!"

I was determined to prove that damn psychic wrong, but this was awfully fast.

"Where on the page is it?" I always read Page Six from right bottom to top left like some kind of weird Hebraic ritual. There's no bad place on the page, but there were a couple of spots of choice real estate.

"Bottom, middle. Your name is black and bold."

"Holy shit!"

I knew Vinny wouldn't like the article and it probably ruined any shot of Pandora actually showing up, but right then, it was way too cool to worry about.

Running to the corner, I bought every copy of the *Post* they had. I was afraid to look—what if Maryann was kidding? What if it was only in her copy? As I pressed the button for the elevator, I opened the top paper. Just as I found Page Six (which hadn't actually been on the sixth page of the newspaper in a million years), the door opened. There was no mistake. Vincent Santerini and Andi Stone, bolded, immortalized, on Page Six— together. A negative prophecy overcome—a dream come true. The elevator door opened and closed at least a dozen times before I finally got on.

In a haze of pseudo-celebrity, I speed-walked over to the club, lost in fantasies of impending fame. What if Pandora did show up? What if tomorrow's paper contained a photo of Vinny, Pandora and me—smiling, arms circling each other's waists? What if the club was packed and had a line outside that snaked around the block? The "what ifs" had to exceed the reality.

Frankie had set up an office for me downstairs in the basement. No windows, fluorescent lighting and a large desk with a phone. It was all I needed. A few minutes after I arrived, the phone rang.

Picking it up, for the first time I said, "Hello, JamGirl."

"Hey, Andi. It's Lenny. Excited?"

"I'm a wreck. But yeah, crazy looking forward to it."

"You're going to love this, a nice little capper to your big day. It turns out that Barry Schoenbaum is from the Bronx and said to ask you about Joey."

"No! Really? I had a feeling. Joey? Wow. He was the third stooge."

A bit reluctantly, Lenny added, "Barry wants you to call."

"It's been twenty years. How weird."

After relaying Barry's info and wishing me good luck, he said he'd see me later. Nervously, I punched in the number.

"Hi, Barry Schoenbaum's office."

"Hi... um... this is an old, um, friend."

"Andi?"

"Huh? Yeah. How'd you know?"

"Barry said you'd be calling and to put you right through."

Okay, so at least he thought this was cool too.

Almost immediately, a deep, resonant, somewhat familiar voice said, "Andi, is that you?"

"Barry, hi. I can't believe this! I've known Lenny for years and we just figured this out the other night."

"It's crazy," he said. "I took Lenny's class the session right before you. I can't believe we never ran into each other in a comedy club."

"Are you a comedian?" I asked.

"By night. By day, I'm a music promoter."

"You're a *what*?"

"I work at Pacific Records. I'm VP of promotion."

"Please tell me you're playing with me," I pleaded.

"Why, what?"

"I'm a music promoter and I'm having a big opening tonight."

"Where?"

As soon as I said The Stone House, he started laughing—hearty, genuine laughter.

"What's so funny?"

"My office is around the corner, literally two blocks away."

"Shut up!"

"I'm serious. Come meet me."

"No way, I'm a wreck. I speed-walked here this morning. I have zero make-up on. This is not gonna be the way you see me for the first time in twenty years. Come to my opening tonight. I'm putting you on the guest list."

"I will, but come on Andi, I can't wait. Come meet me. Please."

I was charged and curious.

"Lenny said you mentioned Joey. Are you still in touch?"

"I was just the best man at his wedding."

"There is so much catching up to do."

"Exactly, so come over and let's get started."

"Barry, this is a huge day for me, I have so much to do."

"Five minutes, that's all I ask. We'll say hello and I'll let you go."

Silence.

"Please, Andi. Come on."

"I can't. Really."

The thought of my sweaty unmade-up self wouldn't let me relent.

"I'll see you tonight."

I had a few more hours of calls to make, but I was so distracted that I had no memory of time elapsing. Lenny called back and asked if I'd hooked up with Barry.

"Yeah, thank you so much. He's gonna come to the club tonight."

"Oh, great. How fun," he said.

About an hour later, a delivery guy entered my office with an enormous bouquet of long stemmed white roses.

I opened the card and read: *"Roses are red, these flowers are white, hope you have a successful night. Barry."*

As I was admiring their magnificence, Vinny bounded in.

I don't think he'd ever seen me without makeup. In fact, I know he hadn't. Normally it would have made me self-conscious and crazy but, for once, I wasn't thinking of him.

"Nice flowers," he said as I was re-reading the card.

"Yeah," I sighed, totally playing it up for all it was worth. "Beautiful."

I enjoyed watching him trying to find a clue as to who sent the roses. He didn't want me, but he didn't want anyone else to want me either. It was clearly bugging him. *Ha!*

"Thanks so much for doing Harold's show. I know it's gonna have a huge impact on tonight." I didn't mention Page Six and he didn't either.

"My pleasu..."

My ringing phone interrupted him. As I lifted the receiver, I looked at him, thinking he would take his leave. But he just stood there.

"Did they come?" I heard the newly familiar voice ask.

"Yes, they're gorgeous. You made my day—in more ways than one," I said, swinging around in my secretary chair.

It wasn't conscious, but boy did that make Vinny nuts. He held his ground.

Barry continued, "Won't you come meet me? Come on, surely you owe me that?"

He had me now.

"Five minutes. On my way home," I conceded.

I offered no explanation to Vinny when I hung up the phone. After a few minutes of loitering in my doorway, he said, "See you later, Andi."

"Yeah, see you tonight, Vinny. Thanks again."

He skulked off as I glimmered in glee.

I spent another few hours on the phone, mostly recounting to everyone about finding Barry after all of these years. How strange. Twenty-odd years ago, we were making toilets out of snow and co-starring in dozens of plays and musicals. A lifetime later, separated by a borough or two, we'd both taken Lenny's comedy class within a month of each other, did improv at the same exact time, then stand-up, and ended up two blocks from each other working as music promoters.

Barry was wildly successful, not a club jumper like me, but we shared a common thread. We'd probably been at the same events a bunch of times over the years and undoubtedly knew a lot of the same people.

A little before 5:00, I was getting increasingly nervous. (Nothing a quick bowl in the loo wouldn't exacerbate.) The opening. Meeting Barry. Having Lenny, Barry, Vinny and Jim Fellows in the same room at the same time. And Pete, even. Holy shit. Seems like Theresa had gotten this one right. The moon was most definitely not in Libra that fateful day.

Rushing to leave myself enough time for a quick stop at Barry's, I called his office. His assistant put me right through.

"I'm on my way, really racing. Can you meet me downstairs? We'll get a quick hug and then I'm off."

Barry started to protest. Realizing I might change my mind, he agreed.

"How will we know each other? Lenny said you're no longer short with blond hair."

He laughed. "I'd know you anywhere."

"I don't think so, Barry, it's been a long time."

"Trust me," he continued, "I'll know you."

"I'm out the door right now, see you in five. Please be downstairs, I'm really running late," I said, already on my way.

As I sped around the corner and up Sixth Avenue, I smiled. Barry had never seen me in make-up, so my appearance to him this day would be a lot less jarring than it was to, say, Vinny. I was a 14-year-old hippie with hair to my ass and young dewy skin the last time I saw Barry. *Yikes!*

I felt totally self-conscious, with sunglasses covering the dark circles under my eyes, and my workout clothes horrifically out of place amongst the throngs of well-dressed business folk. Entering the lobby of a magnificent Sixth Avenue skyscraper, I saw people everywhere; I had no idea which of them was Barry. Then I saw a man that a week before I would have passed on the street without a second glance, but today, I knew.

Dressed unlike the hundreds of suited businessmen walking by, he was wearing black jeans and a black t-shirt. I'd later come to learn that was his daily uniform. About 5'9", 165 pounds, his medium brown hair was pulled back in a small ponytail; there was no mistaking his vibrant brown eyes, characteristic Schoenbaum nose, or his determined gait. We smiled as we moved towards each other.

"Barry Schoenbaum," I said, as I gave him a tight squeeze.

"Andi Schwartz, huh, Stone, or should I call you JamGirl?"

"Alright, alright. Just call me Andi."

"Like I said, I'd know you anywhere," he said, perusing me head to toe.

Embarrassed, I replied, "It's amazing, twenty some years, yet, looking at your face, you're just the same."

We hugged again. His assistant cleared her throat.

Barry, realizing his faux pas, stammered, "Sorry Andi, this is Renee. Renee, Andi."

She held my hand for a moment in hers. "This is the coolest story ever!" She was in her early twenties, I'd say, ridiculously thin and attractive. Her skirt hit shorter than my T-shirt.

I started moving as I said, "We have so much catching up to do, but that's for later. I really have to run. Promise me you'll come to the club tonight—you too, Renee. You're on the list, plus… a hundred."

I gave Barry a kiss on the cheek, waved at Renee and ran off without glancing back, sure that they were both watching my exit. Barry always loved the opposite sex. Renee, I assumed, checked out other women. It's what we do.

As soon as I hit Avenue of the Americas, I jumped in a cab. What a day—and it'd barely begun. Not helping my anxiety level, the traffic was rush hour miserable. When we finally got a few blocks from my apartment, I paid the driver, jumped out and jogged the rest of the way. Racing past Carlos with a quick hello, I flew up the stairs. Who had time for elevators?

I had a date with destiny—and with Lenny—Barry, Vinny, Jim and Pete. This was going to be one hell of an interesting evening.

JamGirl jams it

An hour later I was showered, made up and dressed. I wore a dusty pink, beige and wine-colored, floral print, short party skirt, trimmed in black lace, with a matching cropped jacket, which sported enormous shoulder pads. (In 1990 that was stylin'.) I added black fishnet stockings, a black lace camisole, motorcycle boots and ultra-spiked my hair. Those were the days.

The butterflies were overtaking my stomach. Praying that some miracle had occurred and the beer stench would be gone, I realized that was impossibly wishful thinking. As my cab turned the corner off Broadway, the club coming into view, I saw the JamGirl marquee in place for the first time—my name in lights—on Broadway. Not exactly as I'd imagined, but it still made my head spin.

Bobby V, already on duty, was guarding the ropes. He was, without a doubt, the best doorman in the business. I wouldn't have considered doing a night without him. Chatting for a moment about the guest list, there was nothing I had to tell him. He knew exactly how to build a night, how many people to let in, how many to hold on line, who to keep waiting and who to let pass—he was gifted. What he brought to the evening was as important as any of the elements.

As I entered, Frankie was down on his knees, bless his soul, smelling the rug. Layering Lysol and shampoo, it was an improvement, but it was what it was. Deodorizers hung all over the place. It smelled like a great big taxicab. At least it was familiar.

Workers were everywhere, cleaning and readying for the night. Anthony was setting the lights, pink-hued and low, exuding a flattering glow. Vinny, spinning disks for the crew while preparing his first set, had everyone singing along and dancing as they worked. The vibe was already cool.

I slipped into the VIP room to catch a moment alone, take a few deep breaths and a toke on my one hitter. It could only help the smell. The place looked far more festive than usual. Frankie had placed fresh flowers and candles in strategic locations, which added a welcomed touch. It was very dark, in a good way. There were lots of small tables with couches and comfortable chairs around. I hadn't spent any time in this room (having barely spent any time in the club at all, except for visiting Vinny once on his birthday), but I suspected tonight might be different. The VIP room offered a perfect respite from the masses that I prayed would fill the outer rooms. Vinny had already cued up a long play reel-to-reel with a perfect mix, set at optimum volume, for conversation and mood.

I made my way over to the bandstand, where Brian Feld, whom I'd chosen to lead the jam, both for his musical gifts and his extraordinary knowledge and connections, was in the midst of a sound check. Well thought of and respected by the players, he filled me in on the night's invited guests. Greg Allman and Ace Frehley had promised to stop by, as well as dozens of the best players in New York. Almost every musician that had ever played for me at Rock Bar and I-dee-o planned to sit in.

Aside from the debut of Andi Stone's After Midnight Rock Jam, Pastor Pete and His Disciples were opening the show. Certain crowd pleasers, they had loads of fans and an uncanny ability to win over every room they played. No matter what else happened, whoever came or didn't, the music was assured. We were going to rock.

The first set was scheduled for 10:00 p.m., followed by the Moretti Brothers' new band, Pack of Cats, at 11:00. (Despite the garlic-Caesar dick dog rushing the year before, compliments of James Moretti, I didn't hold grudges.)

Rock 'n' roll never begins on time, but Pete had such a loyal following, I trusted the club would begin to fill up a little before 10:00. Sure enough, at 9:30 they began arriving. By 10:15, there were at least a hundred people waiting for the show. At 10:30, when The Disciples hit the stage, it was closer to two hundred people. Before the set ended at 11:15, it was more like four hundred. That number doubled yet again before the jam began. The place was packed.

Lenny arrived with Barry just before Pete took the stage. It was still quiet enough for us all to have a drink and a little conversation. Very subtly Lenny began staking his claim. He was standing just slightly in front and to my right, preventing anyone else from getting too close. It was a little awkward, but not nearly as uncomfortable as it became when Maryann told me that Jim Fellows was in the house. Then, as if on cue, Vinny came out of the booth when the band took over.

There they were, all in one room at the same time, just as predicted. Lenny (with hair like mine), Barry (the medium), Vinny (the dark devil), Jim (the grey-haired) and Pastor Pete (the fair), even though he didn't really count. *Damn, that Theresa was good.*

Since Jim was a professional contact, it was my duty to make him feel welcomed. As I approached him from behind, Steve gave him a high sign, tipping him to my presence. Turning around, Jim kissed me smack on the lips. It didn't go unnoticed by Lenny, Barry or Vinny, who were all, simultaneously, staring at me. Shit! Score!

It was great for Jim to see the success of the night, and it was terrific for Vinny and Lenny to see I had other admirers. Eventually, they acknowledged that they recognized each other and were chatting. Oh, to be a fly on that bar.

Making my way over to them, I put an arm around Barry and the other around Vinny, while winking at Lenny. After a lifetime of being at the mercy of men, this was a feast for the starving.

"I see you've met. Vinny, did you know that Barry and I went to school together? We go waaay back."

Vinny laughed.

"No, really, sixth grade."

I knew in that moment he'd never use that line on me again.

It was the early days of MTV. Two of the original VJs showed up at the exact same time as the paparazzi. The Page Six suggestion that Pandora might pop in had helped bring the crowds and the press. Now that it was leaked, I was certain she wouldn't come within a mile of the place. But it had served its purpose. The hype was sufficient. Did I really need to see Pandora and Vincent together?

I was not to be tortured this night.

I watched Lenny and Barry goofing around at the bar. Barry was clearly enjoying all the young scantily clad eye candy, while Lenny was stealing glances at me. Every time Jim Fellows came near, I could feel Lenny's steely gaze. Without knowing anything, he sensed everything.

The cash registers were ringing like one-armed bandits on a senior citizen day trip to Atlantic City. Frankie looked as happy as Frankie could look. He was over by the DJ booth most of the evening chatting with Vinny, who was doing what he most loved to do.

In between sets, Vinny had the crowd on its feet. When the bands came on he slipped into the VIP room and spun there for the special guests, which soon included a gaggle of rock stars, past and present. Greg Allman and Ace Frehley had arrived. Martha Quinn (an original MTV VJ), Stuttering John of Howard Stern fame, as well as the guys from Danger/ Danger were holding court in the VIP room. The girls were swarming, not sure whom to hit on first.

Jim had been waiting for The Disciples to take the stage. He wanted to get a handle on what I claimed was a "sure thing." They did not disappoint. Pete's fans knew all the words to all his songs and acted them out in a "Rocky Horror" sort of way. Even first timers were soon singing. It was a very powerful audition.

I could see Jim and Steve were taking it all in, especially the legions of young eager girls jumping and jiggling in time to the music. As soon as the set ended, they beelined straight to me.

Jim took my hand. "I like it. I like the whole thing. Great night, babe. We'll talk. I have to get back Downtown. Care to walk us out?"

I couldn't help but notice Lenny watching. Shrugging my shoulders, I mouthed, "Be right back," as I led Jim and Steve towards the door. When we got to the entrance Jim pulled me outside and gave me a big kiss, right on the lips. Startled, I laughed.

"Not the reaction I was expecting," he said.

"Not the goodbye I was expecting," I replied, still kind of dizzy.

"A few people might be surprised," Steve added, with a laugh.

"What does that mean?" I asked.

"Nothing," Jim said, shooting Steve a "*What the fuck?*"

"I'll call you tomorrow. Enjoy your night. You deserve it. You done good, kid."

He tried to pull me towards him, but I backed up. "Easy cowboy, I have to get back in there. I'll speak to you tomorrow. Thanks for coming."

Pecking them each on the cheek, I shot a questioning look to Steve, who shrugged as I headed back inside. Bobby V bowed low as he opened the door for me. There were at least fifty people in line, chatting him up, trying to get in. We were cooking.

Before I'd gotten to the main room, I ran into Lenny looking intently at a poster of the night's lineup. Being doggedly pursued was completely foreign to me, but I was enjoying my unease. Taking Lenny's arm, I led him into the VIP room, now packed. Introducing him around, I began to relax.

The Moretti Brothers were setting up. I was doing my best to encourage them to hurry before the momentum was lost. Pete was schmoozing his fans and having his girls work the crowd, getting names and addresses for their mailing list.

Bobby V must have picked that moment to loosen his hold, because the club instantly got more crowded. It was getting difficult to navigate through the room. As soon as they opened their set, James and company commanded the stage, providing a perfect bridge to the jam that was to follow.

Lenny, Barry and I toasted our reunion. Just before midnight, Barry begged off.

"I've got an early meeting. I'll call you tomorrow."

The three of us together was a bit awkward. I think we were all relieved to see it end. Lenny remained at the bar, occasionally chatting, always watching.

Jam Master Brian had done his job. There were players everywhere angling to get on. Ace Frehley and Greg Allman did their time and the place went nuts. The jam rocked on for hours. Around 2:00 a.m., Lenny asked me to walk him out.

"That was amazing, Andi. You're amazing."

"Thanks, Lenny."

All too aware of Bobby V only a few feet away, he smiled, gave me a quick kiss and said he'd call me in the morning.

The paparazzi were getting restless, waiting for the money shot.

"When's Pandora gonna get here already?"

"That was purely conjecture on your part. I never said she was coming."

The annoyed shutterbug persisted. "Other than a few has-been rock stars and TV personalities, there really isn't anyone of note on hand."

A pack of gorgeous women passed us, interrupting his disappointment. He took off after them.

More than eight hundred people had come through the doors that evening, but all I could think about was that damn asshole's complaint.

Unseen, I slipped downstairs to my office and got stoned.

Complaint—what complaint?

By 3:00 a.m., only the hardcore remained. Vinny continued spinning while the musicians and wannabe's continued to drink. A handful of couples at the bar were playing out the "will you go home with me" dance.

At 4:00 a.m., Frankie turned on the house lights and ushered the few last holdouts to the door. After counting the money, he, Vinny, Bobby V and I hit the street. It'd been a long day/night. Relaxing for the first time in days, exhaustion took hold. I begged off the breakfast invite. There were hugs and congratulations all around.

"Thanks you guys. Thanks for everything."

Frankie, uncharacteristically, smiled.

"Thank *you*, Andi. Ka-ching."

The new math

Late the next morning, Lenny called.

"How about dinner tonight to celebrate?"

"Sure, that sounds great."

Minutes later, the phone rang again.

"Hey hot stuff, free on Saturday?"

"Barry?"

What's a single girl in her mid-thirties to do?

As a teenager, I didn't have the slightest romantic interest in Barry. Why was he suddenly so darn attractive? Perhaps it had something to do with the fact that I was no longer a foot taller than him, or that he'd grown into his nose, lost the pimples and the cracking voice—all replaced by a handsome guy with a good body, a great job and a state-of-the-art StarTAC cellphone? Or, maybe it was just so romantic to think that after twenty plus years of living parallel lives, I was destined to end up with the boy next door.

Granted, he was Lenny's writing partner, but he was my best friend first. What about the code? Did it apply to this? If so, for whom? Lenny, Barry, *me?* Was I getting ahead of myself? *What happened to the damn power of now?*

"Yeah, I'm free, Barry, but right now I'm running to work. Sorry, I gotta go."

"Since you'll be in the neighborhood, come up and see my office. I'll take you to lunch."

After a morning of congratulatory calls, I arrived at Barry's office a little after 1:00. Renee, Barry's assistant, was expecting me and led me into his inner sanctum. Barry's office had luxurious beige carpeting, gold records lining the walls, a huge desk dominating the center of the room and a floor-to-ceiling window, running the length of the room, overlooking Sixth Avenue.

"Well, this is where our similarities end. You're successful."

Barry blushed a bit, but I could tell he was pleased.

"Hey Renee, did I tell you that Andi and I went to grade school together?"

"Yeah, about a million times. Cool. I wasn't even born then."

I faked silent choking as she left the room.

He took me to Mr. Chow's, a very serious, high-end Asian restaurant (although, back then, we called it Chinese). The maitre d' obviously knew Barry well and greeted him warmly. As he escorted us to the best table in the house, I couldn't help but wonder how many women Barry had brought here before me. Gauging by how everyone was fawning over us, I'd say many.

After ordering way more food than we could possibly eat, he explained, "I like to taste a little bit of everything. Besides, we have twenty years of lunches to catch up on. I'm packing in a few right here." Almost to himself, he added, "I always wondered what happened to you."

"How weird is it that we've been doing so many of the same things all these years and never run into each other?" Mid sentence my eyes caught sight of the three dishes being presented by the waiter. If he was trying to impress me, it was working.

"You know your nostrils are flaring."

"Are not," I said.

"Are too."

"So?" I replied, suddenly blushing.

"That means you're flirting."

"I am not! I don't know what you're talking about."

Damn him for being so observant.

Not only had Barry enjoyed great success as a music promoter, he was also doing stand-up and improv and making a name for himself. Additionally, he had a handful of writing projects in the works with Lenny and a couple of other comics. Everything he tried his hand at worked. He seemed to know everybody in both the music and comedy worlds—A-listers across the board. I had no doubt he was destined for even greater things.

Jeez. And I thought I was ambitious.

At my office later that afternoon, the phone was ringing off the hook. Jim Fellows called from Boston.

"Steve and I had a great time. We want to meet with you when I get back in town." Changing his tone he added, "I can't stop thinking about you."

"By the way," I said, trying like hell to sound casual, "what was Steve implying the other night? I got the distinct impression there might be other parties involved? It's no problem really; I'm juggling a bit myself right now. Unless of course, it's something serious. You're not married are you?"

Dead silence on the other end.

That damned woman's intuition.

"Goodbye, Jim."

One down, four to go.

Sweet-talking Pastor Pete wasn't a contender either. He was fun, but not my type. He wanted all women for a moment or two. I wanted one man, for always.

Two down, three to go.

Vinny. Hell, I barely saw him anymore and still had no idea what he thought of me.

That left two.

Lenny and Barry.

Which was one too many—especially amongst friends.

Promptly at 8:00 Lenny arrived, seeming as uncomfortable as I was. We were talking around Barry, neither of us mentioning his name. I hoped a joint would help. It didn't.

"I wanna take you to my favorite neighborhood dive. Like Italian?"

"Men or shoes?"

He laughed. His appreciation always thrilled.

"Last night was incredible. I'm really proud of you."

"That stand-up gig you and Mona booked me on at Rock Bar four years ago opened the door for all of this."

"Maybe you should be taking me to dinner," he said.

The ride uptown was quiet.

An old time, frenetic, Westside café, V & T's bordered on cliché with its red and white checked tablecloths and homemade Chianti. It was jammed tight with Columbia students, so Lenny and I sat close in a small corner booth.

It was a bona fide date. After years of friendship, neither of us knew how to do it. I certainly didn't. I'd never really dated anyone in my whole life. Whenever I was interested in someone, it was usually flirt, kiss, screw and then eat. That usually took weeks, months, even years sometimes. Eating first was awkward.

After finishing the exact same meal—salad, penne and chicken parm—Lenny suggested we have coffee at his place.

"Fair is fair. I saw yours," he said.

We'd both moved into new co-ops within a month of each other. I did it with help from Cookie and Si. Lenny's was a steal-of-a-deal in a price controlled, ridiculously affordable development. For each of us, it was the first time we were living solo in years, decorating to our own tastes, without interference. After hearing about all the similarities, I was definitely curious.

Sure enough, Lenny's apartment was comfortable and familiar. Other than the ultra plush maroon carpeting, his place was also primarily black and white. Where I accented with wood antiques, he used touches of grey and silver deco.

He offered me a glass of wine. (It was odd to be drinking out of my wine glasses at his place.) When I went to the bathroom, it was my towels I dried my hands on, and when he showed me his bedroom, it was my sheets on his bed. I certainly felt at home. Sort of. In reality, I was anxious. Once we smoked, I got completely paranoid.

Sitting on the couch, Boz Skaggs playing softly in the background, I felt like a lamb being led to the slaughter. But this was Lenny—sweet, patient Lenny. He'd never rushed anything. Why was I so uncomfortable? I just wanted to leave.

Lenny had other things in mind. He'd waited long enough. He leaned in for a kiss.

"I sure wish you would've done that the other night," I said, backing away. "Now I feel like I'm cheating."

"On Barry? We went out first. Besides, he and I have spent the past few years together. I think I'm the one cheating on Barry."

"But I wasn't even sure that was a date. This is a date."

Again, Lenny leaned in for a kiss. I kissed back for a moment and then inched away. Still exhausted from the night before, hell, the weeks before, I yawned.

"I'm sorry, it's nothing personal."

"I understand," he said. "I'll take you home."

He called around noon the next day. I realized I missed him. Hmmm.

Now, seeing Barry seemed wrong. What a fucking loony toon, crazy bird I was. Here was one of my best friends from childhood, whom I hadn't seen in ages, living a life so similar to mine. I wanted to know him again, this time as a man. When we were kids, I thought he was cute. But he was short and, at times, annoying. Plus, then, there was Ray Santo. Ray was tall, dark, handsome and completely unattainable—the bad boy that every girl in junior high wanted. Ray flirted with me constantly but it never went anywhere. (Where was it *supposed* to go? It was junior high.) Reminiscent of Vinny, Scotty and so many of my other favorite wastes of time, I obsessed about Ray for years.

As a kid, I began unrequited love affairs with teen idols from afar. Sajid Khan was the first. He had his five minutes of fame; I had my two years of obsession. There was a Beatle and a Monkee. Barry Cowsill followed, then Michael Parks, who I actually had a close encounter with a few years after my fixation and learned: be careful meeting your heroes. He was too willing. I was too young. Availability was plainly not attractive to me. It was the unattainable that always stole my heart and made mincemeat of my brain.

Thinking back, I could trace this dysfunction to my first true love. Not quite twelve when I met Alan, he was sixteen, in high school and very cool. Tall, lean and blue-eyed, he had wavy brown hair that swooped down low on his forehead. With a menacing smile, he walked with sexy confidence—a real life James Dean.

Alan's parents owned the Catskill Mountains resort my father worked at in the summers, during the late '60s to early '70s. Most of the guests spent a week or two there, and the truly affluent spent the whole summer with their wives and children, from late June until Labor Day. The husbands came up on weekends and, I suppose, generally had their mistresses in the city while their wives were running after the waiters, lifeguards and social staff.

Dirty Dancing summed it up brilliantly. Alan was Patrick Swayze to my Baby, only we never danced, nobody put me in the corner and it took me three years to get him.

The first summer, when I was not quite twelve, I snuck around trying to put myself in his path whenever possible. He was a waiter in the children's dining room. I'd coincidentally show up just in time to help him set-up— three times a day. He'd laugh and pat me on the head like a puppy. I lived for the moments I spent with him.

On Labor Day, the last day of season, he said, "When you're fourteen, you're gonna be my girl."

Little did he know I considered that a deal set in stone. I spent the next two years planning and living for the day.

I saw him every day for the next two summers, suffering through a yearly, ten-month separation, relieved only by a one-week, mid-winter visit. His sister, Sue, was one of my closest friends, which enabled me to be around a lot. They had an apartment on the hotel grounds where Sue and I spent many an hour listening to Frank Zappa and watching old black and white detective movies with her grandma. Alan would always happen through at one point or another. I worshiped him; he knew it, and he seemed to take delight in my adulation. Occasionally, I reminded him of his promise, which always made him laugh.

Did he think I was kidding or something?

When I was fourteen, a few months shy of my fifteenth birthday, I arrived for the season jumping out of my skin, bursting with anticipation of fulfilling my long cherished dream. As if it had been hours, instead of months, I headed straight for the children's dining room, picked up some silverware and began setting tables without uttering a sound. It took a moment or two for Alan to notice. He looked up at me with what appeared to be genuine delight. I flirted with a new confidence. This was to be my summer, after all.

Was I crazy, or was he flirting back? Had something truly changed?

"Wow Andi, you've really grown up this year."

"I'm working as a mother's helper and bunking with the other girls," I proudly responded, as if to verify that fact.

It was the first summer I wasn't staying with my dad. He was however, still on the grounds and close at hand. Gratefully, I was a stealth teenager.

Alan invited me up to the shacks that night, signaling my coming of age. The shacks were (as they sound) run-down, wooden huts in the woods, which were used as waiters' quarters. Alan shared his shack with Bill, his best friend. On that first evening, frightened and excited, I headed up there after work. It was about 9:00 p.m. on one of the longest days of the year, so it was not quite dark.

Unsure which shack was his, I began to panic until I heard, "Come senators, congressman, please heed the call..." Dylan. Now certain I was in the right place, I mounted the steps, albeit cautiously. The door swung open at the sound and there was Alan, still in his black and whites, his shirt unbuttoned, revealing his perfectly toned torso in a tight white t-shirt beneath. As much as I wanted to be there, I was terrified. I was only fourteen and three-quarters.

It was the '60s though. 1969 actually. Things were different then. I'd recently smoked pot for the first time and had had a somewhat intimate encounter for no other reason than to be more skilled for Alan. I knew with total certainty I'd sleep with him that summer. I hadn't gone past first base until a few weeks prior, but I was determined and ready for him to hit a home run. *I was?*

Alan and I sat on his bed while Bill and Freddy (their other good friend, who was older, sadder, funnier and drunker) sat on Bill's. We defended civil rights, the Black Panthers and Students for a Democratic Society, and vehemently attacked the war on Vietnam while we sang along to Dylan and smoked a joint.

I was a young socialist, having already done my share of demonstrating. Alan and Bill were out-and-out commies. Extreme activists, they swooped me up in their passion as I was trying to seduce Alan with mine. We spent the next couple of weeks meeting nightly, engaging in like behavior.

Fittingly, on July 14th, Cuban Revolution Day, I popped over to see Sue. Matter-of-factly she told me she'd locked herself in the bathroom earlier that morning. Stuck in there for a while, Alan happened by and began working on the lock—she on one side of the door, he on the other.

With the safety of the big wooden plank between them, Alan, a very close-to-the-vest, private sort of guy said, "Do ya know who I like, Sue?"

"Who?"

"Andi Schwartz."

"Whaddya say?" I interrupted, freaking out.

Sue and I had never discussed my obsession with Alan, but she wasn't stupid.

She smiled. "Go for it."

I didn't know what to do, how to breathe, walk or talk. Floating, flying, soaring, it was one of the purest feelings of bliss I've ever known—three years in the making. I've had my share of those, but this was the first. Cherry breakings are always historic.

I don't know how I got through that day. I couldn't bear waiting one more minute for Alan to declare his love.

When I saw him in the dining room at dinner, he looked over at me and smiled. "See you later?" he asked, innocently.

"You bet," I replied, with a bride's wedding night blush.

I spent a long time showering and picking out the perfect ripped bellbottoms and BVD. Heading up to the shacks slowly, laboring every step. I didn't know what, if anything, would happen that night, but I sensed the times they were a changin'. Just knowing he had feelings for me, that he had said them out loud, was almost enough.

Alan, unaware that I had spoken with Sue, was his usual self, singing along to "Positively Fourth Street" and smoking a doobie when I entered. Bill and Freddy were playing gin rummy. Alan motioned for me to sit next to him, offering me the joint. Taking a long, deep hit, I was hoping to calm the terror I was feeling. He was big man on campus. I was an inexperienced little girl pretending to be a grown up. But I loved him. I'd loved him for as long as I could remember. I wanted to give myself to him, but I had no idea how.

As the night wore on and we got higher, we also got giddier and more playful. Alan lay down and pulled me next to him. Bill and Freddy were still playing cards. Even though we'd all been talking, smoking and singing for hours, at that moment I was unaware of anyone or anything, except Alan. Looking at him, I suppose the love was spilling from my pores and eyeballs, because after three years of dreaming, wanting and praying, he finally kissed me. He had kissed me before on the cheek, the head and the hand even, but he'd never kissed my lips with his. Boy, was he doing that now.

We kissed and kissed and kissed some more. My eyes were shut tight. When I did peek, I saw his were too. Freddy, deciding they'd seen enough, grabbed Bill, turned out the lights and split.

Once they did, we did the deed. It was over quickly—very quickly. It kind of hurt, wasn't really pleasant, but we had, at last, consummated my love. Knowing I had to get back before curfew, feeling embarrassed, shy and euphoric, I took my leave.

Sailing back to my room, lit from within, I kept saying over and over "Alan Rosenbloom and Andi Schwartz."

"I know how you feel about him, but do you have to keep saying it?" My roommate Julia asked, a bit annoyed.

Looking away, I blushed.

"You dog. You did it!"

"Sssssshhhh," I pleaded.

From then on, most nights played out the same: Alan and I hung out in the shacks with Bill and Freddy, who'd eventually leave when the kissing began. The lights were always turned off, the sessions short. Alan never spoke of his feelings for me, never displayed any sign of affection other than when we were alone in the dark. We never held hands or walked arm in arm; we were always feet apart and unconnected. Young and insecure, I longed for more.

Mid-summer, Alan and Bill headed off, a la *Easy Rider,* with jeans, pot and a "rebel with a cause" attitude, to explore the USA by motorcycle. Despondent seeing them go, Alan assured me that, when they got back, they were going to get an apartment in the city and fight the good fight for freedom. I had visions of visiting them on weekends and being their "Wendy." That thought kept me sane for the remainder of August.

Just prior to Labor Day, Sue got a call from Alan expressing his love of Ohio and the struggle of the working class there. He'd decided to stay, as his efforts were needed. I was blindsided.

For the next few months, I wrote to him incessantly. Receiving a note or two back, it was always about the struggle and never anything personal at all. He could've been writing to his aunt.

I had plans with Sue to stay at her family's apartment for the holidays and prayed Alan would be there. It was all I could think of, every waking minute.

On the drive upstate, my heart was bursting. Filled with hope, as soon as I arrived, Sue greeted me with, "Alan just got here. He brought a couple of friends with him."

I decided to reserve judgment. As I was unpacking, Alan came into Sue's room. Running to hug him, he tensed a bit before responding.

"Good to see you Andi, let's go talk."

Let's go talk?

Leading the way to the family room, with a view of the snowy mountains, he sat in front of the roaring fire. It was the perfect setting for romance, but I sensed that was not on the agenda.

"You know Andi, I think it makes sense for us to just be friends. I'm so far away and all."

Well, there it was.

My heart sank.

"I haven't been with anyone since you," he continued.

"Neither have I," I said, with renewed hope.

Desperate to find a way to change his mind, I added, "I think friends can still be close."

He looked at me for the first time that day,

"You mean no strings attached, just be close and that's that?"

"Sure, why not?" I didn't mean it at all, but if that was the only way I could have him, I was willing to try.

Pete and Taylor, a couple of intellectual radicals from Ohio, looked the part. We all did, with our blue jeans, flannel shirts and work boots. Sitting down as Alan introduced us, Taylor was old (at least 25), short and stocky, wore no make-up and was sort of butch. *She couldn't possibly be the reason he was dumping me.* And yet, as we began talking, I noticed Alan revered her every word.

After dinner and a lively dissection of Lyndon Johnson around the fire, everyone retired to their respective rooms for the night. I was bunking with Sue. As soon as I'd gotten washed and into pajamas, I heard, softly, from down the hall, "Andi..." Then, "Hey, Andi, come on in here a minute, would you?"

It was pretty clear from Alan's tone what was on his mind. And maybe it wasn't just sex he wanted, maybe he'd had a change of heart. Sue shrugged and extended her arm towards the door.

I walked slowly down the long corridor towards his room, still smarting from our earlier conversation, praying for a turnaround. Sticking my head through the door, I could see Alan, lying in bed, covers pulled up to his bare chest, his arms on top of the blanket. He motioned for me to sit down next to him.

"Did you mean what you said about friends being close?"

Disappointed and hurt, but so longing for his love, I forced a smile. I guess I thought if we made love he'd realize what a horrible mistake he was making and change his mind.

He turned out the lights as I slid in beside him. We kissed, but it was awkward and somehow unfamiliar. It had been about six months—but still. Fumbling around, we went through the motions, but it was awful and over very quickly. All I wanted to do was leave, which was clearly the same thought Alan was having, as he seemed relieved when I said good night and went back to Sue's room.

The rest of that vacation was a nightmare. Alan and I had little to do with each other. He spent an awful lot of time with Taylor. Sure enough, soon afterwards, I found out they were engaged. They married about a year later, holding the reception on my seventeenth birthday. I was in attendance, playing the good friend, but I cried my eyes out for weeks before and after.

Some years later, while driving cross-country on my way back to college, senior year, I was staying in Ohio for a couple of days and called Alan, who was now a dad.

"Hi Alan, it's Andi. I'm close by. Can you meet me for a drink?"

"Um, yeah, sure," he said in hushed tones. "Where?"

It was clearly a secret rendezvous for him. I guess I was now the other woman.

How many times have I been the last girlfriend before a guy married someone else? A lot. I wonder what that means?

When I got to the local saloon, Alan was waiting for me, looking older, less James Deanish, more marriedish. We had some awkward conversation, both begging off before long. He had a family to get home to and I had a boyfriend waiting to ignore me in Tucson. Grateful that I'd shed my baby fat, and was now a young woman and looked it, I prayed that I'd left him wanting.

There was closure in that meeting, kind of. It certainly helped me to stop fantasizing about him.

Many years later, while visiting friends in upstate New York, I tracked down Sue. Paying her a visit, I got to meet her son, and she, mine.

Showing me some recent family photos, she spoke of Alan and Taylor and their two grown kids. Alan was beefy and balding. I tried to find his essence in his eyes, but it was hard as the picture was taken from far away. If not for Sue showing me the photo, I never would've believed it was him. I asked for his phone number and she reluctantly gave it to me.

At Christmas that year, I called. It turned out that he and Taylor were divorced. Sue hadn't said a word. He had long ago given up his crusade and was now a real estate agent trying to "act."

I subtly (as a Mack truck) tried to get him to tell me how he felt about me back in the day. He was as withholding as ever, simply reminding me how young I was at the time. And then that truck hit me. *I was jailbait.* A nineteen-year-old boy and a not-quite-fifteen-year-old girl; he could've gotten in a whole heap of trouble—especially with my dad, who was close at hand the whole time.

With that knowledge came some peace, but it was based purely on conjecture. As was his custom, Alan left me in the dark. Which set the stage nicely for my relationships to come.

———————— **Just the three of us** ————————

Saturday morning, Barry called asking if I'd like to come up to his place for a while before our childhood friend, Joseph, joined us for dinner.

As we were hanging up, Lenny beeped in. There was something so sweet about him, about this. Good old-fashioned dating, so foreign to me. Historically it was, "You're cute, I love you, where's my key?"

On the other hand, I was always a bit of a klutz, juggling was never my thing. How was I going to keep two balls in the air? (Hmmm... actually more like four.)

I found myself dressing for Barry. I'd only seen him a couple of times, but it was easy to ascertain that he liked young, pretty, thin girls—lots of them. He'd never been married and most of his relationships barely moved past dating.

In my mid-thirties—I was ancient for a man like him. Not my thinnest, having regained a few post-Nutrisystem pounds, I was self-conscious, constantly comparing myself to magazine perfection.

Arriving at Barry's at 4:00, I climbed the stairs to his fourth floor walk-up on the Upper East Side. Even though he explained that he'd lived there since college, it looked like he'd just moved in. The walls were bare. Albums, cassettes, laser disks and boxes were everywhere; there was very little furniture and poor lighting. Considering how successful he was, I was shocked. He still lived like a struggling student. Wearing black jeans and a t-shirt, his hair pulled back in a ponytail, he looked exactly the same as he had every other time I'd seen him.

Taking me into his bedroom, he sat at his desk and showed me photos that he'd scanned from our youth. It was horrifying to see my twiggy haircut and my non-twiggy prepubescent body. Fleshy and stoop shouldered, I was wearing turquoise and pink, very '60s short-shorts, with a sleeveless, mock turtleneck—my twelfth birthday party. I remembered that day clearly. We played spin the bottle. I was shy and afraid. Barry was being goaded to spin it to me. He did. I remember my disappointment that it wasn't Ray Santo.

This was a new day. Barry was desirable. His bohemian lifestyle did not impress, but the serendipitous nature of our reunion, coupled with his success, certainly did. Where I was struggling to find my place as a music promoter, Barry had worked at two of the biggest record labels in the world and was a VP at both. I currently had the lone basement office alongside the ladies room in a smelly club; Barry's was on the thirty-fifth floor on Avenue of the Americas, with an assistant, a secretary and a full staff. He was also earning at least five times what I was. I'd abandoned my dream of doing stand-up; Barry was working road gigs as a middle act and writing a screenplay with Lenny.

More than any of that, he was the proverbial boy next door. All the signs pointed to this as "meant to be."

"Wanna smoke?" I asked, pulling out a joint.

"No!"

"Mind if I do?"

"Yes!"

Quickly putting it away, I felt like a scolded thirteen-year-old all over again. I sat on the floor and pretended to be looking through some Laser Discs—he had thousands. My mind wandered to Lenny. Sweet Lenny. Once it had, I couldn't bring it back.

"Are you thirsty?"

I nodded, realizing I was. He returned with a glass of water, straight from the tap, sans ice. Carrying a bag of red shoestring licorice, he offered me one. As he tied his piece into little knots before eating it, rather than fess up that that was exactly the way I ate it too (in defiance), I proceeded to eat mine the traditional way, one bite of the long rope at a time. I wanted a grown-up, not Peter Pan. *Like I could change him with licorice?*

While I was busy pondering those and other deep thoughts, Barry leaned in. Jolted back to the present, I was excited at the prospect of his kiss.

At that precise moment, the intercom buzzed. Joseph announced his arrival.

"Saved by the bell," Barry mumbled, standing up.

Joseph bounded up the fourth floor walk-up without even breaking a sweat. His pockmarked skin was the only reminder of his awkward adolescence. Despite that, he was ruggedly handsome. Where he was a tad gangly in grade school, he'd filled out, and now had a great physique and stood proud and tall. Looking like money, he was wearing an expensive, well-fitted suit, freshly shined designer shoes and a million dollar smile. He lifted me up in his arms and gave me a squeeze. I'd always adored Joseph. One of my fondest memories was of us trick-or-treating without costumes—shamelessly begging for candy when we were way too old to be doing so.

Joseph and Barry had been best friends all their lives. They still bickered about everything and annoyed the hell out of each other. But, like an old married couple, they were bound together. So many memories of the three of us came flooding back: walking to school, playing in the snow, eating pizza, laughing—a lot of laughing.

Joseph owned his own real estate office and was doing quite well. Newly married, it sounded like there might be trouble in paradise. Not so much by what he said, rather by what his face conveyed when he spoke of her. I knew that face well, having worn it for too many years myself. He didn't have children, but there was longing when he spoke of the possibility.

We got to talking about the pizza of our youth—Gloria's on Lydig Avenue. There was never anything quite like it. I've spent my life searching.

"Goldberg's has the same sort of taste," Barry said, ordering a couple of pies, to punctuate the point.

The three of us ate at a little wooden table under a bare yellow overhanging bulb. Not the best ambience, but he was right, the pizza was sensational and had that old familiar taste. Eddie had turned me on to Queens Pizza in Brooklyn Heights, which also had it. Other than those three places, I've never come across it. It was simply... the taste of perfection.

"You know, Andi, we always wondered what happened to you. Barry never got over you."

Barry didn't argue.

After we ate, trying to decide what to do next, Joseph picked up the newspaper.

"Lenny's doing a set around the corner at 10:00. Let's go check him out. I've never seen his act."

After a bit of coaxing Barry agreed. Lenny was just taking the stage as we arrived. Grabbing a table in the back, I was caught off guard by how funny he was. Somehow I hadn't remembered this small detail of his life. We laughed. A lot. At least Joseph and I did. Barry was more intent on watching me laugh.

As Lenny left the stage to wild applause, he caught sight of us as he headed towards the outer room. Seeing him in his element, handsome and adored, got my heart pounding.

We gathered at the bar in awkward silence.

Now what?

Stammering, Lenny chipped the ice, "Let's have a drink."

He turned to the bartender.

"These are on me."

We were all relieved to have something to do.

"I'll have a Jack and water," I said, smiling at him.

Lenny's eyes widened. "My kind of girl." Almost before the words had left his lips, he shrugged, embarrassed.

Barry looked over in disdain. "I'll have a coke," he snarled.

What's that about? I wondered. As if reading my thoughts, he added, "I don't drink," without further explanation.

Joseph and Lenny both had a scotch. Moments later, as the elixirs began taking effect, we relaxed a bit. Except, of course, Barry, who was getting hyped up on caffeine and sugar. Tapping his leg, he was pacing around in little circles, watching my every move.

"You were terrific Lenny," I finally blurted out.

"You were great. Barry was right about you," Joseph said, smacking Lenny on the back.

Barry didn't say anything.

Joseph jumped back in, "I hate to break up the festivities, but I have to get home. The old girl's probably freakin' by now."

With that, Joey shook Lenny's hand, adding, "Great to see you man—funny shit!"

He smacked his hands on Barry's shoulders (an act of encouragement perhaps?) and turned to me. "You look better than you did twenty years ago Andi, and that's saying somethin'. See you soon, I hope."

Giving me a hug, he was off.

The three of us stood there.

With a big, exaggerated yawn, Barry sort of sang, "I'm pretty beat. Think it's time to call it a night."

Grateful to break up this little ménage, I said, "Yeah, I could use a good night's sleep myself,"

"Can I give you guys a lift?"

"That'd be great, thanks, Lenny," I said.

"Come on Barry, I'll drop you first," he said, as he instinctively took my arm.

"What a guy," Barry mocked under his breath.

He'd always been moody. I'd forgotten. Obviously Lenny knew this side of him. Nonplussed, he led the way, holding the passenger door for me. I slid in and made room for Barry. He sat as close to the door as possible and pulled me to him. Lenny rounded the car and got in. We drove the three blocks in silence.

"Well, here we are," Lenny said, doing his cheerful best.

"Thanks for the lift. Uh, speak to you guys." Barry slammed the door behind him, a bit too forcefully to go unnoticed.

Opening my window, I called out, "Good night, Barry, I had fun. I'll call you tomorrow."

"Night, man," Lenny seconded.

Barry waved without turning back, continuing on his way, head down.

"Well, that was nice and awkward," I said.

"My favorite shampoo!"

Lenny got the intended laugh.

"This whole thing is awkward," he added.

"You're telling me. You were great tonight by the way. I forgot how funny you are."

"Gee, thanks."

"I always knew you were funny, but you were great. Great!"

We drove the rest of the way in anxious silence.

"Well, that's me," I said nodding to my entrance. Lenny faced me. Very tentatively, he leaned over and kissed me gently on the lips.

"Have any plans for the Fourth?"

"Barry asked me if I'd like to hang out with him, why?"

"Too bad. I go to this great beach party every year. Lots of comics, musicians and people you'd enjoy. Charlie Johnson from the Harold Burns Show hosts it. He's an old friend of mine—a great guy who really knows how to throw a party."

"Wow, sounds great. Let me see what I can do. I'll call you tomorrow. Good night, Lenny."

"Good night, Andi."

As I entered my building, I turned and saw he hadn't moved a muscle. He was just sitting there staring at me. As I waited for the elevator, I was trying to figure out what the hell I could say to Barry.

It was giving me a headache and I deserved it. I had no business breaking plans with Barry because something better came up. On the other hand, the potential networking was huge and could really benefit my career. But was that really what was motivating me? Or, was it simply wanting to be with Lenny and have fun with a bunch of cool people? A little of both, I guess—a lot of both.

Reintroduced to Barry's mopey side was deterrent enough from wanting to spend the potentially festive Fourth of July with him. He didn't drink, didn't smoke pot and I couldn't possibly not do either on one of the biggest party days of the year.

I called Barry.

I wanted to bring it up immediately and get it out of the way. I was anxious, but I just couldn't bring myself to break the mood, he seemed so happy. *Was it really Barry I was thinking of?*

Finally, I spit it out in one breath, without pause "Lenny's going to a party at Charlie Johnson's on the Fourth and invited me, thinking it could possibly be a great opportunity for my new nights as there are always a lot of players there."

"Sure, go," he said, letting me off the hook without further discussion.

Relieved, but overcome by guilt, I offered to meet up with him after the party. Guilt or gluttony? Was I just looking to have both men and eat them too?

Unsure of how the hell I was going to tell Lenny about this latest development, I decided to wait until we were on our way to drop the bomb—lest he change his mind and I end up home alone. *Which was exactly what I deserved.*

At about 3:00 p.m. on the Fourth, Lenny showed up wearing an old pair of short shorts, a tiny, tight t-shirt and a goofy hat. I began questioning my choice.

Wasting no time, "Lenny, I promised Barry I'd see him later, so I can't make this too late. I feel so guilty about the last minute change in plans."

Pulling out of the parking space, Lenny nodded, "I can live with that." Silence.

"By the way," he said, "since you're not doing stand-up anymore, would you mind if I used the punch line from that Kennedy joke we wrote during that private session?"

"What?"

"The one that ended, '...that's like Oswald saying, Kennedy shot first.'"

"Yes, I mind. I paid for that joke!"

No lightweight, Lenny, he'd wasted no time in getting me back. Right between the eyes!

With that, I moved as far away from him as I could get. Already keeping my distance, thanks to my guilt and that outfit, this development had me hugging the door. *What was I doing here? What had I done?* Karma had wasted no time on delivery.

We got to Charlie's on the early side. A few comics were milling about drinking, smoking and waiting for the fun to start. Lenny was chatting away. I had little to offer.

After a ridiculous amount of eating, a bunch of guys wandered inside. Soon, Lenny was playing piano, Keith somebody was on guitar, a few guys were banging percussion and everyone was singing. The amount of alcohol consumed went a long way toward explaining why it did not sound particularly musical. Not really a drinker, my one beer wasn't helping my appreciation. I wanted to run. Mercifully, someone lit a joint.

Far from the exciting day of networking I was anticipating, I could've gone to McShitsky's on my corner and accomplished just as much. Take away the brick wall and the lights, put them in ill-fitting clothing and comedians are just a bunch of schmegegges.

We all headed down to the beach at dusk as the drinking got into high gear. Everyone was having a ball—everyone except me. And Lenny, I suspected. He couldn't possibly have missed my discomfort.

As the fireworks ended, I reminded Lenny that I had to get back to the city. Good-naturedly he said his goodbyes as we headed to the car. I got the feeling his friends thought he was about to get lucky. Oh, he was lucky all right.

The ride back to the city was even more uncomfortable than the one coming from the city. Lenny, a bit lit and feeling no pain, had command of the car, but I was nervous as hell. In a fine mood for most of the trip, it wasn't until I asked him to drop me on the Upper East Side that he seemed to remember where I was headed. Long, awkward silences prevailed, and the air got thick.

As we approached Barry's corner, I saw him standing there watching the cars go by. I hoped Lenny didn't notice.

"I'll jump out here," I said, still on the far side of the street.

"Don't be silly, it's a green light. I'll drop you in front."

Just as Lenny said those words he must've caught sight of Barry and Barry of him, because Barry started walking down the street, away from the car, without acknowledging us or turning around.

"I better just jump out."

As Lenny stopped the car, I leaned over and kissed him briskly on the cheek. "Thanks Lenny, it was fun."

"I get the feeling it really wasn't. Sorry."

"It's totally not your fault. I brought it on myself. I apologize for being such lousy company. I did a stupid thing and, unfortunately, all of us paid the price."

"It's cool. Call you tomorrow?"

"Great. Thanks, Lenny. The fireworks were spectacular!"

"You like fireworks? Wait till you catch up with Barry."

Feeling a certain relief as I got away from Lenny, I was filled with dread approaching Barry, who was walking half a block ahead of me and wasn't slowing down. Let the punishment begin!

"Hey, Barry, wait up."

He stopped walking, but didn't turn around.

"You'll be happy to know I had a horrible time. It was so not good. Things are getting all mucked up. Lenny and I were much better friends, we weren't meant to date. It was so uncomfortable."

Barry didn't say a word.

"I'm sorry, Barry, really sorry. What I did was awful."

Walking again, without picking up his head, he mumbled, "I have to think."

We went to a billiard hall and played some pool. Barry continued to ice me for the duration of the evening. It was damn chilly for a hot summer night. I knew I had it coming, but I couldn't wait for the night to end.

The next day, we had brunch. Softening a bit, he brought up his lousy Fourth of July just enough to remind me that I was a very bad girl.

In work mode, the rest of the week flew by. Lenny called as promised. We agreed to see each other Thursday at my club. I was relieved it would eliminate the dating pressure.

Lenny showed up early, before the insanity started, as was his custom. Wearing black jeans, black t-shirt and a black leather jacket, he looked incredibly sexy. It was far from his usual attire. His efforts to fit in were not lost on me.

"The other night didn't go so well," he said, looking down.

"It was my fault. I really appreciate your taking me."

"How's Barry?"

"Still punishing me."

We caught each other's eye and laughed.

One of the musicians was having trouble with the sound guy and called me over to settle the dispute. "Would you excuse me a minute, Lenny?"

"Sure, of course. You know, Andi, you just keep getting better at this. It's amazing to watch.

"Thanks, Lenny. I owe it to you."

Walking away I remembered why I liked the guy so much. Who was I to judge him? I was the schmuck.

The club got busy really quickly. The next thing I knew, an hour had passed. As I made my way to the bar, I noticed Lenny was gone. I'm gifted at making a bad situation worse.

As the evening was winding down, Maryann and I shared a nightcap. Reaching for my wallet to tip the bartender, I dropped my purse. As I leaned over to retrieve the scattered contents, I noticed a piece of paper under my stool. There was familiar writing on it. Notes. Flipping it over, a perfect likeness of me was staring back—a pencil sketch that could almost have been a photograph.

"Look at this," I said, offering it to Maryann.

"That's incredible. Who did it?"

"Looks like Lenny did."

As soon as I got home, I called him. It was really late but he was a night crawler like me. He was still awake and sounded surprised but happy to hear from me. I decided not to mention the sketch, not yet anyway. I filled him in on the rest of the night.

After a few minutes, he asked, "Are you free for dinner on Sunday? I'm working in Jersey for the weekend, then I'm off on a cruise ship for a couple of weeks."

With the Fourth still fresh in my mind, I hesitated but, remembering the pencil drawing and how great he looked, I asked, "What time?"

On Saturday, I had brunch with Barry. Somehow we got to talking about fear of sexually transmitted diseases. My fear, that is. I had taken a test as soon as Eddie and I had split up and hadn't seen any action since, save for Eddie himself a couple of times. Barry had been with a bevy of babes, he'd never been tested, and, if you factored in all the guys they'd been with—well, that was a risk I was totally unwilling to take.

"I guess I've always felt that what you don't know won't hurt you," Barry said with a shrug.

"That attitude has killed about a dozen of my friends."

I don't know why I'd even bothered to bring it up. Barry kept his distance all day, continuing to punish me. We had no physical contact. His mood certainly didn't warrant affection, but I couldn't help but wonder if he was even considering making a move. We'd come a hair's distance from kissing that day in his apartment when Joseph showed up. It remained on my mind but if it were still on Barry's, he was sure doing a great job of hiding it.

"Want to visit the old neighborhood next Saturday?"

"Totally," I answered immediately, thinking that perhaps it would shake him out of this funk.

On Sunday evening, Lenny arrived all spiffed up. He was wearing a nice pair of slacks, a freshly pressed, button down shirt and shiny, well-polished shoes. He took me to a very expensive, romantic bistro in the village.

I was feeling uneasy, like I had no right to be there. There seemed to be something so dishonest about seeing two men, even though Lenny and Barry certainly both knew about each other (hell, they knew each other, period). Never having played the field I didn't know the rules, but suspected I was breaking more than one.

Rather than avoid the subject, Lenny dove right in. "I still can't believe you and Barry went to school together."

"It's amazing. Especially that you were the link. Everything is happening so quickly. It's very confusing."

"Must be the pill I dropped in your drink."

Nothing like a man who can make a girl laugh, no matter what.

On the ride uptown, knowing this date was drawing to a close and having no idea how to finish it, we were both awkward and clearly uncomfortable. Lenny did what he did best and had me laughing. The funniest person I'd ever known, he found the humor in everything, and had the perfect expression for it.

I can't remember what he found to satirize that evening. Knowing Lenny, it could have been anything from the garbage on the street to the president. Laughter was a perfect release and we finally relaxed in a way no wine or pot could manage. As I moved closer to Lenny, he took my hand. There's something so sexy about sitting close to a man while he's driving and has to concentrate on the road and then doing everything possible to subtly distract him. I miss bench seats.

Lenny double-parked when we arrived in front of my building. Making awkward small talk (I wish I could've read the bubble over his head), we said goodnight, then simultaneously moved closer.

To say that Lenny's kiss surprised me would be the understatement of the decade. It was perfect—sensuous, warm and sexy—very sexy. As attracted as I'd always been to him, it was in a sort of innocent, "you're my friend" way. There was nothing innocent about this. This was magnetic, head spinning.

Carlos, my doorman, was craning his neck from behind his podium to get a better view. Lenny disengaged long enough to pull into a parking spot on the corner.

All the years of knowing had led to trusting, which unleashed a deeply felt connection that was manifesting in some very hot necking.

I hate that word. When I was eleven I caught my divorced parents together. Afterwards I asked my mother what they were doing. "We were just necking," she said. Taking that literally, I couldn't figure out why they would want to rub necks.

The windows must have steamed up, as we didn't see, were completely unaware, of the car that was sitting along side us, until they started honking to get Lenny's attention. (Leave it to a New Yorker looking for a parking spot to decimate a first kiss.) Embarrassed, I straightened up.

"I should go."

The couple was impatiently staring. Lenny shrugged in resignation.

"Can I call you when I get home?"

"Please do!"

I leaned over and kissed him one last time, gently on the lips.

"What a revelation," I said, more to myself than to him. Without waiting for a reaction, I was off. Before heading into my building, still reeling from this unexpected turn of events, I gave a last look. Lenny was stopped at the light, his head out the window, facing back towards me. I blew him a kiss. When the light turned green, he was honked from behind to move on. As he drove out of sight, I could still feel the warmth of him. I touched my lips, still amazed at how good it felt. What in the world had taken us so long?

My mind was reeling; Josephine, the astrologer's, words dancing in my brain. "You know him, you just don't know you know him." Could Lenny possibly be "the one?" What about Barry, the boy next door? Surely there was a message there. I knew him too. After twenty-something years, he resurfaced, having lived an almost-parallel life. He was successful as hell, which Josephine had promised. It was meant to be, wasn't it?

Lenny was all I could think of. After the disaster of my initial kiss with Vinny, I figured it had to mean something that it was so not right from the get-go. That's a sign, isn't it? Not like Vinny was even a choice, anyway. He didn't want me. I was pretty sure Lenny did. Hey, wait a minute... Vinny, Lenny... they kind of sound alike...

Barry? Too soon to know. And that kind of sounded alike too.

Upstairs, I washed, undressed and had just gotten under the covers when the phone rang. Lenny's voice was soft and sensual. Why had I never noticed this side of him before? From day one I'd adored him, but I don't think I'd ever thought of him as this incredibly sexy thing. I'd entertained the thought of marrying him more than once, but I don't think I ever really thought beyond the liking. I had no idea how much I'd be wanting.

"I'm gonna be away for a couple of weeks, working a cruise. I'm not crazy about going, but it's a personal favor for Captain Stubing. We dock in Manhattan, mid-voyage, to pick up new passengers. Care to join me for lunch aboard the Love Boat next Saturday?"

"I've never been on a cruise ship. I'd love to."

Now officially dating, we said goodnight and I drifted off, smiling. So infrequently surprised, the night had been totally unexpected and thrilling. I was in uncharted waters and loving it.

I woke the next morning as happy as I've ever been. My new gig at The Stone House had lots of promise, I had a potential new man and plans that night with the boy next door. Lenny... Barry... Lenny... Barry... what a TWAT!

Once Lenny left on his cruise, Barry had the upper hand and decided to make the most of it and truly torture me. He invited me back to our old neighborhood to wander around and reminisce.

We walked the two blocks from the subway station to my old house in the Bronx. Walking around back, I peeked in the knee level window. It looked so small. A basement apartment, my memories of it were as dark as my old bedroom now was.

Cookie worked long hours selling ads for the Yellow Pages. A latchkey kid, I came home to an empty house. My father and brother lived across the street, but it was far from an ideal life for an eleven year old.

I didn't like the feelings that were resurfacing. Barry, sensing my discomfort, led the way back to the street towards his old house. We wandered into his backyard. Warmer memories began to take hold.

Passing Francine's place, the name on the door still read Mancuso. On a lark, we decided to ring the bell. Her mother answered the door looking much the same as she did twenty years prior. We, of course, did not, and she pleasantly inquired as to who the hell we were. Once we explained, she insisted we come in for some tea.

After catching us up on Francine and her family, she asked, "Do you have children?"

Looking at each other, we burst out laughing, explaining our recent reunion. "How romantic. It's destiny, no?"

One would think so. Barry and I smiled at each other. He seemed to forget for a moment how angry he still was at me for the Fourth of July and, of course, Lenny.

After lingering for a few more moments, we left a note for Francine and a promise to return. Heading down the once familiar Lydig Avenue, we were both struck by the change in sights, sounds and smells. What was once a predominately Jewish neighborhood, was now, almost exclusively, not.

Very few remnants of our youth remained. Thankfully, Gloria's was one. I had to have it. The price was certainly not as I remembered. What was once a 15-cent slice of pie was $1.50. I don't know why that shocked me, it was the going rate all over. The young man making the pizza, no longer the son of the Italian immigrant owner, was now a paid by the hour Latino. The pizza, once uniquely delectable, was now lukewarm and pedestrian.

Offering Barry a bite, I said wistfully, "They say 'you can never go home again.' I guess they're right."

Barry, chewing contemplatively, added, "You know why you can't go home? They've changed the locks."

I laughed, grateful for the levity in this moment of utter disillusionment.

Carvel was two doors down, the local hangout for my brother Jeff and his friends, where I tried desperately, for years, to fit in. Barry got a cone, offered me a lick and even the ice cream was not as I remembered. Feeling sorry for myself, I dropped my half eaten slice in the garbage can on the corner and ran smack into a woman who looked vaguely familiar.

"Have you lived here long?" I asked her.

"All my life," she replied, smiling. "Do I know you?"

"I think you knew my brother, Jeff Schwartz?"

"Knew him? I blew him!" she said, laughing heartily at her own joke. "Just kidding. How is Jeff?"

Bringing her up to speed, I promised to say hello for her. Only she never did tell me her name. There was something oddly comforting about it nonetheless.

Barry went to the payphone on the corner to call his dad to arrange a pick-up spot since we were going to join him and his second wife for dinner. In an instant, he was screaming at the man, turning blue. Embarrassed for him, embarrassed for me being with him, it was reminiscent of too many maniacs I'd spent my life with. It was scary. Surely Lenny never carried on like that.

Extremely agitated, Barry motioned for me to join him on the corner. Too afraid not to, I complied sheepishly. I was terrified he would turn his wrath on me. My stomach flipped. We walked silently towards the rendezvous point on White Plains Road.

"I can't believe TJ Music is still there," I said, trying to break the ice with genuine enthusiasm. "I wonder if the Madnicks still own it? Let's go in."

Hooking my arm in his, I started walking towards the store. I was yanked back a step by Barry's unyielding stance.

"We've got to meet my father."

"We have a few minutes, come on," I said, holding the door. Barry grudgingly followed, looking like an eight year old being forced to ingest a teaspoon of castor oil.

Behind the counter, a tall, tanned, handsome guy with a fresh pump from a recent workout was reading the newspaper.

"Danny, is that you?"

"Yeah, who's asking?" he inquired, before looking up.

His eyes began at waist level, slowly working their way up to mine. Squinting for a second, as if to better focus, there was silence, slow recognition and then a smile.

"Andi? Andi Schwartz? Holy shit, get over here!"

We embraced over the counter.

"You remember Barry Schoenbaum?"

"Yeah, sure," he said, shaking his hand without taking his eyes off me. "You look incredible. No wonder I had a crush on you."

"Crush on me? I had a crush on you!"

"If only I knew... this could have been us." He said, offering me a photo of his wife and kids.

"They're beautiful. Can't say I've been as lucky. Divorced, no kids. Ah, me."

Having had enough of this, Barry loudly cleared his throat. (Wow, people really do that?)

"Well, this was great, but we've gotta run," Barry said, pulling me towards the door.

"Great to see you, Danny."

"You, too, Andi. Don't make it another twenty years."

When we got outside, I was furious. "That was incredibly rude."

"Do you know everyone in the Bronx," he sneered.

"What's with you? What changed your mood?"

"Nothing, I'm fine."

"Good," I said sarcastically.

"Good," he mocked back.

Within a minute or two, Stan and Stella Schoenbaum, Barry's dad and stepmom, showed up at the corner of White Plains Road and Pelham Parkway, as arranged. We hopped in the car, doing the introductions as Stan pulled away. He looked just the same and I told him so. He was quite pleased with that, not knowing that he'd always looked old to me. All parents did. Stan was tall, thin, about sixty-five and balding. Stella, his second wife, was about fifty, wore a lot of make-up and even more perfume. I could sense their mutual affection and attraction. Happy for them, I wondered if I'd ever have that with someone over the long haul.

"So, did you kids have a good time?" Stan asked, good-naturedly.

"You gonna call me a kid when I'm fifty?"

"Barry, give him a break," I pleaded.

"Don't tell me how to talk to my father."

"Be nice," Stan said, embarrassed.

Turning on the radio, within a few seconds Stan was singing along to "Mack the Knife," as was Stella, followed by Barry. I couldn't decide what was worse, the fight or the fun.

As we arrived on Arthur Avenue, I settled into an old familiar calm. Back in the day, all New York Jews knew—Saturday night's Italian, Sunday is Chinese. It was sacrosanct. Arthur Avenue is to Italian food as Bourbon Street is to gumbo. The smells immediately took me back. There's something about the foods of youth that remain—never forgotten, forever craved.

I must have been about four when I had my first slice of pizza on 161st Street, across from Yankee Stadium. It was sitting on a piece of white wax paper, the cheese oozing off the crust, sticking to it. It smelled like fresh baked dough, tomatoes and oregano, and tasted like chewy heaven—the mozzarella stretching a foot and burning the roof of my mouth. A few blocks away was Hebrew National, with the best garlicky hot dogs, coated with spicy brown mustard, hot yellow sauerkraut, that made the roll soggy with its juice, and whose taste lingered for hours, as it repeated and repeated. The House of Wong's huge, crunchy eggrolls, stuffed with finely shredded cabbage, bits of roast pork and whole tiny shrimp were to die for.

I've chased those flavors, just as I did my first high, never again finding either. But this Arthur Avenue baked ziti was sure close to Crossways in Fallsburg—and that's saying a lot. It saved the day.

On Saturday morning, I awoke excited and hopeful. It was to be my first time on a cruise ship. I was missing Lenny and wanting him. After shaving my legs, perfuming from head to toe and putting on my best undies, I called Maryann to get permission—validation—for my dishonorable intentions. Mercifully, she didn't judge. In fact, she encouraged me to go for it. She said all the right things: "You and Lenny have known each other for years. You're both single, consenting adults. Why not?"

I took a few hits off a half-smoked joint. I hadn't been with anyone in a while. What if he didn't make a pass? *What if he did?*

Arriving at the pier at exactly noon as planned, the ship looked enormous from my vantage point. I searched for the entry plank. To my horror, I noticed there were at least half a dozen of them before me. Clutching the instructions Lenny had provided, I stood there paralyzed. A worker, mercifully noticing my panic, offered assistance. Kindly escorting me to the guest entrance, I stood transfixed, in awe of the vastness before me.

He gave me a gentle nudge. "She won't bite."

"But, he might," I replied, with a wink.

A podium and ship's officer flanked the top of the walkway. The crew was bustling, eager to complete their duties to allow for a few much-deserved hours on land. A handful of passengers milled about. It was transition time—the incoming cruise had disbanded, the outgoing not yet ready to receive guests.

ID was required to board, even for lunch. As I neared the officer, searching my bag for my driver's license, my purse became, as it always did when I was looking for something, a black hole. Just as I was getting frantic, Lenny appeared. The sight of him evened me out. Within a moment I produced my license.

Taking my hand, Lenny led me down the main corridor, pointing out the sights along the way.

"This is a high-end cruise line, with a mostly older clientele. The food is top notch, the people watching—not so much. Hungry?"

"Starving!" That about summed it up for a lot of things that hot summer day.

Entering the dining room, Lenny led me to his table near the large floor-to-ceiling window. It was a deuce, set for one. I couldn't help but think how lonely two weeks at sea with a bunch of seniors must be. He'd been living this solitary life for a week already, with another to go. Poor Lenny.

When a drop dead gorgeous cocktail waitress approached, with legs longer than linguini, it dawned on me that, on a ship with a thousand passengers, there had to be hundreds of young men and women tending to their needs: waitresses, chambermaids and showgirls. Oh my. Poor Lenny, indeed.

Wearing a baby blue button down shirt, which accentuated his eyes, Lenny didn't shift his gaze away from me for a second. Not even when leggy linguini girl delivered our wine. It was heady to have his total attention, and what appeared to be his appreciation of the tight, white, scoop neck jersey I had donned for his viewing pleasure.

Struggling to make conversation, both of us were clearly nervous about where things were heading.

"I'll have the Chinese chicken salad," I said, grateful for the waiter's interruption.

Without skipping a beat, Lenny added, "I'll have the same."

A couple in their seventies approached, wearing matching sailor outfits. The wife was nudging her husband.

"Sorry to interrupt your lunch," the husband began, glaring at his wife. "We really enjoyed your show last night."

"Thank you very much."

"You were wonderful," kvelled the wife, in heavily accented New York Jewish.

"So, you got the twenty bucks?" Lenny asked, with a wink. "I hope you enjoyed your cruise."

"We've decided to stay aboard for another week. Can't wait for your next show," the wife said, as her husband waved, pulling her on their way.

"Hell, now I have to write some new material," Lenny whispered to me, only half joking.

Even though I was famished, I barely touched my food and noticed Lenny hadn't eaten much either. I suspect we both had other things on our minds. I know I sure did.

"Would you like to see my quarters?" Lenny asked, after coffee.

"Your nickels and dimes too. Ba-dum bum. You taught me well, Kemosabe. Do you have a staff cabin?" I continued, not really caring, just trying to buy time.

"It's more like a staff infection."

"Right back at me, Henny."

"It's a passenger cabin, but don't be too impressed. Wait until you see the size of it. I can take a nap, shower and dress without moving."

I figured he was exaggerating. As he unlocked the door, I saw he was not. It was the tiniest room I'd ever seen. The closet (I use the term loosely—three hangers on a chopstick) was on the immediate right. The bathroom, opposite, on the left, was about the same size. Sitting on the bowl would force one's knees into the shower. One additional step straight ahead put us in the living room/bedroom/den, which consisted of a desk the size of a toddler's, bearing a lovely fruit basket which took up its entire surface. A tiny chair was pushed underneath. If pulled out for sitting, there wouldn't be any floor space in the room at all. A TV hung from a bracket on the ceiling, facing what looked like a smaller than usual single bed, resting against a wall with a porthole. Despite its size, the room was cheerful and bright.

"Welcome to luxury at sea," Lenny offered, good-naturedly.

"It's everything I imagined and less," I responded, more to be funny than because I meant it.

Tiny or not, I was duly impressed. Lenny was off to exotic ports on an extremely luxurious liner. This cabin held little purpose, other than to sleep. And, um…

"How do couples live in this space for a week?"

"This is why most cruises end in childbirth or divorce," he said with a smirk.

"This is a single," Lenny continued, "double rooms are at least six inches larger."

Sitting on the bed (there wasn't much choice), we were straight backed, with our feet touching the floor. We were about to change the course of our relationship and we both knew it. That's a lot of pressure. So I jumped him.

Mid-kiss we rolled a bit too far and fell off the bed. Laughing, we got back up and tried again.

The bed was so small there was no leeway on three of the sides. Lenny's elbow caught my hair. Screaming from the shock of it, I totally freaked him out. As he tried to straighten up to apologize, I yanked him back down. Within moments, our history unfolded with our clothing.

Just as I had foreseen the inevitable, so had Lenny. Ironically, some condom company had done a promotion at my opening night. Lenny had grabbed a handful of freebies from the men's room and had them handy.

Despite having little space for creativity, we sure had fun. Exhausted and satisfied, I rose to freshen up, embarrassed by my nakedness in front of Lenny.

"Uh oh."

"What's wrong?" I asked, already inside the tiny john.

He didn't have to answer. Along with the two glasses of wine I'd had with lunch, out popped the condom. As if that weren't enough, it was broken—so much for freebies. It was way more stress than a new love affair needed.

Calmly, I freaked the fuck out! Lenny didn't know how to comfort me. It was the worst possible time of the month and I'd have to wait two weeks before knowing if there were to be consequences for my actions. Actually, I was seeing Barry the next day; I'd begin payment immediately.

Sunday morning at 9:00, Barry and I were scheduled to meet at the Hampton Jitney. At 9:15, Barry plodded up. He'd overslept, something he did a lot. He seemed to spend an inordinate amount of time sleeping and almost as much time kvetching about being tired. I found the whole business exhausting.

I was hoping that getting away from the familiar would distract him from my recent misbehavior on the Fourth of July. It also seemed like the perfect opportunity to see what, if anything, was to become of us.

And yet, I couldn't stop thinking of Lenny. Despite the lousy ending, his absence did make my heart grow fonder.

When we arrived at Cookie's, I suggested Barry take the guest room, choosing to bunk on the couch. Barry didn't argue. Si wasn't pleased.

Used to defending my ~~boys~~ men, I tried 'splainin'. "Barry sleeps late and, since you're up at the crack of dawn, he won't interfere with your morning routine."

Under his breath, Si muttered, "Another winner."

"Give him a break, Si," I whispered, pleading for his understanding, "He's the VP of a huge record company, he makes big bucks. On the weekends he likes to sleep in."

"I don't trust a man who sleeps all day. He seems moody."

Smart guy that Si.

Cookie's friends were having a poolside BBQ and had invited Barry and me to come along.

Not knowing anyone there, I was grateful for the bustling margarita bar. Barry sneered and ordered a coke as I took my first lick of salt. Everyone was in a Jimmy Buffet state of mind—everyone except Barry.

"I love watching a bunch of idiots get smashed," he sneered.

"They're not idiots, they're not smashed and, from what you told me on the Jitney, you spent the better part of your life doing exactly the same thing. Sounds a little self-righteous, no?"

"It's just not my idea of a good time."

"So, what is? I've been trying to figure that out. We don't seem getting anywhere."

"I just wanna take things slow."

"What's that supposed to mean Barry? We're not twelve anymore."

"I thought you were so worried about safety and disease," he said, daring me to contradict him.

"I am. But sometimes you have to take a chance, move forward, albeit cautiously."

"Like you're doing with Lenny?" He spat.

"Look Barry, I've been straight about this from the start. Lenny and I were on a date when I found out about you. That relationship was moving forward before you entered the picture."

"And I guess it's continued developing?"

"Barry, I don't know what I'm doing here, I've never 'dated' in my life, let alone two men at once. I know I'm not handling this well, but I just want to do the right thing—be sure. Lenny and I are at a different place than you and I are."

"That's why I'm taking it slow," he said, defeated.

Realizing the party wasn't helping, I said my goodbyes to Cookie and Si and set off in search of neutral ground.

Italian food seemed like a good option. We went to Baby Moon—as close to the real thing as one could get in West Hampton.

Away from the margaritas, Barry relaxed, smiling for the first time all day. I was reminded of his charm, of which there was plenty.

Our phone conversations were animated and flirtatious. He was very attentive, calling me numerous times a day. Our first few meetings were exciting and filled with promise. How could I blame him for getting bitter? It certainly appeared I was setting him up for a fall. But I wasn't. Really. It was anybody's ballgame.

Lenny was swinging for the fences; Barry was barely chipping at the ball. Like Roger Maris in '61, Barry was misunderstood, the underdog, quietly going about his business, head down. Lenny was The Mick, the hometown favorite, charmingly bold.

How would I have felt competing for someone's affection? Historically it brought out the fight in me. It certainly did Lenny. I liked it, the old knight in shining armor thing. Duel to the death. Fight to the finish. Lenny was engaging. Barry was retreating. What's more attractive?

And yet, Barry was being a friend, thinking of Lenny. Or, was he just protecting his cojones? Probably both. Lenny, on the other hand, was in survivor mode, single-minded of purpose. And it was working.

173

to be

·as going to kiss me that night with the moon pulsing
ı chickened. And I was left wanting. Again.
the beast in me and it needed to be fed. I yearned
ep, I impatiently waited for morning.
ᴜ crack of dawn, "stage-quietly" started the coffee. I'd
ρ for a bit, but sat up to let him know I was awake so he could
ᴜs pretense. Si hated to be quiet. With me awake he began moving
ᴜout as if no one slept. Cookie was already washing up. As far as Si was
concerned the day had begun—for everyone.

Barry woke around 11:00, duly noted by Si. I made Barry French
toast, and we headed out for a day in my folks' speedboat.

After stopping for lobster rolls at a dockside bistro, Cookie and Si
gave us a ride back to the city. Having shared the weekend, a bond had
been formed and conversation flowed easily. Cookie warmed to Barry,
forgave him his moods, and was now conducting an animated inquisition
of celebrity info, which Barry proudly provided in the plenty.

Si dropped Barry off first. I got out of the car as he pulled his bag from
the trunk, meeting him behind the opened hood. The long-sought kiss did
not come. Barry leaned over and gave me a peck on the cheek. Painfully
reminding me once again that he was moving s l o w l y.

I longed for Lenny. Pushing my fears of pregnancy away, I replaced
them with lustful vignettes in which I was thin and confident, seducing
the object of my affection with bold salacious moves I would never, in a
million years, actually do.

Jim Fellows called early Tuesday morning, all chummy and flirty. Did
he think he'd distract me and I'd forget he had a wife? Having already
breached that terrain in my marriage, I was not about to go there again. I'd
learned that lesson the hard way. Despite what Frank knew about Eddie, or
didn't know, I knew. It was my worst personal failure.

Barry, back on phone duty, was once again attentive and exuberant.
One of his major clients was performing that night, followed by a company
dinner. Barry invited me to tag along.

He spent most of the evening on his cell phone wheeling and
dealing—business or mystique? I enjoyed the show but couldn't help
feeling uncomfortable with all the skinny, couture wearing girls filling
the VIP booth. I felt much as I do when I get my hair cut on Madison
Avenue—the imposter, with my faux Prada purse and semi-precious
baubles.

I didn't get high before the date and made a point of letting Barry
know. It was a big deal for me. I also didn't drink at the concert, or at the

dinner, hoping that would bond us somehow. I guess it worked. Midway through the main course Barry whispered, "I got tested you know."

"No, I didn't know," I said, surprised.

"I got my results back the morning we went to the Hamptons. That's why I was late."

"Oh, I'm sorry. That explains a lot."

"No," Barry said laughing, "I'm negative."

"So why the doom and gloom?"

"I used that as an excuse to keep my distance. Once that question was answered, there was no place to hide."

"What's that supposed to mean?"

Who was I kidding? I knew what it meant. Barry and Lenny hadn't written together since the whole thing started. They'd been friends for years, just as Lenny and I'd been. Now their friendship was suffering. No one knew where they stood. This was a mess of my creation.

I could think of no comfort to offer.

When he took me home, saying goodnight was even weirder than before. He'd gotten a clean bill of heath, but the cure proved more deadly than the disease. There were to be severe consequences for all of us, no matter how I proceeded. We'd entered dangerous waters and there was no way we were all coming out unscathed. Someone was going to sink. In a way, we all would. I knew that, but selfish me pressed on. I wanted to be kissed, to know.

Barry took his time, seeming to ponder the potential. Thinking that at last he was weakening, I parted my lips in anticipation. I prayed he'd slam his body and mine against the wall, and lay one on me. It was not to be our fate. Not that night. Forever the master of control, he waved, and was off.

The next morning I was awakened by the ringing telephone. "Remember me?" Ah, Lenny.

He was back.

Just in the nick of time.

"I'm opening for Jake Richards tonight. Wanna come?"

Not yet nearly as famous as he was soon to become, Jake was already a big deal. Not long before, a mutual friend had introduced me to him at a street fair. I was tongue-tied and lame. He virtually ignored me. A huge fan of his for years, I never missed him on Johnny or Dave. It was exciting to get a chance to meet him again in a better context. More than that, I couldn't wait to see Lenny.

There was only one dressing room backstage at Kennedy's. Normally, both acts shared it. Jake was arguably the most respected stand-up of the day. In reverence, we hung at the bar. Just before his set, Lenny wandered back there for a moment, first escorting me to a table. I noticed that as Lenny took the stage, Jake wandered out and watched a good portion of Lenny's act, laughing appreciatively. It made me like him even more.

Lenny joined me at the table for Jake's set. The combination of seeing him perform live and Lenny's connection to him, all heightened the experience. I laughed so hard, I cried.

I was still high from the rush following his set when Jake joined Lenny and me for a few minutes. Jake was staring at me and I was quite flattered. It wasn't until a later trip to the restroom that I realized the cause.

I played Nelly Forbush in a high school production of South Pacific. They built a straw shower for the "I'm Gonna Wash That Man Right Out of My Hair," number. Trying to be authentic, they had running water so that I could really wash my hair, right there on stage. It wasn't quite working during dress rehearsal. The first time I did it was opening night. Gales of laughter followed me out of the shower, through the rest of the number. My confidence soared. It wasn't until I got backstage and began changing for my next scene that I noticed the black sludge running all over my face.

I discovered waterproof mascara for the duration of the run, but had neglected to wear it that night at Kennedy's. Who knew?

I guess Lenny didn't want to embarrass me but, shit! To Jake I'd be forever the lame-o.

After I fixed my face, Lenny and I had another drink. He had me laughing in no time. Sharing a joint on the car ride home, as we neared my building, the "what happens now" panic began to set in. Lenny dutifully double-parked. Not without forethought, he made sure we were well out of view of my doorman.

Signal number one: He planned to kiss me.

And so he did.

Just as I was beginning to get lost in his kiss, I remembered our unfortunate last encounter and the fact that I was still not in the clear. It kind of put a damper on things, but not for long. Lenny kissed with me with such passion, coming from someplace so deep, my negative thoughts quickly dissipated.

Signal number two: He had more in mind.

Basically speechless at that point, I indicated for him to park. Straightening up, I headed for the front door. I gave Carlos a little wave as he and Lenny exchanged a few baseball scores. I continued walking, each step marked and deliberate, taking my time, allowing Lenny to catch up. Just as the elevator door opened, he placed his hands on my waist, guiding me inside while nibbling the back of my neck. There's something so damn sexy about being kissed from behind, unable to see one's seducer.

It didn't take long for my fantasy of being slammed against the wall to come to fruition. Lenny spun me around and kissed me so fiercely my head clunked loudly against the back of the elevator. Startled, he pulled back apologetically. I laughed, and then so did he, as I yanked him back to me. As the door opened, we spilled out, falling on the floor. Laughing like idiots, we struggled to get up.

As I fumbled for my keys, Lenny's hands were slowly searching my body, again from behind. He soon found what he was seeking. As he attempted to cup my breasts, I wiggled away, embarrassed at the prospect of being eyed, via peephole, by Valerie, my nosy neighbor.

As we got inside, kissing, undressing and banging into everything in our path, we weren't graceful, but it sure was fun. Steps before reaching my bed, tangled in our partially removed clothing, we fell yet again. Our relationship really required mats.

I took no time for music or candles, we'd had all the romance we needed—years worth.

I didn't have to remind Lenny to be careful.

"Don't worry, Andi. I purchased top-of-the-line protection, guaranteed not to break or they take the kid."

Just as he had been slow and methodical, taking his time to romance me, so was he in his seduction.

We made love for hours, until just before daybreak. Exhausted, barely able to move, I didn't put up a fight when he began getting dressed. Sitting on the edge of the bed as he put on his shoes, he turned back to face me. His eyes searched mine, like a puppy needing affirmation. I smiled.

Normally, I would have been wounded beyond repair if a man left my bed before morning. But I knew Lenny would be back. This was more than sex. It was the beginning of love.

I was in deep REM when the phone rang about an hour later, the sun now shining through the still-opened blinds. As I rose to close them, I felt a trickle between my legs.

Lenny's voice was stifling his excitement. I figured it was the aftermath of our passion, until he started laughing.

"*What*? What's so funny?"

We'd had fun, but it wasn't really funny. Well, parts of it were, I guess.

Lenny, trying to control his laughter, actually had to take a moment to compose himself enough to speak.

"You know, when I left, Andi, it was dark. I just got dressed and split." He paused.

"Yeah, *and*," I said, just wanting to get back to sleep.

"Well, I didn't think much of it at the time."

"*And*," I repeated impatiently.

"When I said goodnight to Carlos, he smiled, then did a sort of double take. He looked at me in what I can only describe as horror."

"*Horror?*"

"I was so distracted by you, that I didn't give it much thought. As I got into my car, I was stopped at the light. I noticed the cabbie next to me. He looked over and nodded casually. Then he did a double take. He, too, looked at me with that same startled expression."

"You're kidding? Why? Did you forget to put your shirt on or something?" I was trying to figure out where he was going with this.

"Not exactly. But, by this time, I was curious, so I looked at myself in the rear view mirror. The sun was just beginning to come up. I noticed my face was covered..."

"Your face was covered in *what*?" I demanded.

"Blood."

"*Blood*?????"

With that I threw the light on. There was blood EVERYWHERE. On the sheets, the pillows, the floor. *Holy Shit!*

I was horrified. And relieved. No unwanted pregnancy. But what a way to find out!

Anyone else and I would have been mortified and joined a nunnery. But it was sweet Lenny. And, I figured, any man who was going to have enough blood all over his face to be seen by a cab driver, in another vehicle, in the dark... I'm thinking... that man... he just might be a keeper.

The ole tomato

Lenny came over the next night with something on his mind.

"What's up with you and Barry?" he asked, pacing madly around my small living room.

"I don't think I can take much more of this, Andi. It's not only murder with you, Barry and I can't look at each other anymore."

"I'm so sorry, Lenny. I've got this thing in my head that this is the most important decision I'm ever gonna make, and I better get it right."

"Right now, your most important decision is Chinese or Italian. I'm hungry, let's go eat."

Relieved I was off the hook, we went around the corner and had some chicken parm. Lenny was more pensive than usual. I suspected he had more to say.

Smoking a joint back at my place after dinner, we were sitting very close. I turned to speak, then stopped myself. He was silently pleading. I knew what he wanted. But was I ready to give it to him? I wanted to be. And yet...

We went to bed, but it was very different than the night before. Our lovemaking was tentative, almost fragile.

Lenny dressed to leave.

"Won't you spend the night?" I asked, trying not to sound as disappointed as I felt.

"I can't sleep anywhere but in my own bed. Even then, it's tough. I'm a total insomniac. If I stay, I'm gonna spend the whole night staring at you and making little noises to keep you awake."

I took his leaving as a rejection of me, no matter how valid his reason. How could I choose him if he wouldn't even spend the night with me?

"Stay with me, please?"

Did I sound as desperate as I felt?

He stayed—surprising us both. By extending his comfort zone, he was definitely swaying my vote.

As we lay there, neither of us even close to sleep, the words finally came.

"I'm falling in love with you, Andi."

I snuggled close, willing him to stop there.

It was not to be.

"I think it's time. Me or Barry."

Well, there it was at last. The ole tomato.

I was crazy about Lenny and definitely falling for him, but I couldn't ignore the signs. Barry had resurfaced for a reason. Wasn't the girl supposed to end up with the boy next door?

Barry and I had a date scheduled for the next night. He was going to pick me up, see my apartment, and then take me out to a late supper.

I had something else in mind.

Determined to make an informed decision, I planned my seduction carefully. I put on my tightest jeans, lowest scoop neck, clingy, jersey top and fuck me pumps.

Barry arrived, shockingly on the same page. He was carrying a dozen perfect, long stemmed roses—red this time. The message was not lost on me. I showed him around the apartment, which took less than a minute.

As I was putting the flowers in water, the phone rang. The machine picked up.

Silence and then, "Hi, this is Andi, leave me a message."

After the beep, Lenny's voice, sounding anxious, almost strangled, "Hey Andi, it's me, just wanted to say hi."

Neither Barry nor I acknowledged the intrusion, not verbally at least.

I poured him a Coke, put on Sting's *Nothing Like the Sun* (does it get more obvious than that?) and joined him on the couch.

"Dance with me," I said, leaping up, yanking at his unwilling arms.

He struggled a bit, but finally gave in and rose hesitantly. We'd only taken a step or two when the phone rang again.

"Hi, this is Andi, leave me a message."

Beep.

Silence.

"Andi, hi. It's me, I ah…am going a little crazy here."

Silence.

Barry and I sort of froze. Just as we were easing back into motion, the phone rang again. I raced over and turned off the machine.

"I'm sorry Barry. I'm so sorry, but I've got to know what's going on with us."

"You've got to know? *You've got to know?*"

Barry, looking almost insane, scaring me a little, did what we were both there to do.

Could this be that little blond boy? Amply aroused and possessed, Barry eased me down on the couch lowering himself on top of me, never taking his lips off mine. The phone rang again.

And again.

Having waited more than half of his life, Barry finally let go and was not to be deterred. He was skillful and passionate, not quite what I expected after all of the stalling.

The phone rang again. I couldn't not hear it, couldn't block it from my mind. "Barry," I started.

He smothered my mouth with his.

The phone rang again. I struggled free. "Barry, I have to answer it."

He was furious. And had every right to be.

I raced to the phone.

"Hi," I whispered.

There was no hello back.

"Choose."

I held the phone away from my ear and just stood there for what seemed like an eternity.

"I'll call you back."

With Lenny, I could be myself. We had the same taste in almost everything and shared a passion for pot.

The psychic's words reverberated in my head. "You know him, you just don't know you know him." That was true of Barry and Lenny. "He's an Aries or an Aries type." Barry was a Sagittarius, another fire sign. Lenny was a Taurus, but his moon was in Aries. *Shit!*

I walked slowly to the couch, totally unsure of what I was going to say. And then, my heart spoke.

"I'm sorry Barry."

Without a word, he grabbed his jacket and never looked back.

I was furious with myself and ashamed. I'd done exactly what Barry feared I would. But it wasn't like that, really. Only it was. My selfish need to know. Why hadn't I acted like a grown-up and just made a decision, without massacring everyone?

Barry was the innocent victim set up for the fall. *Or was he?* If he'd kissed me, romanced me from the start, might things have been different?

Probably not.

Almost as soon as Barry left, the phone rang again.

"I'm yours," I blurted out, without hesitation. "You better not be fucking with me."

Without discussing it, Lenny and I both knew we were moving into new territory, the land of exclusivity—strange, scary and thrilling. We were now a couple. *A couple of what?*

It was too soon to know where it was headed. What I did know for certain was that if he fucked me over, I was going to hunt him down and kill him.

SIX

WILLINGNESS

Tea for deux

It was a new world, the early days of MTV and video jocks. Music in Motion, a small New Jersey music channel, approached me about VJing. They wanted to capitalize on my nights by having me interview the players and then present my live show on the air. It was all pretty exciting, giving me a new avenue to perform. I hadn't realized how much I'd missed it. Years of studying acting and being on stage had led me somewhere, but the damn destination kept changing.

The same week, Jim Fellows offered me a promoting gig for an art opening at Buddy's. He assured me it wouldn't interfere with my Thursdays at The Stone House; it would just give us a chance to see how we worked together. His club was very avant-garde, because of its celebrity namesake (Don Bud—rock legend) and the gallery upstairs, which attracted known artists and photographers, as well as their famous subjects.

Jim was making Lenny crazy. Lenny didn't like him or trust him, not one little bit. Jim was a party boy who wanted who he wanted and was fairly relentless in his pursuit. The fact that he owned a hip club and gallery and was the ex-husband of a '60s superstar only added to his cred. That he was bad boy didn't hurt either.

The event at Buddy's turned out to be the opening of Rick Black's photo show. Rick had shot Sam Anderson's first album cover—a rock classic. For over a decade, it'd been plastered on posters and t-shirts everywhere. Even though he'd been working steadily ever since, none of his subsequent work exceeded his debut. It was his "American Pie."

I was out of my league, never having moved in those circles before.

My dad's wife, Roxlyn, was an artist. Never liking her was a good enough excuse to not pay attention to what she loved. I was young, fifteen when they met, and all I knew was she was taking my daddy out of the city to the far reaches of Long Island suburbia. She owned a big house in a sleepy town that was dark, isolated and, for me, epitomized loneliness. She thrived in the quiet. It deafened me.

After a lifetime as a Catskill Mountains Master of Ceremonies, she pushed my dad to retire from the one thing that fed his soul and his ego. She didn't like it there with those people. Only she was one of those people (Jewish), but she didn't see it that way.

Almost twenty years younger than my dad, she was so much older in so many ways. She dressed like a hippie with bad taste, well past the '60s. She spoke with a singsong insincerity and wore a huge, omnipresent, unmoving smile—which made the hairs on the back of my neck rise. She was like a Moonie, without Reverend Moon.

During the academic year, my dad taught Hebrew, traveling great distances between two schools to make ends meet. It was an exhausting existence, six days a week. He lived for the summers, when he was center stage. Once performing was taken out of the mix, he lost his passion. As the years wore on, he became more and more listless and unhappy, until he drove Roxlyn away with his worries and complaints.

He did a few gigs here and there, but it wasn't like the old days when he sang night after night, receiving praise and adulation. Once the regular dose of applause was gone, so was his vigor. Thanks to Roxlyn, he'd given up the stage and I'd forfeited any interest in anything "art," a mature decision indeed.

I approached Rick's show as I had every project to date. After doing some research, I wrote a press release, designed an invitation featuring his famous shot, and then plastered the press and club-going public with them.

Music in Motion was given the exclusive in exchange for mass promotion. We shot a series of commercials at the club, creating quite a stir, as there were cameras and lighting crews up East Third Street for hours. Even though they were Jersey-based, they ran the ads constantly. Word did get out.

I picked bands that would complement the mood and create a similar vibe for the reception to follow in the club downstairs. Fortuitously, I was able to land some players who had been sidemen for Sam Anderson back in the day.

I promoted the evening everywhere, including JamGirl on Thursday nights, which understandably did not please Frankie and Steve. The beer stench was getting to me anyway and my crowd was growing tired of the place. It'd been a hip novelty for a few months, but it had lost its charm. The nights were still busy, but were ever so steadily diminishing. We all knew it was probably time to pack it in.

Thankfully, the Rick Black opening was a huge success. The red carpet sizzled as Music in Motion filmed the arrivals. The streets were lined with interested passersby trying to catch a glimpse of the invited. Rumors spread quickly as to who was there and better still—whom they thought was there. I interviewed the attendees who were game (most of them didn't realize it was only Jersey cable), as they admired Rick's work.

After the cocktail reception in the gallery, everyone headed downstairs for the show. Little Steven (Bruce's guitar player, before *The Sopranos* brought him acting fame) showed up and agreed to be interviewed. Joan Jett came too. I didn't ask her to go before the cameras, knowing how much she valued her privacy. Thankfully, her pitch-black hair and leather-clad form were unmistakable in the crowd shots.

Lenny and I were now inseparable. My apartment became our midweek city flat and his place uptown was our weekend country home. I maintained my routine of waking early, working out, getting high, followed by my promotion and publicity responsibilities in the afternoon. Lenny slept in most mornings, unless he had something cooking. Other than Wednesday, his teaching day, his afternoons were fairly flexible. Auditions were erratic, some weeks far busier than others. Often, he spent the day with me as we made our calls and conducted work from home. It allowed plenty of time for falling in love.

We began our nights at the comedy clubs. Lenny would do a set, then a quick hang at the bar with the other comics. From there, we'd head to the land of rock—hear a band, hang out and push my nights. We were, for a time, insiders in both worlds, and they synched well together.

Lenny had been making his living doing stand-up since before the massive influx of the untalented, desperately trying to jump on the "I'll get my own sitcom" bandwagon.

While still in high school, he'd dared to do some open mike nights at one of the only comedy clubs that existed in New York then. Within a short time, he "passed." That meant late-night spots that paid. Five dollars it was, and probably still is. The money wasn't the point. The validation and exposure was all that mattered. He was part of an elite crowd whose high rankers included Seinfeld, Reiser, Maher and Murphy—when they were starting out, and on their ascent. Being on the inside of all that was a huge accomplishment for a young guy with a dream.

Lenny was a good comic, a smart one—observational, as they started calling it. He wasn't wacky, didn't have an offbeat look, or unique character. He was tall, blond, blue-eyed and attractive. That probably cost him.

He quickly moved from MC to middle, and within a few years he was headlining—one of the lucky few that earned his living doing what he loved. A road warrior, he worked New York City midweek, and the great big US of A on weekends. Partying till dawn, sleeping until noon, he shared beers, joints, stories and condos with the most fertile comic minds of the day. Lenny was a great audience for them. He laughed heartily at other people's stuff, which was pretty unusual in that business. He was kind, sincere and well-liked.

He made a respectable living, but the big money and fame eluded him. It wasn't from lack of talent, just a lack of trying. He was a bit complacent and accepting of his level. Rather than hungry and driven, he was happy and satisfied. He was young and single, so why not?

There were two things that set Lenny apart from the crowd. For one, he understood the Tao of humor. He had the ability to construct a joke as close to perfection as possible. Other comics, even those more successful than he, would welcome his suggestions. He could also impersonate almost anyone. Dead-on. He'd call people and have entire conversations as their manager or a club owner, and not get found out. He could've been an *After Midnight Live* staple. He should've been. But, why try when you can hang out and party after your set, instead of running to three other clubs to work some more? He just didn't want it badly enough, I guess. Or, maybe the Mary Jane numbed his ambition.

In spite of it all, Lenny and I were both doing pretty well financially. Combined, even better. We afforded ourselves a good life, especially since most of the luxuries were provided for us gratis. The weekends we spent away in swanky hotels were high points. The comedy clubs picked up the tab. There were a few dives but we had fun in them too. Lenny typically had gigs in the tri-state area, within a few hours drive from the city. Usually, hungover and worn out from my Thursday nights, we'd leave town early Friday afternoon, stop midpoint, have some food, and talk through the night before in detail.

After checking in, Lenny would shower and prepare for his first show. Usually we'd eat at the club between the early and late set and hang out with the other acts afterwards. If they smoked, we hung out; otherwise we didn't stay too long. Booze just didn't do it for me. I needed pot to feel right. And, who needed the extra calories?

Saturdays, we'd sleep late and go out for breakfast, something we never did in the city. Usually we'd go to IHOP, where we'd indulge in road food—meals we wouldn't think of eating in real life. We spent the afternoons sightseeing, window-shopping or both. Sometimes we'd hit a mall, great fun for Manhattanites.

After a late lunch, we'd head back to the hotel for showers and then do the night routine all over again. On Sundays, after another forbidden late breakfast, we'd hit the road, often stopping along the way, getting high and taking our time returning to the real world.

There's something very romantic about traveling and hotel rooms. On the road, we could leave the world behind as we embarked on our journey. Even when returning to a familiar haunt, there was still an air of adventure and mystery to each trip. Added to that was the buzz of seeing Lenny gussied up in his stage clothes, handsome as hell under the lights, commanding the attention of hundreds of admirers hanging on his every word. I could see the desire in other women as they came to meet him after the show. There's nothing sexier than a smart, funny man, except a smart funny man who's wanted by others.

I was madly in love with my best friend. We talked about everything, all the time. I kept no secrets and assumed the same of him.

With Eddie, I had purged my past, learning the hard way that it was not a wise move. As sympathetic as he would pretend to be initially (usually post coitus), once we got into fight mode, he would fling it all back in my face. My teenage abortion became calculated homicide. My previous marriage was viewed as manipulative Hebraic abuse (mine) of a poor innocent (Frank). My attempt at stand-up was seen as pathetic ramblings of a needy JAP.

Lenny was different. He didn't judge. He listened. He empathized. He accepted.

For the first time in my life, I felt unconditionally loved. No matter what I told him, or what he saw for himself (my actions always betrayed my words, revealing the true monster that lurked just beneath the surface), he still wanted me and treated me with respect. He seemed amused by my compulsions and intrigued by my obsessions. The psychics had promised and he'd been delivered.

The best of times, there was plenty of hope and dope. Our careers were on the rise, but the scene was changing. Suddenly, stand-up comedy was ubiquitous, available on a hundred-plus cable channels. You couldn't turn on your television without seeing a brick wall and a guy telling recycled jokes. Fewer and fewer people were willing to pay $100 for a night out. Lenny was still working steadily, but he often had to scramble, not knowing until the last minute where he'd be appearing that weekend.

Lenny's manager, Sol Fink, was a well-dressed, middle-aged schmoozer, who looked and sounded like he'd just stepped off a movie lot—a walking cliché, from his onyx and gold pinky ring, to his textured black nylon knee socks. I liked him a lot. I think he felt likewise—kind of. Despite our mutual affection, I drove him crazy as I filled Lenny's head with grand dreams that Sol wasn't sure how to actualize. He wanted me to stop, to let him run the show. I was not to be deterred, knowing Lenny was capable of great things. Not only did he possess extraordinary talent, he had incredible fortitude and perseverance. All he needed was a little push.

No longer managing Eddie's band (that ended when the romance did), I was putting increased energy into Lenny's career, which was not sitting so well with Sol.

The fickle music scene, where venues stayed hot for seconds it seemed, was keeping me jumping. I club hopped a lot that next year. Thursdays were my constant, until they weren't—becoming Wednesdays for a short while. I was sure that would be the end of me.

I survived, finally settling in on the Upper East Side, at a place I hoped would be my home for the long haul: Blue Room, so named after its owner's unforgettable azure eyes. I went back to being a full-time, in-house publicist, booker and promoter, and reclaimed Thursdays.

Fay, my therapist, always says that when one partner drops the ball the other one picks it up. That was sure true with Lenny and me. It seemed just when I was losing a venue, he was scoring a huge gig. I'm not sure if it worked as much the other way around. I comforted myself hoping I made up for it in other ways.

My life had always been steeped in high drama. If there wasn't tumult, I created some. Attracted to the crazy life, I instigated the mess. Lenny and I had plenty of tsuris, but we also had each other. No matter what was going on with our careers, life was good. He gifted me with stability, a treasure I'd never known.

A river in Egypt

As far back as I can remember, I was a cautious, play it safe, good girl, quiet and obedient—the seemingly perfect daughter. I allowed Cookie to mold me as she wished, which to my horror, was almost always in sharp contrast to what I desired for myself. I coveted my best friend Marla's long blond hair. Mine was brown and Cookie insisted on a "Prince Valiant." Short cuts were fashionable, but I was no Jean Seberg. I had baby fat and lacked cheekbones. Hell, I was six.

I was the kid that always had a sweater when the other kids were in shirtsleeves; the one still wearing tights when all the other girls were in knee socks. Afraid to skate, to bicycle, always hedging my bets—if there wasn't a rail or someone to hold on to, I just didn't try.

My brother, Jeff, was the antithesis of me. Fearless, wild and athletic, he and his bunch of crazy friends were always looking for trouble. Torturing me whenever possible, he played on my fears and vulnerability. Luring me into a game of cards, he'd choose *knucks,* forcing me to continue until he drew blood. He noogied me until I had bumps all over my head and he inked in the ears of my beloved Patty Play Pal.

Even though I had Marla, she had Jenny. Marla was my best friend and I seemed to sometimes be hers but, at other times, she leaned toward Jenny and I was crushed. The three of us often played together, but I always felt like the odd one out. They both had more clothes, more toys and long hair.

We lived in the Bronx, blocks from Yankee Stadium. In those days, the Grand Concourse was a middle-class, Jewish neighborhood. Cookie and Jerry the ideal couple: young, good-looking and happy. I have the 8-millimeter home movies to prove it.

When I was eight, they took a bold step and moved us to Howard Beach, Queens. Suburbia. It was all two-family homes, no apartments for as far as the eye could see. That was the shit back then. I don't know how they afforded the three-bedroom, two-bath rental home. I didn't care. All I knew was that I no longer had to share a room with Jeff. I could close my door and the torture would stop. Yet I was nervous having a big room to myself that bordered the back yard, which had a creek running through it. About a week after we moved in, Jeff told me rats lived in the creek and they liked to come through the windows and bite kids on the neck. I slept with the covers rolled tight under my chin until the day we left that house.

We played in the street out front with the other kids on the block. Good Humor, Bungalow Bar, Chow Chow Cup and the Carvel truck drove by nightly in the warm weather. Times were different. It was way before missing kids appeared on milk cartons. We walked to school without supervision and came home to our housewife mothers who had the cookies and milk waiting.

Life was good. Not perfect.

When my Uncle Henry was getting married, he asked me to be a junior bridesmaid. I got my first grown-up gown, nylon stockings and small (but high for an eight-year-old) heeled shoes. A few weeks after the wedding, Sheila Lipshitz's mother complained to mine that they had a Bar Mitzvah to go to and she didn't want to spend all the money on an outfit for Sheila. (They lived in a big house and Sheila had every doll and toy imaginable. It was not as if they were poor.) Without a word, Cookie went into my closet, took my precious gown, nylons, garter belt and shoes, and handed them to Mrs. Lipshitz. I wailed, locking myself in my room, trying to understand how she could betray me and take what she had given. I never got any of the stuff back. In retrospect, I can appreciate the thriftiness of Cookie's choice. Yet, the way it was done, without discussion or explanation, was so painful. Those clothes represented a coming of age. As carefully as I had chosen each article and cherished owning them, it contrasted stunningly with how swiftly and thoughtlessly they were taken away.

With Cookie, conditional love was business as usual. I was forever disappointing her. Therefore, it was okay to change her mind and take back. As a child, it was devastating. Didn't feel too good as an adult either.

One day, when I was about ten, I remember walking to the ocean from my aunt's cottage in Atlantic Beach. My mother looked down and began to laugh.

"You have your father's toes. Look how long they are!" I hid my feet for years after that.

When I was eleven, in a new home, going to a new school, knowing no one, she bought me a puppy. Without any instruction, she expected me to train and care for him. When, after a week, he was still peeing on the newspaper in the house, she took him away while I was at school, again, without a word.

On my wedding day, as my mother helped me with my make-up, she kindly pointed out that my eyes were different sizes. As I walked down the aisle, instead of focusing on all that awaited me, I thought instead of my freakish right eye.

It's amazing the things we remember. Oh, the stories Jack and Syd will one day be sharing!

My parents were the ideal couple. Young, attractive and well-liked, they were the centerpiece among a large social circle of other young couples with children. I remember laughter, parties and large frequent, family get-togethers. It was very *Donna Reed*. Except Jeff was no Paul Peterson.

Sitting at the kitchen table one Thursday evening when I was nine, I could see my mother's reflection in the mirror as she put on her make-up in the bathroom nearby. I was eating a vanilla cone with peppermint dip from the Carvel ice cream truck.

"Where you goin'?"

"To the doctor."

"Why?"

"To talk."

"About what?"

"About Daddy."

"The good part or the bad part?"

Without waiting for a reply I continued, "Are you gettin' a divorce?"

Expecting a quick "of course not," instead, she began to cry as I watched her in the mirror. Filled with dread, without even knowing what made me ask, I now knew the terrible secret she'd been keeping. The world started spinning around me; somehow I knew that life would never be the same. My ice cream cone fell to the floor. To this day, the smell of peppermint makes me nauseous.

Flashing to the previous Mother's Day, Dad had given her a present on his way out to play tennis. A scarf, I think. Something bland and unromantic. I remember my mother's disappointment. Had that been the beginning of the end? I couldn't remember any other clues. They never fought, not that I had witnessed. They danced like Fred and Ginger. They laughed. They drank Martinis and smoked cigarettes.

I guess there were signs. The previous summer, I was forced to go to sleepaway camp for the month of July, where my mother had taken a job as a counselor. My father and brother went to the Catskills, as usual, only, this time, without us. I joined them in August, while my mother remained at the camp for the rest of the summer. That should've been a tip-off that something was wrong, but I was so young.

I didn't have any friends at camp and had just survived moving from the Bronx to Queens only months before. I'd barely connected to a few girls when my parents separated.

Jeff insisted on living with Dad. I fought to have the same privilege, but Cookie wouldn't hear of it. Whisked away from my father, my brother and what had become our new home, I moved to a small apartment on the other end of town with my mother. Only I barely saw her. She took a job and I became a latchkey kid at nine. Too far away to play with my friends, living with my mother was tantamount to being alone. Not only was she barely physically present, she was emotionally unavailable as well.

On November 9, 1965, barely 10, I walked home from school alone, as was now the norm, and let myself into our apartment. The days were short. It was already getting dark as I sat eating greasy Wise potato chips out of the bag, watching *Dark Shadows* on TV. The picture slowly started to fade, then flickered and went off. Just as I was rising to check it out, the entire apartment went dark. Pitch black. Even the streetlights were out. I thought about the shelter drills at school. Did the Russians bomb us?

Groping around for the front door, afraid to go outside, I was more terrified to stay inside alone. Slowly turning the knob, I peeked.

We lived on the main floor of our apartment building, directly across from the entrance. The super was in the lobby cursing in Spanish. "Chinga tu madre!" As his flashlight's beam swept past, he must have caught my eye, for he doubled back and walked towards me.

"Where's your mommy?"

"Working," I said, trying hard not to cry.

"What time does she get home?" He was taking his time, speaking very deliberately. I knew he was trying to comfort me and I was grateful for his effort.

"What happened?" I asked, not really sure I wanted to know the answer.

"It looks like a blackout."

I stared at him blankly. He assured me the lights would no doubt come back on in no time, although his face held no such promise.

People were congregating in the lobby as I remained frozen in the doorway, trying desperately to figure out what to do. What if my mother was stuck in an elevator somewhere? Or worse? What if she never came home?

As the gravity of my situation began to settle in, the tears flowed. A heavy-set, grandma-type must have heard and slowly inched towards me, as if not to frighten me further. Just as she opened her mouth to speak, I saw behind her the silhouette of my mother, highlighted by the edge of a flashlight beam. Running, I threw my arms around her. She thanked the woman and led me inside.

Conflicting emotions bubbled to the surface at once. Anger—how dare she leave me alone? Sadness —I was sure I was the only child in New York City without a mommy when the lights went out. Fear—what if it happened again? Anguish—how could I ever come home alone again? Despair—why couldn't I live with Daddy and Jeff? Shock—I ran into my mother's arms for comfort. We were like two Barbie dolls. Stiff, arms outstretched, unable to connect. We were never comfortable being physical with each other.

Now terrified to come home by myself, I really started working on Cookie to let me live with Dad and Jeff. She refused to listen. I couldn't understand why she fought so hard to keep me. Usually she'd fix dinner and then I'd go to my room and watch TV while she read in the living room. I can't remember ever spending the evening together, except for a few rare nights when we went shopping at Korvette's and maybe to Howard Johnson's for some fried clams and a frankfurter. Sometimes, for a real treat, she took me to the Chinese restaurant on 108th Street for spare ribs, egg roll and fried rice, which came to the table in high-stemmed silver dishes with domed lids.

Did she keep me with her so that she wouldn't have to eat dinner alone? In no small measure, I think she did.

Dad, no longer able to bear the constant reminder of the life he no longer lived, moved with Jeff to an apartment in Pelham Parkway, a much nicer section of the Bronx than the Concourse. It had tree-lined streets and lots of like-minded Hebrews.

Even though I only saw Jeff and Dad on the weekends, I always knew they were close at hand—just in case. But now they were in another borough—it might as well have been the moon. Dad called every night and picked me up from school on Fridays. I dreamt of that moment all week. Sundays sucked. I woke up with a feeling of dread. I could barely enjoy the day, so filled with grief over the thought of leaving.

My dad did all he could to distract me, filling the days with fun. As soon as he got home from teaching Sunday school, we'd head out to a movie, a walk in the park, ice-skating—something great. Yet, the inevitable loomed. My stomach was always flipping, tears welling just on the other side of my lids. We'd hold hands, walk arm and arm, anything to stay connected. He knew how miserable I was without him. He felt my pain and surely had his own to deal with too.

One Saturday, we went shopping at a hip store on 8th Street in Greenwich Village. My dad was very cool—handsome, dating young women, singing in the Catskills, and at the top of his game. After he tried on a bunch of outfits, I helped him pick out a fashionable (at the time), pair of white bell-bottom pants, matching turtleneck and a gold medallion necklace. He still wears those pants—thankfully, not the medallion. As hip as my dad was in the '60s, he got sort of frozen there.

Walking down the street arm in arm later that afternoon, wearing his new duds, he took me to see *Play it Again Sam* on Broadway, starring Woody Allen and Diane Keaton, snagging front row seats. Days like that gave me a sense that Jerry was flush. He was a sport, a big spender. I had no clue that he was living beyond his means and barely making ends meet.

Cookie countered by taking a job as a traveling saleswoman for Revlon. She moved me in with her brother, Henry, his new wife and baby—on Long Island. Now even further from my Dad, I was inconsolable.

At Henry's Levittown two-story tract house, Cookie and I shared the attic bedroom; only she was rarely there. I felt like Cinderella, unloved and unwanted. Basically, I was living with Henry, and Jill, who understandably resented my intrusion on her young marriage.

It never dawned on me that maybe my mom needed someone to watch her kid so she could go make a living. The $15 a week that Jerry paid in child support afforded little, even back then.

All I could see was my hatred for mean old Cookie. She abandoned me in suburbia, in someone else's home, where she barely slept—just to keep me hers for the rare times when she was around.

I began to get sick. A lot. Mr. Green, my fifth grade teacher, spent his days chewing the ends of his tie and speaking unintelligibly. Between my extensive absences and my lack of "mumble" comprehension, I was in danger of being held back. Appreciating the gravity of the situation, during the summer Cookie moved us to the Bronx, into a little basement apartment across the street from Dad and Jeff—and Barry: my ticket to heaven.

Prince Valiant haircuts segued to the "Twiggy." The coif didn't alter much, but everything else sure did.

Mrs. Smith, my sixth grade teacher, sat me front and center. Focusing on my strengths, she romanced me out of my shell. Always painfully shy, I flourished under her tutelage. For the first time, I loved going to school. Good grades fed my previously non-existent self-esteem; social popularity was a welcomed by-product.

Barry and Joey were the first to befriend me. Outgoing and fun, they made a point of paying attention to the new girl, inviting me to walk to and from school with them.

Once again, coming home to an empty house, Cookie softened the blow by enrolling me in after school classes twice a week at the local community center. I signed up for cooking; they assigned me drama. There are no accidents. When I walked into the theatre, there sat Barry, looking as surprised and happy to see me as I was him.

Howard Dent, the acting coach, sensed something in me, a sadness, a knowingness, and guided me to shape those feelings into art. What he encouraged me to believe was my life's purpose. Watching my every move, listening to my every word, he cast me as the lead in everything.

Barry and I co-starred in school plays and community theatre for the next four years.

The days contrasted dramatically with the nights.

When my mother got home from work, she'd read the newspaper in her room while I did homework in mine. Then we'd both watch TV— *Peyton Place* or some other adult show—but not together. I did so alone in my bedroom, with the contrast on dark and the sound down low, so she wouldn't get wise.

I ached for love and attention. Cookie showed me neither. I guess she was lost in her own loneliness.

I sprouted boobs and got my period—exactly on my thirteenth birthday. With the blood came a set of balls. I smoked or, should say, choked, my first cigarette. I took to sneaking them daily from my mom's purse.

Seeking peer acceptance and affection, I searched in all the wrong places—solely attracted to emotionally unavailable bad boys, even at thirteen. If it's true that we all seek the familiar, primarily our mothers, I was adhering to the stereotype.

Barry was adorable, attentive and crazy about me, but all I wanted was Ray Santo. Ray was tall, dark, handsome and completely dismissive. I had a crush on him all through junior high, in between my summers spent obsessing over inattentive Alan.

Never part of the *in* crowd, I'd always been on the outside looking in. Pot afforded me the change I was seeking. More fun and less afraid, my popularity grew.

Cookie kept reading her paper, not seeming to notice the changes in me. My dad continued to treat me as his good girl and I did nothing to dispel the myth. We all lived in denial, a long way from Egypt.

———— Dropping a bomb with the ball ————

Thirty-five years old, my clock was not only ticking, the alarm was screaming 24/7—with no snooze button. After only a few months with Lenny, I began dropping hints as subtle as a brick to the head.

My mission was greatly aided by the owners of Blue Room, two of the most insanely good looking, attentive and appreciative bosses imaginable. Hired when the club was still under construction, they included me in decisions and valued my opinions. As if that weren't enough, they loved fun and encouraged that ambiance wherever they were.

"Peeps," so named for his stunning blue eyes, was a huge, raspy-voiced, clean-cut, old-fashioned, retired football player. Still in amazing shape, he was a gentle giant. Billy, his partner, was a modern day hippie. A thirty-something Tom Sawyer, he had long, wavy, dirty-blond hair, a turned up nose and a pair of blues that weren't too shabby either. Together they were lethal—known as much for their skin-tight blue jeans as they were for their eyes

Lenny couldn't help but like Peeps and Billy, nobody could. They were nice. And as much as he knew I adored him, Lenny was obsessed with what he imagined might be going on between them and me. My long hours spent in the downstairs office with Billy drove him crazy.

Cookie and Si adored Lenny and wanted to know what the hell we were waiting for. I wasn't getting any younger, thank you very much. I was also Cookie's only hope at grandchildren. My brother Jeff, three years older than me, had never married, and it was doubtful that his rotation of stripper girlfriends would ever produce a wife, let alone a mother for his children. As much as Cookie yearned to remain young, she coveted what her friends were now enjoying—kids without the work. She pressured me, and I passed it on to Lenny as gingerly as a dancing elephant.

On New Year's Eve 1990, about five months into our relationship, Lenny took the holiday off for the first time in years. Inviting a few couples over to his place to help us celebrate, we sipped champagne, ate Sevruga caviar, danced and pretended to be sophisticated, urban adults. At 11:45, Lenny put the TV on so we could ring in the New Year with Dick Clark. The couch was against the wall, perpendicular to the television. I was turned away from Lenny, facing the tube. He was holding me around the waist from behind.

As the ball began its descent, we all counted along, out loud, "10, 9, 8, 7…" Lenny turned me around to face him. Before I could put thoughts together and figure out what was going on, he was getting down on his knee, taking my hand.

At exactly "5, 4, 3," he whispered softly, "Andi, will you marry me?"

Without a moment's hesitation, at "1," I said, "YES!"

It was so fast, so discreet; no one else in the room knew it had happened. They were caught up in their own moment.

Lenny took me into the bedroom, presenting a "too-large-to-be-a-ring-box," heading my expectations off at the pass.

"This is just a token. I wanted you to be able to pick out your own ring."

A bit disappointed, I opened the box to see a small silver heart on a chain. With it was a tiny key.

"You now hold the key to my heart."

In an instant, Lenny had turned the moment around. I threw my arms around his neck, kissing him fiercely.

Almost without pause, I picked up the phone. Cookie and Si were over the moon. My dad was distracted, which hurt my feelings. Samuel, Lenny's dad, was joyful and inquisitive, as he was about most things. Ellie, Lenny's mom, never much liked me, and was underwhelmed.

A few days earlier, Samuel and his wife Claudine (his former student, many years his junior), had a Christmas party. Both philosophy professors, their friends were an eclectic mix of intellectual eccentrics, which led to lively debate and loud arguments. There were no hard feelings; it was sport.

Everyone was having a ball—everyone except Ellie. She looked miserable, as she often did. Her life had been severely challenging. Wearing her trouble for all to see, it weighed her down, stooping her narrow shoulders. She was a tiny thing. Barely eighty pounds and in her 70's, she looked older than her years from a lifetime of trauma and disappointment. She was all bones and sharp edges. If that wasn't intimidating enough, she was German, her accent thick, and her voice so deep she was often mistaken for a man.

Amazingly, she'd not only survived the Holocaust, she'd spent the entirety of the war as the head nurse in the Jewish hospital in Berlin, losing almost everyone and everything she loved. Adding further assault to great injury, at the end of the war she was severely burned by an American soldier as he cleaned the floor with kerosene.

She decided to join her older sister, who had escaped to America before the worst of the war. On the long ocean voyage, she met the love of her life. Samuel was a young and handsome merchant marine—nurturing and protective. He took that tiny, broken woman and tried to make her right. Attending to her every need, he made her the most important thing in his world. It was just what the doctor ordered—for both of them. He needed to save her. She needed to be saved.

As with all rescued creatures, her gratitude bound her to him for life. They married soon after arriving in America. He could do no wrong, ever. Even when he fell in love with Claudine, years later, Ellie remained devoted. For the first few years, she suffered her loneliness with her young son, Lenny. Once Claudine had children of her own, Ellie became their nursemaid. She attended them regularly, developing a relationship of tolerance with Claudine, who, as a Buddhist, accepted all things. Ellie learned this was her ticket to keeping Samuel in her life. She held a firm place in his new family, traveling with them and sharing holidays, and came to accept her station.

Lenny had always been very available to Ellie. They often had coffee together and kept no secrets. She was tolerant of the marijuana and the women, as long as they didn't get too close.

When we first began dating, Lenny called Ellie numerous times daily, always checking in from the road as well. But I began to cut in on her time. Where Lenny once confided to her everything, he no longer had the same need. He had me.

At Samuel and Claudine's annual holiday party, where everyone was having a grand old time drinking and arguing, Ellie was sitting at the table with Claudine, who was looking over at Lenny and me. "Looks like there'll be a wedding in our near future."

"Ach, Leonard won't get married until I'm dead!"

Not only was Ellie's voice dark and thickly accented, it was also very loud, unmistakable above the chatter.

The room stopped. It was such a strange thing to say, especially out loud. But with me in the room, it was shocking. It was clear Lenny and I were in love and headed towards matrimony. Clear to all except Ellie. Maybe she thought if she said it out loud she could will it to be so.

I'd overheard her, as did half the room. Somehow Lenny did not, and for a while, he didn't quite believe me. Ashamed that Ellie would say such a thing, he knew her well enough to know that it was certainly possible, given her prior track record. I was not the first girl to feel her wrath. She had caused many a tear before I came along.

I wonder if she didn't actually help things along with her declaration. Could Lenny's proposal have, in some way, been a reaction to that embarrassment?

What must Ellie have thought when only a couple of weeks after the party Lenny proposed?

He soon got an earful.

Ellie wasn't the only one raining on our parade. I was troubled by my father's lack of enthusiasm. It didn't add up.

When I announced my engagement to non-Jewish Frank many moons earlier, my dad disowned me. It was incredibly hurtful and seemed so out of character. Jerry was a Hebrew teacher and came from an orthodox home, but still. Months later, when Frank agreed to convert, not because of Jerry's rebuff, but rather because of my stepfather's acceptance, Jerry relented. But the damage had been done, more for me than Frank. Frank brushed it off. I was mortally wounded.

It was one of those life-changing moments. I realized my father's love, which I'd always believed was the surest thing in my world, was conditional. That was an extraordinarily painful day. He swiftly changed his mind and I forgave him, but something had shifted.

It proved even more confusing when he showed no joy this time. I was to marry the perfect Jewish boy. Jerry was crazy about Lenny, as was just about everyone who knew him. Why this indifference?

I soon found out. The morning after our engagement, New Year's Day, we were wakened early by the ringing telephone. Roxlyn was shaken.

"Jerry's in the hospital. A gardener found him early this morning unconscious on the walk path. Can you come down?"

Roxlyn was being evasive. Even from 1,000 miles away, I could tell she didn't have her Moonie grin on. Unclear as to the cause, I sensed it was bad—very bad. Although he was now conscious, I was clearly needed.

The thought of leaving Lenny, my brand new fiancé, to stay with Roxlyn and visit Jerry in the hospital was too depressing for words. I was not a good daughter. I was a selfish woman in love. I did not want to go. But go I did, tearfully leaving Lenny at the airport, unsure of what I would find when I got to West Palm, or when I'd return.

Roxlyn filled me in on my dad's mounting depression, slightly hinting that there might be trouble between them. They had been married for almost twenty years and not once had there been any hint of discord. This shift might well explain his having consumed a few "too many" pills?

Jerry was not himself, but he began rallying a bit. I stayed until he left the hospital three days later with assurance from my brother that he would arrive immediately following my departure. Roxlyn seemed scared. That really shook me. She'd always maintained a freaky serenity. The fact that she was cracking was unnerving. I had to get out of there, away from her. Sleeping in the same small apartment, just the two of us, had left way too much time for us to talk, something we were never any good at. Plus, the hours upon hours spent at my Dad's bedside were heartbreaking. Absent was his usual joie de vivre. It was clear the marriage was dissolving. It explained his cry for help.

Sure enough, news arrived a couple of weeks later that Roxlyn had left him.

Jerry had always been handsome and vital, never having any difficulty attracting women. Now though, in his early seventies, retired, with little money and fewer resources, when Roxlyn left, so did his mojo.

———————— Falling in love with Mary Jane ————————

When I arrived in New York, Lenny hugged me tight, gave me a lusty kiss, and lit a joint as soon as we pulled out of the airport parking lot. Living in close proximity to Roxlyn, I'd white knuckled it for three days. Lenny had anticipated my need.

Pot was the great healer of all things and had been for as long as I could remember.

Soon after my thirteenth birthday, I was lounging on my brother Jeff's bed, a day-glo Beatles poster of Sgt. Pepper's Lonely Hearts Club, stared down at me. As it started to get dark, I noticed that the first letters of the words, Lucy in the Sky with Diamonds, popped out in hot pink

"LSD, what's that?"

"Acid—for tripping," Jeff said, incredulously.

"Have you ever done it?"

"Nah, I just smoke pot."

"Really, what's that like?"

"I don't know… it's great."

"I wanna try."

"I don't have any right now."

Jeff's crowd was cool and hung at the local Carvel after dark. A few nights later, his friend Bo, as if anticipating my curiosity, took me in hand, inviting me back to his place to smoke. Scared out of my mind, I allowed myself to be led.

Bo's parents weren't home. They had an enormous apartment with lots of rooms, one leading into another. Starting out together, in what I assumed was the den, Bo produced a small wooden pipe, and filled it with a greenish brown substance that as soon as it burned, produced an extremely pungent aroma.

"It's keef," he said, handing me the bowl. "It'll get you fucked up."

I knew how to inhale, having already developed a rapidly increasing cigarette habit. Drawing the smoke lightly into my lungs as I would a Lark, I coughed a little and shrugged. Bo, obviously experienced in turning on a novice, smiled knowingly, patiently instructing me on the proper technique for smoking dope. The next go-round, holding the smoke deeply before exhaling, I coughed incessantly. Bo smiled approvingly.

I've heard about people not getting high the first time. That was not my experience. As soon as I released the smoke, with it went a lifetime of fear and pain. Relaxing, I eased into an oblivion I came to worship. After another hit or two, I lay down on the caftan-covered couch. Floating peacefully, I remember lying on my back, lifting my right arm straight up in the air. For some reason, I remained that way for what felt like hours, not moving or speaking, simply being. I don't recall why I was allowed to be out so late, how I got home, or got past Cookie, but somehow I did.

I kept it a secret from Barry and Joey, but did confide in my girlfriend Joanne, who was a year older than me and very mature. It turned out she had been pinching her brothers' stash for months. We took to getting high whenever she could manage some.

Marijuana freed my soul. While high, I was daring, outgoing, skinny, pretty, smart, funny and sexy. As soon as fear, insecurity, pain or loneliness crept in, a hit or two would ameliorate it.

By the time I was in high school I was a daily smoker. In college, I was a round the clocker—wake and baker. Every one of my boyfriends was a stoner, too. Weed was always plentiful. There were a few brief periods of non-smoking, I won't call them sober days, because I drank, although very modestly. Other than a brief dalliance with Boodles Martinis, I rarely drank to excess. As functional as I was stoned, was as dysfunctional as I was drunk. I hated being out of control and nauseous. Overindulging with booze usually brought me to both.

Initially, I didn't get high before classes, performances or work but, eventually, I relaxed those rules. That produced a mixed bag—about a nickel's worth. On the one hand, I was incredibly paranoid, on the other, fearless and edgy.

Marijuana rarely got in my way as far as I could tell, with few exceptions. My first awareness that perhaps smoking was detrimental came with my re-introduction to Barry. He had no tolerance for drinking or smoking and was very vocal in his disdain. The first time he came to my apartment I made the mistake of smoking in front of him, regretting it immediately. He was crabby as shit all night after that. I took to toking up before I saw him.

While Lenny was at sea and I was spending most of my time with Barry, I tried to kick pot completely for the first time. I enjoyed being clear. A few unknowing folk even commented on how much nicer I seemed. *Really?* I couldn't keep it up for long. When I was jonesing for a joint, it didn't take much to change my mind.

With Lenny, I could be my true stoned self. What a relief.

When we started planning our wedding, we were getting shit from everyone about what we should and shouldn't do—especially from Ellie, Lenny's mom. It was sucking all the joy out of it so we went to see my therapist, Fay.

Somehow the pot came up.

"How much do you smoke?"

"Not a lot anymore." I said, casually. "A toke in the morning, one in the afternoon, maybe a couple at night. A joint all told during the day," I added, proudly.

"You're an addict, you know," she said matter-of-factly.

"Bullshit." *Addicts have needles hanging out of their arms.*

I was appalled, misunderstood. How could she say that? If only she knew how much I was really smoking.

"Do you believe her, calling me an addict?" I asked Lenny as we made our way back to the car.

"Pure bullshit," he said, lighting a joint.

Fay planting that seed worked on me daily. I don't think I ever enjoyed pot quite the same way again. Her words echoed in my head. Guilt and shame became part of the equation. Damn that bitch! What a goddamn buzz killer.

I do, part two

A few months before the wedding, Lenny took me on my first cruise. He was contracted to do three shows a week, which came out to a few hours of work in total. In exchange, he not only was compensated handsomely, but he also got to bring me along; both of us enjoying full passenger status.

Unlike the ship we'd launched, um...lunched on, this liner was one of the oldest and grandest. We had a surprisingly large cabin, with enough room to walk around, twin beds—not ideal, but doable—and decent closet space.

Most tables in the dining room were for six or more to encourage social mixing. When the comics brought their wives or girlfriends, they were almost always seated amongst a group of favored passengers to keep them happy and entertained. Somehow, we lucked into a table for two, spared the small talk and left alone to amuse only each other.

Prior to my life with Lenny, I'd barely been anywhere. Frank and I honeymooned in the Bahamas and I'd been to Mexico a few times with Seth, my high school sweetheart. We camped out on the beach and ate on the cheap.

I was unprepared for cruise ship glamour. Once again the imposter, I felt like Kate Winslet appeared to feel in *Titanic,* only I never got wet, except when I chose to. Moonlit nights, piña coladas while the steel drums played, lobster and shrimp, plenty of weed, sunbathing, working out and sightseeing on magnificent isles. We were fit, tan and madly in love.

As soon as we returned home, things got insane. Working full time to get Blue Room on the map, traveling with Lenny on the weekends and trying to figure out the whole wedding thing, kept me on my toes.

Where to do it? Whom to invite? Who would pay?

Cookie had already thrown me one over-the-top Jewish wedding. How many of those should any parent back? She offered Lenny and me some cash if she could stay out of the whole deal. We gratefully accepted, but that left all the planning to me.

I wanted something more intimate and mature the second time around, but it was Lenny's first, and hopefully only, wedding. I wanted it to be all that and more for him.

Barry had moved to LA some months before, saving us that awkwardness. With all of our grandparents deceased, neither of our extended families were very close, basically gathering for weddings and funerals. I resented Ellie, and Lenny's intellectual aunts, who didn't seem to think much of me. I wanted to be surrounded by the people who celebrated us—our friends, the family of our choosing—not the ones that despised us, me, um... *shit!* I guess I was wielding my power, showing them who was boss. I justified only inviting the family members who were active in our lives—the ones I absolutely had to. That didn't go over real well.

Pricing restaurants and halls was a nightmare. There was no way we could afford even the hundred or so guests we had narrowed it down to. Then a light bulb went off. Publicist that I was, I envisioned marrying right there at Blue Room. It was freshly renovated, everything brand spanking new, all stainless steel, black, white and blue. A restaurant as well, it was extremely upscale for a rock club. Peeps got only the best. There was a large stage, perfect for a ceremony and band to follow, and it had a dance floor.

The more I thought about it, the more sense it made. I figured I could get the club a decent amount of publicity hatching such a stunt, and in the process get a cut-rate deal on the space and food. The kitchen served fabulous, way better than average, Chinese, which fit in nicely with a Jewish wedding. Since we weren't having extended family, I didn't have to worry about my orthodox relatives, so there was no problem with the non-kosher cuisine.

I asked the choicest sidemen to play. Together they formed my dream band, graciously agreeing to do it for dirt. We saved a fortune, and were spared the usual schmaltzy wedding band that charges big money to play cheesy muzak.

Our family rabbi agreed to officiate and bring a chuppa—the traditional canopy under which all good Jews wed.

I tried to sweeten the deal for Peeps and Billy by choosing a slow club day—a Monday—Labor Day. Knowing it would be a dead night for them, they were grateful for the guarantee. We agreed on a fair price, where they would make more than they would have otherwise, hopefully get some free press, and Lenny and I would save a bundle. What I hadn't figured in was the aggravation factor.

The staff decided they deserved to party like everyone else since they were our friends too. They ate, drank and danced, leaving the rest to me.

There I was in my fitted, white, satin, tiered, strapless, Pilar Rossi, knee-length cocktail dress (perfect for a second wedding), running down to the kitchen to try to get the hors d'oeuvres out. I was in a sweat before the "I dos."

Lenny and I had spent the night before apart—superstition and all that. Our first night alone in a long time; it added an extra touch of magic to the day.

Before the guests arrived we posed for pictures, signed the ketubah (Jewish marriage license) and did a quick rehearsal with the wedding party.

Paulette, my new aunt–in–law, angrily reminded me of all the relatives we'd forsaken. Lenny's dad, Samuel, was arguing with Ellie and wouldn't pay attention. As the wedding planner and bride, I was trying to get things moving and be a gracious daughter-in-law, failing miserably at both. We finally got through it once, just as the guests began arriving.

Disappearing downstairs, hoping not to be seen until the ceremony, I was pacing like an alley cat in heat. I knew this was right and meant to be. Why was I so nervous?

Who knew what was going on up there?

I hate being out of the loop on anything. I'm one of those people that sleep little, afraid I'll miss something. The last to bed, the first to rise, I'm persistently suffering from exhaustion. It was self torture for no purpose other than fear. *What exactly do I think I'll miss at 1:00 am?*

Flex, a renowned pianist, who, for love and friendship, took the most thankless role of all, played electric organ while our guests took their seats. As the room filled to capacity, he began processional music. Jerry had already given me away once. Far from Daddy's little girl at thirty-five, I realized I was giving myself to Lenny, so I asked Jerry to walk Ellie down the aisle. Always the gentleman, he agreed. Samuel and Claudine followed, and then their children, Clarisse and Brad. Cookie and Si were next, followed by Lenny's groomsmen, then David, his best man and finally, Maryann, my maid of honor. Bean, my friend since college should have shared that honor. I shied away from it—what bride had a male attendant in those days? I wish I'd been more innovative—another of my life's regrets.

As Flex began the traditional bridal march, I raced down the aisle. (Quick, lest that gorgeous young man change his mind.)

Taking my place next to Lenny under the canopy, the depth of my good fortune filled my heart with love and my eyes with tears. *Shit, not now.* I wasn't wearing waterproof mascara. I can't have a Nelly Forbush moment at my own wedding. *Control, Andi, control!*

I stole a glance at Lenny. He never looked more handsome, radiant and in love than he did on that day. I couldn't even discern his terror.

Rabbi Resnick began,

Hebrew, Hebrew, Hebrew…

"With happiness and joy, we thank God for his blessing of love, which we celebrate today, formally consecrating the love of Andi Stone and Leonard Blakeman for each other. May they always rejoice and may their love be graced by the light through their mutual affection. Open their eyes to the beauty and mystery of the love they hold for each other. May their life together embrace and enrich in the promise of this moment so that all who know them will call them truly blessed."

Hebrew, Hebrew, Hebrew...

The Rabbi instructed Lenny to put the ring on the fourth finger of my right hand, as is Jewish tradition. I looked down to see that it was not the mate to my engagement ring that we'd purchased, but rather the matching band to Lenny's that I coveted. I was overcome.

Lenny whispered, "I wanted you to have it. I have the other one for you as well."

A man that could surprise me, not once, but twice—I was truly blessed.

Lenny repeated after the rabbi. "By this ring you are consecrated unto me as my wife in accordance with the law of Moses and the people of Israel."

Then I repeated, "In accepting this ring I pledge my love and devotion."

The Rabbi read from the ketubah.

Hebrew, Hebrew, Hebrew...

"This ketubah, witnessed on the second day of the week, the second day of the month, the holy covenant of marriage was entered into by Leonard Blakeman, bridegroom, and Andi Stone, his bride, Blue Room, First Avenue, New York City." (Titters of amused laughter.)

"Conscious of the solemn obligation, Lenny made the following declaration to his bride, 'Be thou consecrated unto me by the laws of Moses and the people of Israel. I will love, honor and cherish thee. I will protect and support thee and I will faithfully care for thy needs in accordance with Jewish tradition.'"

"Andi made the following declaration to her groom, 'In accepting the marriage ring I pledge you all of my love and devotion. I take upon myself the fulfillment of all of the duties (*duties*, what duties?) and covenant upon a Jewish wife.'"

"The bride and groom then together declared that they have signed this ketubah of their own free will, without reservation. They intend to be bound by this holy covenant so long as they shall live. Amen."

The Rabbi had me take Lenny's ring, placing it on his ring finger. (How come his ring doesn't go somewhere else first?)

"With this ring you are my husband and a sign of my love and devotion."

"My dear Andi and Lenny," the Rabbi continued, "I have to share with you that yesterday was my wedding anniversary. My wife and I have been married for thirty-four years, but the two of you created some problems for me. For the past month or so my wife has been trying to get me to take a haircut; I didn't dare because I wanted to be able to look in keeping with the ambiance when I did the wedding here."

The crowd roared. Rabbi Resnick went on: "So we've been going back and forth at it and somehow, as we always do, we resolved it. I know that people always talk about a wedding as a very solemn moment. It's really not so much solemn as it's serious, because it's festive. It's a time to laugh, to look forward and ahead with all of the verve and delight that I know the two of you are going to share. It's always a pleasure to stand under a chuppa with a young couple who are willing, who mean enough to one another to stand in public. It's easy to say 'I love you' in private; it gets a little more difficult when you stand in front of a hundred or so people. I know the two of you are used to standing in front of people, waxing eloquent and getting laughs, and yet I've been watching you both for the past hour and there's some nervousness, a bit of quivering, because it is a serious moment."

"It's a very beautiful time to be getting married. This coming Sunday evening in the Jewish calendar ushers in Rosh Hashanah, the New Year. In a special and meaningful way, the two of you have really ushered in your own Rosh Hashanah, New Year. There's a special beauty in being able to connect your private life with a period of the year in which people from Jewish tradition think and care very deeply about relationship. That's what Rosh Hashanah is about, about mending what's happened and looking forward to a new start. And, I would suggest to you that if you could take your example from the High Holy Day services and here too, it's a serious day, but not a solemn one, it's an upbeat day because, in our very characteristic Jewish fashion, we know we have it made. We might not be exactly what we wanted to be last year but we can start fresh with a brand new year. If the two of you, for all the years to come, could take each day as a Rosh Hashanah, have that same sense of excitement, that specialness that you feel for one another and recycle it, over and over again, so that, when you've been apart, the world lights up when you come together, the world feels better because you're there for one another.

"In a few moments, we're going to step on the glass and I'm always asked why we do it. We step on the glass to inject a certain sense of sadness and it's almost a lesson to the bride and groom. The lesson is that we're getting married for the totality and range of relationship. We're getting married to enjoy—to laugh together. I've learned, as I peek at my own marital roots, that it's really not that difficult to get somebody to love you when they laugh with you. It's more important to have somebody you love when times are hard. You both know that it's not that difficult to find somebody to laugh with you. You just stand up there in front of a microphone and, if your routine is good, they laugh. It's not that easy to get somebody who is willing to cry with you, and certainly not easy to get somebody who discovers that in sharing the difficult times, the relationship is made even stronger.

"In the outside world, we are supposed to be good winners and good losers. You know, if you're a good winner and your day's been great, you can't boast. If the day's been lousy and everything has been wrong, you're not allowed to cry about it; it's not being brave, it's not being adult. But, within the bonds of marriage, you can boast to one another and know that's really what you're there for, and cry with one another and know that you're also there for one another in those times.

"So, you're getting married, and I know that if I stand here for an hour I really could not tell you what it means to have the most challenging, most difficult, most wonderful of human relationships, to be somebody's mate. You, my friends, will discover that as the years pass by. Just keep in mind that you want to constantly recycle the relationship, keep it fresh, keep it new, keep it vital and make sure that it remains the most important thing you have going on in your lives. Every day a Rosh Hashanah. If you do that, then this moment will be a precious one for all the years to come."

The room was moist with emotion. Rabbi Resnick nodded to Dad. Jerry, taking his cue, sang the Hebrew blessings with showbiz passion. Everyone cheered.

The Rabbi continued, "It's always the singers who get the applause."

The crowd laughed uproariously. The joke, though funny, got even more than it deserved because everyone's nerve endings were so close to the surface. We were raw. Rabbi Resnick had touched us.

He put his arms out in front of him, over our heads (sort of, he was not the tallest man), and began to chant.

Hebrew, Hebrew, Hebrew…

"May the Lord bless you and keep you. May the Lord give kindly and with grace as you share the years to come. May he make his presence felt in your lives and those precious to you, his most wondrous of blessings, blessings for peace. Peace for you and all of those assembled this day. Peace for our people of Israel. Peace for all mankind. And, say you, Amen."

"Amen."

"Since the two of you have joined voluntarily in ceremony, in accordance with the laws of the state of New York and following the hallowed precepts of the people of Israel, you, Lenny, and you, Andi, are now husband and wife."

Through the tears and the joy, Lenny and I kissed—a heartfelt soul kiss—lipstick, onlookers and all.

In toon

Exiting the stage hand-in-hand, husband and wife, I was certain that I meant every word of my vows. Quite a different experience than I had the first time around.

When I had walked down the aisle to join Frank under the chuppa with the very same Rabbi, I knew as I took my father's arm, before I'd taken a step, that it was not to be forever. In fact, I can remember comforting myself with that thought. What a shameful act, with enormous ramifications. Frank and I fought for years before our wedding, already holding each other in contempt. What the hell were we doing? Rolling with momentum I guess. I was young, nineteen when we met. I resigned myself to life with him, even though it was completely unacceptable. We shared a passion for poker, pinochle, John Prine, chili, pot, theatre, Reggie Jackson, Mary Hartman and Aggravation—both the board game and the state of being. Beyond that, we didn't agree on a thing.

Lenny and I were different. We perhaps had less in common as far as our interests were concerned, but we respected each other's right to be.

The psychic had promised that my mate would support me and Lenny surely did. We had total faith and belief in each other.

There we were, husband and wife, at a party to honor that fact. Once I got past it taking forever for the food to be served, the music being too loud and the jokes too blue, I had a great time.

We'd taken a few dance lessons to help us prepare for our moment in the spotlight. Our song was Art Garfunkel's, "I Only Have Eyes For You"—a pressured decision we came to when we couldn't come up with anything other than, "Mamma Said Knock You Out," which, somehow, didn't seem appropriate. We'd forgotten "More Than Words," which really was our song. Where are those do overs when you need them?

When the DJ announced us, we took to the dance floor with trepidation. Lenny was a wreck, shaken by the catcalls from his merciless peers—nothing like a room full of comics to make a point. I tried to lead, whispering the old 1,2,3, to no avail. Lenny was distracted. We both just wanted it to be over.

At that exact moment, our videographer must have had a lapse, because the footage from the announcement of the dance until midway through the roast was lost forever.

Once everyone had joined us on the floor, I danced with my dad and Lenny danced with Ellie. Following the hora, David, the best man and Lenny's closest friend since college, took the stage for the toast. Sadly, I was so distracted I barely remember a word of his funny, heartfelt speech. Next up was Gabe Schefman, our master of ceremonies. One of my favorite club comics, he was intelligent, insightful and a sentimental choice, as he was on the bill with Lenny and me for my first stand-up gig at Rock Bar. He brought Pastor Pete up next, who sang some Elvis. Always the showman, he did not disappoint. Next up was Charlie Johnson, whom I hadn't seen since his Fourth of July party.

"Two Jews walk into a bar... they get married." Ba dum bum...

As to be expected, having spent years as shock jock Harold Burns' sidekick, Charlie went for the jugular. "I didn't know Soupy Sales was in town," he said indicating my father, who, with his all white outfit and hair did look like Soupy. "Oh wait, no, it's the Good Humor man." He got a rim shot on that one. From there, it was a tirade on Jews. In a room filled with them, it was a very interesting choice. Tearing into Lenny and me with reckless abandon, he was offensive and hysterical.

We were mercilessly roasted and toasted by a slew of funny men. And we loved almost every minute of it.

The band followed, packing the dance floor. We did the traditional wedding things, in this very untraditional setting—throwing the garter, the bouquet and the cutting of the cake. By the time the after-dinner drinks were served, only the hardcore remained. It'd been a long day.

In retrospect, not inviting the whole mishpucha was a foolish, selfish move. Many of those friends have long faded from our world, where our relatives forever remain. It's one of my big regrets.

But, despite the missing family, the boozed up staff, the mysterious disappearance of the video reel and my double duty as wedding planer and bride, it was a fabulously memorable day.

Si and Cookie took the top tier of the cake back to their place, while Lenny, the presents and I headed to Central Park South. It's customary at Jewish weddings to gift the bride and groom with money. Most of our booty came in little white envelopes.

When we arrived at the Park Lane Hotel, we were taken to a magnificent room overlooking Central Park from twenty-something stories up—directly below Leona Helmsley's suite. We had an almost identical view.

Lenny popped the champagne the management had sent up. Glass in hand, he looked not unlike a handsome Donald Trump—a very handsome

Donald Trump, sans crap comb over—relaxing in his tux on the settee, with the skyline of Manhattan behind him.

I was starving. Both my tummy and my buzz needed to be fed. No way I was gonna smoke in the bathroom and risk getting busted by Leona, so we raced down to 59th Street to share a joint. Very inconspicuous we were, passing a doobie on Central Park South, looking like the top of a wedding cake. We made it back to the hotel dining room just before closing and dined alone, in full wedding regalia.

Once sated, it was time to get down to business. I slipped into the sexy white satin nightgown Lana had gifted me for just such purpose. Lenny donned a plush white terry robe, compliments of Mrs. Helmsley. Atop the enormous king bed with goose feathered quilts and mountains of pillows, we tore into the envelopes. We consummated our marriage, rolling in dough.

In the morning, we ordered room service, allowing ourselves no shame over the $80 extravagance. After a hurried shower, we headed back to my place, stopping first at the bank to deposit our loot, then raced to JFK to board our plane to paradise.

As luck would have it, pleading would not convince the ticket agent to upgrade us to first class. Even though our travel agent was supposed to have put in the request, she'd neglected to do so. She'd assured us that, as honeymooners, it was almost a guarantee. Disappointed, but not about to let the day be ruined, we took our coach seats across the aisle from a Hasidic family, which included a screaming baby. We couldn't possibly anticipate at that moment that the hysteria would last, without interruption, for the next eight hours. No amount of complimentary champagne could drown out the racket. Lenny was a good sport; he acted the jester until the movie started. Even with the headset on "10" there was no way to not hear the crying. The parents didn't seem bothered in the least, barely even trying to soothe the child.

Every time Lenny leaned in to kiss me, that baby was screaming. While we shared a laugh, that baby was shrieking and, when Lenny pulled the blanket up over us, that damn baby was wailing.

As the sun began to set, it became apparent there'd be no sleep that night. I spent the time eviscerating them in my head.

—— Lenny, oh Lenny, here for art thou, Lenny ——

We arrived in Milan at about 8:00 a.m. I spoke un poquito junior high school español, barely enough to help us in Italy. Lenny, although fluent in French, knew no Italian at all, but had a terrific accent—very effective for jokes, not much help in getting around. Thanks to some college charades experience, we managed to rent our mini-car—the tiniest vehicle I'd ever seen.

With our Frommer's, Fodor's, Birnbaum and AAA maps to guide us, we headed for Lake Como. Having not slept a wink, Lenny was operating on pure adrenaline. I was little help. Phobic to drive in America, Italy was completely out of the question. The speedometer went to a hundred and seventy-five even in this toy car, and there were no discernable speed limits on the roads at all.

Almost immediately, we came to our first toll plaza. There was no attendant, no gate and no perceptible ticket machine. Unsure of what to do, Lenny drove through it, accepting it as a wedding gift from our Italian hosts.

"Grazie," he said to the imaginary toll taker.

"Prego," he responded, in a more resonant voice, as the attendant.

"Ragu…" he responded, as himself.

Lenny got a lot of laugh mileage out of that exchange for the next few years.

A good many miles later, the traffic slowed. With creeping horror, it dawned on us that we were supposed to have taken a ticket, which was confirmed as another toll plaza came into view. For our oversight, instead of $5, we had to pay the cost from the beginning of the highway to the end, a $98 mistake. We chalked it up to the crying kid and had a good laugh.

I was married to the man of my dreams, in a beautiful, exotic land, living a dream.

Life was grand.

From Lake Como, we drove to Venice, actually Lido. It was early September. Lido, as it turned out, was the place to be. The Venice Film Festival was in full swing. Who knew it was actually held in Lido? The island was hopping with international film stars. For once, I couldn't have cared less. Loving Lenny was all I had a mind for.

Back home, Scotty Fitzgerald was in the midst of another huge comeback. Now approaching middle age, it was that much more amazing. Even in Italy, the US Open was big news. It was on the cover of every newspaper and the top story on every TV. The world was once again Scotty crazy. Thankfully, at long last, I wasn't.

Our three days in Venice were magic. Taking the requisite gondola ride, every time we kissed, our driver loudly yelled some unintelligible, guttural sound: "Gooooorrrrr." We thought he was kidding, but then noticed by the third time, he seemed to be getting quite annoyed. We never did find out what the problem was. *Who doesn't kiss on a gondola in Venice?* Fuck that. We kissed and kissed. Even though it was not the romantic experience I was anticipating—walking down the narrow streets, exploring the ancient city and kissing at the Bridge of Sighs was.

We couldn't leave Venice without a visit to Harry's Bar. Everyone had told us about Bellinis, an original cocktail, made from the nectar of white peaches and sparkling Italian white wine. When in Venice…

My faux Chanel purse was fooling no one. I felt very out of place as soon as we crossed the threshold. We were fakers and everyone knew it, especially us.

Trying not to act the schnorrers we were, we controlled ourselves, only having our busboy refill the scrumptious breadbasket twice–enough to garner two sneers of disapproval. Our bottle of sparkling water sold for ten times its value. We each had a Bellini and Shrimp Fritti. No coffee, no dessert. The check came to $200.

We ran out of there starving, gasping for free air, in search of sustenance.

What I remember most about walking around Italy was always being attached to Lenny. We never let go of each other. Not for a second.

From Venice, we drove to Florence, the closest I've come to heaven in this life.

We had five days in paradise.

We strolled and explored.

When we arrived in Monaco, land of Princes and Princesses, I felt like Britney Spears in charm school. Everyone was moneyed and haute couture, and there we were in our little white trash casuals.

Eager to relax and settle in for the last four days of our honeymoon, we made our way to San Tropez. Our travel agent had recommended a brand new resort with beach views. We were psyched.

It was drizzling in the late afternoon as we approached town. Within seconds, it was pouring. As we passed a tiny strip of dirty sand and yucky water, we noticed our turn off. Surely this could not be our beach.

About a quarter mile down the road we pulled into an unpaved parking lot. It looked like a deserted construction sight with scaffolding everywhere. Entering the enormous, empty lobby I felt like we were about to find Jack Torrance behind the desk.

Instead, a bored, faux Frenchman appeared.

"Ah, Monsieur and Madame Blakeman. The honeymoon suite, with a balcony overlooking the beach, awaits!"

We didn't hear a sound as we followed the bellman almost a quarter mile, three buildings over. There was not a sign of life, except for one American couple that seemed as shocked as we were. Our room was huge and pristine, which counted for something.

Moving towards the balcony I was greeted by our view of what would one day be beautiful gardens, but currently was an enormous mud hole. Directly in front of us, at eye level, was a huge scaffold. When we went out on our balcony and leaned as far left over the rail as we could manage (getting drenched with rain this day), we could glimpse the dirty patch of sand and water we had passed on our way in.

This was supposed to be our respite after almost two weeks of sightseeing and running around. Promised a beach resort, what we got was a "soon to be resort, near a strip of sand." No wonder we got such a great rate.

Lenny knew that there was no way this would do for his bride. Obviously, we were not the first to freak out, because without too much discussion, the manager ripped up our charge receipt.

Almost 6:00 p.m. and raining harder still, we were a few miles outside of San Tropez with no place to stay and no idea how the fuck to work French pay phones. We stopped at every hotel that looked decent as we neared the town. The first was Le Byblos, which was très magnifique! The only little problem was they wanted more than twice as much as we had paid anywhere else, and we'd paid a bundle.

As I gazed at Lenny with pleading eyes, he looked back with, "You must be kidding me," written all over his face.

On we drove to hotel after hotel in the teeming rain. Almost everything was booked or awful. It was pitch black with a moonless sky, and we were tired and hungry. Barely speaking to each other, Lenny caved.

"Le Byblos it is."

My perseverance had broken him.

We had the smallest hotel room I'd ever seen, but it was gorgeous, with a four-poster canopy bed, magnificent antique chest and a small refrigerator filled with caviar, champagne and truffles. The pièce de résistance was the bathroom, which had a huge sunken tub, twin sinks with vanities, plush white robes, and hand-painted walls of impressionistic figures and foliage that would do Monet proud. The linens were at least eight hundred-thread count and exquisite. Our tiny terrace overlooked an elegant pool with its own café and bar. Figuring we couldn't possibly afford to eat there, we bought fresh baked ham, bread and a few sodas in the town square and smuggled them into our room. We ate and screwed on the four-poster, then bathed and made sweet love by candlelight in the decadent tub.

Wearing the rich, white terries, we stood on our tiny terrace, smoking a joint and surveying the action at the pool below. The guests appeared to be aging tycoons with very young mistresses, i.e., guys with hairy backs and swelling tummies attended by svelte gorgeous women. We made our way to the pool, where the girls were clad in expensive jewelry and little else. Amidst their perfectly tanned, toned bodies, I remained clothed.

Surely they knew we really couldn't afford to be amongst them. I was certain at any moment we'd be publicly revealed, reviled and cast out.

Unlike in Italy, where we were enveloped in warmth, generosity and assistance, as well as encouraged to speak Italian (despite the stammering and errors), in France, we were held in disdain. Lenny had not only studied the language for years, but had spent many a summer in his youth in Paris with Ellie and Samuel. He spoke fluently. A master mimic anyway, his accent was spot on. They were having none of it. Lenny would ask a question in French, they would answer in English every time.

It was as if to say, "We know you're American. Do not dare think you are fooling us, oui?"

I found them to be a generally snotty bunch, deserving of their reputation.

Prior to planning our honeymoon, Ellie had carried on about Lenny and me going to Paris. As much as I wanted to, I rebelled against her suggestion, as a means to reject her. Thanks to my brilliant thinking, we went to France and bypassed Paris. That's kind of like going to Krispy Kreme and skipping the donuts.

SEVEN

HUMILITY

Happy daze

Lenny and I began building our marital life under a loving, nurturing cloud of smoke. We'd both been through our share of dysfunctional, abusive relationships and were relieved to be free of the drama. Soon after the honeymoon, Peeps, the owner of Blue Room, started freaking out about money. He'd overspent and undercapitalized. It became my fault, or at least, my problem. Knowing I was merely a scapegoat didn't relieve the stress.

The scene of our wedding became a hellhole. Peeps was forever pacing around the place mumbling under his breath, constantly threatening cutbacks. Within weeks, he followed through. The place that was once filled with energy and promise reeked of fear and failure. Just as animals can smell it, so could our customers. Once fighting to get in, they were driven out by the stench of doom.

"We can't afford to pay you anymore. I'm sorry." Peeps, said, head down, about a month later.

Basically a good, straight-ahead guy, I knew he felt terrible. I was the one getting dumped, but my heart hurt for him.

"How about the last couple of weeks?" I asked, afraid to hear the answer.

"You got off cheap with the wedding, let's just say we're even."

Ouch.

I'd sacrificed a lot to take the gig. When Barry moved to LA to head up the promotion department of a new record label, he needed someone to run the New York end. The job was mine if I wanted it, with Barry agreeing to match the money Peeps was offering, plus I could work at home and receive full benefits. After suffering the choice for a couple of days, my gut led me to go with the shot at New York club celebrity. It worked in the short term. Blue Room had started as nothing. When I left it was a hot spot—although not for long.

Three months after my forced departure, Blue Room closed. Rock Bar had died about a year after I left there; Buddy's was long gone and I-dee-o had only lasted one season after I split. Even The Café had shut its doors within a year of my departure. I know I had little to nothing to do with most of it, but my bruised ego did think perhaps there was some validity to my Andi Stone Relativity Theory, also known as "Andi's Narcissistic Delusion."

Ambitious, hardworking and failing were not a good combination. Ashamed and determined to prove myself, I immediately set out to find a new home.

It wasn't about the money for me. It was never about the money. Always a fame seeker, I craved admiration and respect. What others thought of me mattered so much, because I thought so little of myself.

Lenny was still doing stand-up on weekends and teaching on Wednesdays. He had a fair amount of auditions and voice-over work, but he was around a lot. Thank goodness for love. I had a lot of fun in spite of my insecure career insanity.

Pastor Pete was playing nightly at the Shangri-la, one of the last original Greenwich Village clubs that featured the best of the hip in the '60s. Dylan was a regular back in the day. Now primarily a tourist trap, it catered to the bridge and tunnel crowd. Even though business was brisk and it was always filled to capacity, the owners sought to restore its once cool vibe. Pete suggested he might know a way to help them—and me.

The owner's son, Josef, was a young Israeli with attitude, who helped propagate the Jewish myth. He was loud, demanding and cheap. Grudgingly, he gave me a shot. Thursdays were mine.

Barely losing a week in the transition (continuity is essential in the promoting world), my crowd, ready for a change of scene, happily followed. A few weeks into my run, Julia ferkin' Roberts herself showed up, with her then-boyfriend, Jason Patric. I owe her big-time for that, even if it was unintended. It got me another column on Page Six, quieted Josef for a spell, and kept my gig running until I was ready to move on.

The Shangri-la, despite its history, never felt quite right for me. Josef was constantly unhappy. The room was stagnant—packed closely with tables overflowing with too many chairs. The magic of my nights was in the music and the mingling. The venue was not conducive to either.

Continuing to frequent B-Bar to promote my nights, I started talking up Don, one of the owners, having heard they were "looking." B-Bar's Wednesdays, for years the definitive Pro Jam, were slipping. They'd lost steam, in some part due to people like me, who diffused the energy by stoking nights in other venues.

They offered me Wednesdays. There was a time when I would have jumped through burning hoops to promote Wednesdays at B-Bar. Now it was disconcerting. The club scene was beginning to wane. My crowd was used to Thursdays. A lot of them didn't go out on Wednesdays anymore. They were getting older, having more success at day jobs and not able to party until the wee hours, night after night, as they had done in the past.

Resistant to change with almost everything, I was afraid to gamble, but ultimately couldn't resist the challenge.

It ended up being fairly effortless to get my crowd to make the shift; everyone loved B-Bar and Wednesday became the new Thursday.

Promoting the biggest music night, at the hottest club in New York, was definitely the shit. I was on top of the world. For about a minute.

My B-Bar gig quickly turned into a nightmare. The owners fought me over every dollar, insisting that any person they recognized had just shown up to hang out at their club. They couldn't explain how Wednesday nights, which had withered to mediocre at best, were once again packed and happening. I knew it was because I'd called every one of those people on the phone that day.

It was a fine, blurry line, as a lot of my crowd did frequent B-Bar from time to time. Chipping away at my door (I was paid by the head), more and more, it became an emotional, as well as a financial, drag. I felt used and abused, coming home after a great night with little to show for it. Still, it was hard to think about leaving, even with all the crap.

Lenny had been doing quite a bit of stand-up on cable TV. It was everywhere then; before the whole thing became overexposed and the comedy clubs imploded. Why not move on to network television—*After Midnight Live*? Lenny was perfect for it. He did hundreds of impressions and was a total chameleon, physically taking on the appearance and demeanor of his subjects. Unlike his stand-up, which was carefully crafted and safe, his true core was edgy and dark. He would've thrived in that groundbreaking environment. Sol couldn't make it happen. Lenny never got an audition.

What he did get were a few commercials that brought in some extra money. As with most performers, for every gig he got, there were dozens he didn't. It was rough on his psyche and mine. He hooked up with a couple of guys who handled corporate events, and usually scored one of those a month, which nicely impacted our finances. Hitting a lucky streak, in a matter of weeks, he scored a hosting gig for an educational network, and started doing warm-up for television shows that taped in New York.

Life was again full of promise.

Married, wanting children

. We were spending the weekend at Cookie and Si's new beach house on the bay when I took the test. In the quiet of the early morning light, I stole away to the bathroom, anxiously conducting my experiment. There was no grace to my actions. I always sucked at science. Missing the target almost completely, I barely had enough reserve to continue. The few moments waiting for the results seemed interminable. We'd only stopped being careful that month. What were the odds? Yet, I felt funny and had a sort of faint hormonal smell, discernable only to me. I was only four days late but, in those days, I was never late. Those were the fucking days.

There was no denying the blue plus sign, once it began to appear. As it got darker and darker my heart raced faster and faster. It was barely 6:00 on a Saturday morning. I couldn't contain it. It was too big. Running back to our room, I sat on the edge of the bed, staring—daring Lenny to wake up. Opening his eyes, slowly at first, alarm crossed his face as he bolted upright.

I held up the white plastic thing. Simultaneously, Lenny looked shocked, thrilled and petrified—exactly how I was feeling. We both started to scream.

We could hear Cookie and Si beginning to stir. Running to their room, I burst through the door, waving like an idiot.

"Hello grandma!"

Cookie joined in the screaming.

Skimming across the bay on a wave runner that afternoon, queasiness consumed me. I wore it proudly, a badge of impending motherhood.

The B-Bar gig became a no-brainer—all the smoke, boozing, drugging and staying up until dawn would no longer do. I was grateful the decision had been made for me.

The following Wednesday, when the money dickering began, I walked.

Lenny was cool about it. I don't think he minded having me away from the rock boys, my life now revolving totally around his. Neither did I. I was determined to make this marriage work.

As if to confirm the direction our lives were taking, right around that time, Lenny discovered he'd forgotten about a little savings account of his. More than he made in a year, he'd somehow lost track of it and was completely shocked when the bank sent him a notice. Or so he feigned.

Years later, he admitted that he'd kept it a secret prior to our marriage, fearing I would marry him for his money. Hell, it wasn't that much.

Suddenly, we were flush. Without my own ambitions to focus on, I put all of my energy into Lenny—his happiness, his libido and his career. I was filling Lenny's head with all kinds of crazy notions about how successful he could be, how much more was possible.

For the next few weeks, as the nausea escalated, so did my excitement. Adjusting to the idea of parenthood seemed as natural as the heaving I was doing on an almost hourly basis. Morning sickness? Who named it that?

My gynecologist assured me that in about eight weeks it would pass. *Eight weeks?*

Dr. Rubin had seen me through my waitressing days, stand-up career (albeit brief) and my rock years. We were friends. As friendly as a woman can be with a doctor who examines her... down there. I'd waited on him, entertained him, and he'd been a guest at our wedding. He was genuinely invested in our impending baby.

When I was about six weeks along, Sol booked Lenny on a cruise to Jamaica. A full-time housewife, I was free to accompany him.

On my first cruise, Lenny had suggested I take meclizine as soon as we boarded the ship. I never had a moment of discomfort. There were no discernable side effects, so I didn't even realize it was working. There was no sleepiness or dizziness; I felt completely normal and chalked it up to being one of the lucky ones who didn't suffer seasickness, not giving the drug any power.

Pregnant, I felt seasick all the time. Most of my day was spent on the floor in the john. The rest of the time, I was in bed, munching on pretzels and drinking Coke. I didn't need motion to wreak havoc on me, my hormones were doing fine on their own. Add any movement at all to the mix and I was immobilized—unable to listen or speak, much less think. We'd flown down to Miami to catch the ship. The flight should have tipped me off. I was about to spend seven days on a giant vomit machine. *What was I thinking?*

As soon as we got off the elevator to our floor, I knew I was in trouble. I was in the early stage of pregnancy where almost all smells are offensive, some insanely so. Coffee maniac that I'd always been, I hadn't had a cup of joe in weeks. Not only could I no longer brew it for Lenny, I forced him to go into the bedroom to drink his morning cup. I was not very nice. I was crazy. A constant state of nausea is enough to break anyone.

Our cabin was right above the kitchen. There was an omnipresent odor of cooking food, as no one ever stops eating aboard cruise ships. We had a lovely porthole, which I immediately covered, because the sight of the crashing waves was not helping one bit. As the ship pulled out of port, we went out on deck to get some fresh air. The cool breeze helped. The waters were calm. For a while there, so were my nerves.

At dinnertime the first night, we hit choppy seas. It was bad for everyone—for me, torture. Just a sniff of dinner had me reeling. I took one taste and that was one too many. Racing back to the room, I heaved for an hour. Poor Lenny didn't know what to do. He set out on a quest for help, returning with Sea Bands (little headband-like contraptions worn on the wrists; they were tight with plastic bumps that massaged pressure points) purchased at the ship's concession. I had almost instant relief. I was saved.

After a day at sea we arrived in Ocho Rios, Jamaica. We headed out in hopes of hiring a car and driver to show us around. The town was a bit frightening—a collection of crudely constructed shacks, filled with under-earning, overeager locals swarming tourists for a quick hustle. Everyone had something to sell. As Lenny approached a line of taxis, three drivers lunged for the fare. One wore a smile.

Lenny, trying to act in control, turned to him, asking briskly, "How much?"

"How much you want to spend, mon?"

Lenny and I looked at each other.

"Tell you what, for seventy dollars I'll take you around for three hours and show you everything worth seeing. Deal mon?

"Deal."

"Welcome to Jamaica, mon. My name is Tyrell and I'm gonna show you a good time today."

He held open the back door, which was hanging by a hinge. I slid across the lumpy back seat of worn thin red leather, avoiding the numerous exposed springs. As he pulled out of the lot, we flew in the air. The suspension was shot, as was just about everything else in the car. Despite the lack of luxury, there was something fun about the amusement park effect. We sat back to enjoy the ride.

Quickly, we were out of the city.

"How 'bout some ganja, mon?" Tyrell asked, looking at us in the rear view mirror, smiling and sure.

Lenny peeked at me with hangdog eyes. "Why not, man? When in Jamaica…"

I shook my head and pursed my lip in disapproval.

Tyrell already had the joint lit and was passing it to me.

"No, thanks. You take it Lenny."

"Come on, Andi, take a hit."

"You know I can't."

It sure smelled good.

"What's one little hit gonna do? Come on. Just this once," Lenny said, as he took a deep drag. I watched him instantly relax as he released the smoke.

It sure smelled good.

After they passed the joint back and forth a couple more times, it didn't take much coaxing when Lenny asked again.

"Come on Andi, just one little hit."

Rationalizing that marijuana was used to fight nausea, I figured it was sort of medicinal, prescribed by Dr. Tyrell.

I took the joint—held it, admired it and smelled it—gingerly putting it to my lips. Having gone that far, I dragged long and hard. It tasted like nothing I'd ever inhaled before—earthy and strong. Holding the smoke in as long as I could stand it, I exhaled slowly, savoring every second.

Now that I'd had a little, I was hungry for more. I allowed myself one last toke, a big one, and then relaxed back into the lumpy seat.

I'd quit smoking pot as soon as we'd decided to try to make a baby. Having not smoked in over two months, combined with the potency of the herb, I was very high, indeed. Lenny was high. Tyrell was high. Giddy and grinning like idiots, we played tourist as Tyrell merrily pointed out the sights.

He took us to the rain forest, and had us get out of the car to experience some of its many wonders. That was no easy feat. Moving at all took way more effort than I had. He had us close our eyes and try to guess what we smelled as he held unknown indigenous herbs under our noses. His simple lesson did more for my understanding and compassion for the need to preserve these natural wonders than any of Sting and Trudie's urgings.

"Hungry, friends?"

"Starving," I said, realizing I was.

Tyrell pulled into a little dirt road that led to an old rundown circular outdoor café counter. "The best jerk chicken in all of Jamaica, mon."

The food was served on paper towels ripped from a roll—no plates, napkins or silverware. I'm not sure if it was the cooking or the ganja but everything tasted better than anything, ever.

Driving back to the ship, I was sated and happy, slumped low in the backseat, more relaxed than I'd been in a long time. Tyrell struck a match. "One for the road, mon."

Lenny's eyes lit up like an airport runway at midnight.

"Not for me, thanks." I said weakly, silently imploring Lenny to not tempt me further by partaking.

Tyrell passed the joint back. Lenny took it and then offered it to me.

"I can't," I whined, not very convincingly.

"Come on, your last time for seven and half months. G'head," Lenny prodded.

It sounded logical. Maybe just one little hit. We were about to board the quease-machine. Maybe this would help me keep food down, which would be good for the baby! I took hold of the reefer, inhaling deeply. Why did he have to remind me it was my last joint for seven and half months? Longer with nursing—it was more likely to be my last hit for a year and half. Enduring a period of abstinence like that deserves one more, tiny little toke. *Hey, give me that thing.*

I was too high and we were about to re-board the ship. I didn't have my arsenal for de-reefer-izing. No perfume, Visine, Handi Wipes, nothing. Complete paranoia set in. Lenny's eyes were completely bloodshot. Mine too? At least we had sunglasses. But we reeked and could barely walk. It would've been scary enough if we were just regular passengers, but Lenny was crew. They throw people in jail for less down there. Holy shit. Jamaican prison.

As was custom, the entire hospitality staff was on deck welcoming the passengers aboard. Where to go, what to do?

We walked to a small stand by the side of the road and bought a lemon drink. Pouring it into my hands, I ran the liquid over my arms, on my face and through my hair. Better to appear badly groomed than stoned.

I'll never know if we fooled anybody, but no one said a word.

Later that evening, after a long nap, I awoke with a severe migraine. Not wanting to risk taking anything stronger, I allowed myself a couple of Tylenol, which was like putting a Band-Aid on a gunshot wound. Smoke pure Jamaican weed, but don't take an Advil. That made perfect sense.

I prayed, swearing that if I got through my indiscretion without harming our baby, I'd never smoke again.

Skipping dinner, I stayed in the cabin all night, bringing up whatever remained of our lovely lunch. Consumed by guilt and shame, I felt justifiably punished for my bad behavior.

For the next week, I was in a constant state of headache. Dr. Rubin didn't seem concerned in the least, assuring me it was a normal side effect of many pregnancies. It seemed every woman I mentioned it to had her own pregnancy headache story. *What to Expect When You're Expecting* had warned of them. My tummy continued to swell and my morning sickness persisted round the clock. I chalked it up to another price of motherhood.

In my tenth week, it was just about time to hear a heartbeat with a doppler— possible, probable, but not an absolute. I was terribly disappointed when it didn't happen. Dr. Rubin assured me that was the way it went sometimes. He was convinced both mother and child were fine. So was I. I was already in maternity clothes and looked well past my almost three months. Must be a big one in there. My size and intuition screamed BOY.

I was scheduled to have an amniocentesis in my sixteenth week. With the increased risk of birth defects in women over thirty-five, it was a no-brainer. But what would I do if the news wasn't good? Other than worry, I had no answer. My life revolved around the baby. It was all I thought about, talked about, cared about—other than Lenny. It was a nauseating, but blissful time.

In my fourteenth week I went back to Dr. Rubin for my monthly visit. I was enormous. The morning sickness had finally abated. We laughed at my girth, chatting away as he began the examination. Stethoscope in ears, he was mid-sentence when he stopped, concentrating on what he was hearing. Or wasn't. He moved the instrument around slowly at first, and then appeared to get a bit frantic. He had me turn this way and that, finally stopping and composing himself into the confident doctor I knew and loved.

He'd always been a straight shooter. In my mid-twenties, I'd had a bi-lateral ovarian cyst. As soon as he examined me, he warned that surgery was the only option—a pretty major deal. It was before lasers, when there was a lot of cutting, six weeks of healing time and a nice big scar. He was so matter-of-fact and swift about the whole thing I didn't have a chance to get too nervous. The surgery and recovery went off without a hitch and I got a nice long break from The Café with pay.

This was different. I kind of suspected he was shook.

Trying to pooh-pooh it, he said, "The baby's sleeping. Must be around back."

When he saw that gave me little comfort, he added, "You can go for an ultrasound, but I'm sure it's nothing to worry about. Your amnio's in two weeks, why don't we wait until then."

I already loved this baby so much; if something was amiss, I didn't want to know.

When I was nineteen, in my first months with Frank, I got pregnant. I envisioned having the baby, even though I was still one myself. Frank wouldn't even discuss it. His high school sweetheart had gotten pregnant their senior year. Even though they'd agreed on adoption, one look at her baby and she changed her mind. Frank did the "right thing"—quit school, giving up his full basketball scholarship and future of promise, went into the house painting business with his brother, and got married. It didn't last long. They were separated within a year. As bad as the marriage was, his devotion to his son was Herculean. He adored Timothy and was a terrific father in so many ways, despite his youth and the miles between them. He carried the bitterness of lost opportunities with him for years. I believe I paid some of the price.

Flying home to my mom to take care of business, on the morning of my scheduled procedure, I began bleeding profusely. Nature took care of it for me. But the doctor still wanted his money. Worried that the fetus would be expelled before he got his check, he put me on the table and sucked the non-life out of me, despite its impending arrival. No anesthesia, no nothing. Figuring I deserved the pain, I lay there silently sobbing. When Cookie came in and saw me on the table, pale and quivering, she passed out and went down for the count. Even though I knew it was for the best, I suffered the loss terribly.

The day after my office visit with Dr. Rubin, Lenny was scheduled to work at a dive in Pennsylvania about two hours northwest. I figured whatever I was going to do could wait for another couple of days. After all, the baby was only sleeping. Dr. Rubin said so.

On Friday, arriving about an hour before show time, I went to the club with Lenny, happy for the diversion, grateful to be away from the skanky hotel room. It was the only really crappy lodging Lenny had to contend with. The beautiful countryside surrounding it made it doable.

On Saturday, we went out to breakfast and for a drive. Starting to feel really crummy by late afternoon, I decided to stay in the room while Lenny did his shows—something I never did.

Just about the time Lenny was hitting the stage for his second show, I started to bleed. A lot. Frantically, I called Dr. Rubin, leaving an urgent message on his service. Calling back within moments, he advised me to lie down and keep my feet up.

"I'll schedule an ultrasound for Monday morning. Take it easy until then."

Hanging up, I wanted desperately to believe the pregnancy was salvageable. I phoned the club and left word for Lenny to call me the moment he got off stage. He was headlining, so that meant at least another forty-five minutes. The passing of time was interminable.

I tried to lie down and stay still. Raising my legs in the air, I willed my baby to miraculously re-root and be healthy.

Lenny was breathless and panicked when he called exactly forty-six minutes later. Racing back to the hotel, we were out the door and on our way home as soon as he'd packed the car and checked out. We stopped at an Arby's about half way, but I couldn't eat. My heart was breaking, my baby was dying; there was no room for anything else inside me.

On Sunday morning, Lenny had to leave for another cruise. Following the last ship to hell experience, we'd mutually decided I'd be better off at home. That lonely, child of divorce, Sunday feeling I'd escaped with Lenny came back full blown. I spent the day in bed, making deals with

God, praying for a miracle. God was my convenience in desperate times. I had no real rapport or understanding. I was simply terrified.

Cookie picked me up Monday morning to drive me to my ultrasound. She looked as terrified as I felt. Forced to drink massive amounts of water prior to the test to ensure an accurate picture, maintaining the deluge of fluid was beyond uncomfortable. I barely dared breathe, let alone move. It didn't serve to distract me, nor did Cookie's nonstop conversation. My misery was not to be deterred.

After an hour, I'd consumed the requisite fluid and was ready. I wasn't really ready, but it was time. Cookie offered to come in with me, but the memory of her passing out all those years ago was still vivid.

Luckily, the technician was a young girl with a sensitive, warm demeanor. In a soothing tone, she encouraged conversation as she prepped me.

"Let's just see that baby of yours."

After subtly turning the screen so I couldn't see it, she moved the instrument around my swollen belly,

"Did you find my baby? Is everything okay?"

I already knew the answer. She tried to turn away from me, but I could see her expression was grave as she bit her lower lip.

"Tell me, please, what do you see?"

"I'm not supposed to say anything until the doctor has a chance to review the pictures," she said, apologetically.

"Please, please, just tell me."

"The fetus is dead," she whispered. "I'm so sorry."

The tears came in a slow, steady stream at first.

"Was it a boy?" I asked, already sure of the answer.

"Yes."

That brought the flood. I'd spent months loving that boy, the child I was now never to know.

"Can I see my baby, please?" Hesitantly, she turned the screen towards me.

"The fetus is very small. I'm going to take some measurements," she said softly.

"I'm so enormous? What does that mean?"

She smiled at me and went about her business.

"What is it?" I asked, trying to read her, as she read the screen.

She was concentrating on the task at hand—using a ruler and the machine to do some calculations. "The fetus died at six weeks. August 14th. It's unusual, but it happens sometimes. The body holds on; the fetus continues to appear to develop."

I barely heard her last words.
August 14th.
We were in Jamaica that day.
I killed my baby in the back of Tyrell's taxi.

Early Mourning

In the deserved discomfort from the D&C that Dr. Rubin performed, I stayed in bed for days, using that as an excuse for my lack of desire to do absolutely anything else. I was staying at Cookie's. She and Si were due to leave for Europe the following day. I was to be alone with my heartbreak. It seemed fitting—the beginning of the just punishment for my inexcusable indiscretion.

I called Lenny on the ship to shore. He was dutifully compassionate, but I knew the loss was different for him; he didn't have the same attachment. There was probably a certain relief at not having the added responsibility of fatherhood just yet.

For me, there was a hole I had no idea how to fill. I ached for my baby, for motherhood—trying to imagine my life without it. Lenny and I were so good together. We shared every detail of each other's lives, surely that would be enough. And yet, how could I be complete without a baby? I'd been a mother's helper, a babysitter, a counselor, a camp director and a student teacher. Children had filled my life. Could I bear not having one of my own?

I'd vowed that if nothing bad happened, I'd never smoke again. Now that I was no longer with child, all bets were off. For a few moments, the pot worked and I was numb. Ultimately, it couldn't diminish the emptiness; it pooled in my chest and wouldn't leave. I ached for my boy with every breath.

I had no job, no baby and no plan. When Lenny returned a week later, I was still stoned, listlessly wandering around the apartment. I needed to snap out of it, to move forward.

How?

We couldn't even think of trying again. The dead fetus I'd carried for almost two months had left me a mess, in mind and body.

Beyond motherhood, I tried to daydream about what I wanted to do. I couldn't come up with a thing. Creative visualization had worked many times in the past: with college, The Giggle Group, The Café. This go round, all I could see was a briefcase, a suit and working in an office, 9:00-5:00. How odd. Where did that come from?

I had no idea what I was qualified to do, but I went to The Sharper Image and spent my birthday money on a black leather attaché.

Okay, now what?

Fate lent a hand. When things fell apart at Blue Room, I'd entertained the notion of starting my own business. I'd been hooking up musicians for years. With computer technology advancing, I thought about forming a database of talent that could be used worldwide for just such a purpose. It was prior to the internet, or at least my knowledge of it.

If a band needed a new drummer—punch in the criteria and then audition only those of choice. Clubs wanting to book talent could listen and watch a taped performance and so on. I did a bit of research with computer geeks to find out what was possible, met with a few businessmen as potential investors, even had my lawyer search out the name I'd chosen and draft an initial business proposal.

When a promoting gig turned up at the Shangri-la, I abandoned my half-baked dream as I had so many before it.

I was in the throes of a full-out depression when my old friend Joseph called. He was recruiting for a couple of friends who were starting a computerized service to be utilized by casting directors seeking actors. He remembered my business proposal and thought it might work to hook me up with this new company. He set up a meeting for the following Monday.

I hadn't expected to be using my attaché so soon.

I put together the most businesslike outfit I could manage—no easy task for this rock 'n' roll promoter. I met with Nate and Morris, briefcase in hand.

Both in their 60s, they were well-dressed and reeked of success. Their offices were atop the building just east of the TKTS booth on Broadway with a spectacular view. There were eight individual offices with windows overlooking Times Square, feeding into an enormous main room with couches and easy chairs throughout the space.

They lead me to a conference room on the far side of the suite, where we sat across from each other and began the get-to-know. I filled them in on my business plan and job experience. Before I even got to B-Bar, they wanted to talk salary. *That was fast.*

They offered me a nice chunk of change, over $50,000 a year. It was less than I was making as a promoter, but it was a regular paycheck, no week-to-week wait and see. There'd be benefits after three months, something I hadn't had since my union waitressing days at The Café. The best part of the gig was my title. I somehow talked them into Senior Vice President. The coolest credit I'd ever had. Also the most bogus.

The company was started without enough capital, and what was available was spent on "show." I was a good, thrifty Jewess. No amount of negotiating skills however, could offset their misguided use of their limited funds. They were spending tens of thousands of dollars on monthly rent but sweated the pennies on everything else.

The casting directors were willing. They had nothing to lose. We provided them with the computers and taught them how to use them. It was the early '90s and all of them were still using paper files. Our service was a gift to them, even if they never cast a role from it. We brought them into the land of speed and efficiency.

It was the actors who got screwed. My original business plan was intended to serve users on both ends. I believed that to be true with this as well. It took me a while to realize that this casting service was only intended to make money, with little concern for the poor actors duped into spending their few saved dollars for a chance at work. They came to us with the promise they'd be in the casting directors' data bank, which was supposed to be used for actual casting.

We did have a number of very successful casting directors aboard, but none were actually subscribing yet (they were getting the computers and the service gratis and only one or two actually used the equipment for the intended purpose). In exchange, we put all of their existing files into the data bank and they continued to use their regulars for the actual calls. Of the hundreds we signed up, perhaps a handful of actors, at best, actually got an audition.

As the company spokeswoman, I gave seminars and demonstrations, getting the vulnerable to turn over their cash. Despite the salary, the office and the title, I felt dirty working there. I spent hours daily trying to get the system used as it was intended—to no avail. It was almost a relief, when less than three months later, they went bankrupt, giving us a day's notice that it was over. I was three days shy of being eligible for unemployment.

With the distraction of the job gone, I plunged, once again, into the depths. I had nothing to focus on other than my desire to be a mother and how damn much it hurt down there. Still in tremendous discomfort, Dr. Rubin assured me that it was all in my head.

Furious at the suggestion that it was my neurosis, at Lenny's urging, I made an appointment with his urologist. I felt like I was cheating on Dr. Rubin, but rationalized that Dr. Katz was not a gyno.

Sure enough, Dr. Katz informed me that I had a severe bladder and kidney infection, caused by retaining a dead fetus for six weeks. He prescribed strong antibiotics that I'd have to take for three months, and advised me not try to get pregnant during that time.

I was crushed.

Had Dr. Rubin trusted my symptoms and referred me to a urologist immediately, he could've saved me from months of discomfort and prevented the infection from strengthening as it did. His ego was better served than I was. Had his office been more up-to-date with sonogram equipment, he would've known immediately that the fetus was no longer viable and could've prevented some of the drama that came to pass. At least, if he'd sent me for a test when there was no discernable heartbeat at fourteen weeks, it would have minimized the physical and emotional trauma, to some extent. I didn't blame him for what happened, but I couldn't stay with him—another costly casualty of the situation.

I could've looked for a job at that point, but rationalized that in three months we'd make a baby. It was far too easy to not work, and to wallow in my misery.

When my infection finally cleared, we were given the go-ahead to start trying. I was elated, and confident that we'd see immediate results. I'd gotten pregnant on the first try, the last go-around.

When it didn't happen after three months, I went bonkers. I was aging by the minute.

We knew we had what it took to make a baby. But, damn it, it wasn't working.

We went to a fertility specialist. Lenny came in a cup and we were both poked and prodded.

We were advised to take my temperature, and have sex the exact second it spiked. But first, I was to douche with baking soda to aid motility, and then keep my legs in the air for at least ten minutes post coital. Total romance killer—but I was determined.

In July, Sol booked Lenny another cruise. I went along, as much for the change of scene as the fact that I'd be ovulating. The first couple of days were perfect.

Just as we pulled into the dock in Bermuda, my temperature soared.

"It's time," I gasped.

"Come here," I ordered.

"Now!" I screamed.

"Where's the damn baking soda?"

Poor Lenny.

Sol and I were increasingly at odds. We genuinely liked each other, but I knew he wanted me dead. Accomplishing the next best thing, he booked Lenny for a weekend out of town with Lenny's ex—Mona. Her new husband, also her agent, suggested we all drive to the gig together.

I wasn't working, had lost my baby and was having no luck getting pregnant. Mona was still doing stand-up, making money, getting laughs and adulation. She made me insane.

On the flip side, she hadn't quite gotten over Lenny's reluctance to marry her, nor the speed with which he had turned around and wed me. I guess we both could've used some therapy that weekend.

Returning home that Sunday night, all was forgiven.

I was with child.

——————— **Cut** ———————

In spite of some lingering fear, my pregnancy was heaven. Morning sickness and excessive weight gain did not dampen my spirits in the least. Immediately bonding with our developing baby, as soon as the amnio confirmed it was a boy, we anointed him Jack and referred to him by name.

One night, somewhere around my sixth month, Lenny and I were watching TV and eating pretzels.

"Mmmmmm… salty," Lenny said, in perfect Homer Simpson.

It was a dead on impression. When I was undressing a few days later, he got that wide-eyed, dumb thing going on again and said, "Oooohhh look, a naked boooooody." Homer became Lenny's alter ego, which, more and more frequently, he'd let out to play. Whenever he dropped anything, he'd exclaim, "Doh!" In the supermarket, he'd stop dead, close his eyes, smile and say, "Dooooooohnuts." If I was doing something he didn't like, he'd cock his head, purse his lips, lower his chin and exclaim, "Maaaaaaarge!" The kicker was one night he fell asleep with a Sugar Daddy in his mouth—the goo dribbling down his chin. When I went to take it out, he clamped down on it with his lips and continued eating it in his sleep. He was Homer and I was his Marge. The names and the play stuck.

Despite a difficult thirty-six hour labor, Jack's birth was profoundly sublime. As predicted, I fell head over heels in love with him at first sight. It was unlike any love I'd ever known. I didn't sleep a wink for the first five days of his life, high on hormones and his sweetness.

On the eighth day, as is customary in Jewish tradition, we had his bris—a religious ceremony of circumcision that is nothing short of torture for a first time mother. Seeing the mohel—an old man with shaky hands, drinking wine—and knowing that he was about to approach my son's penis with a knife, was just too much for me.

I retreated to Cookie's bedroom. We were staying with her for a couple of weeks so she could help us with our adjustment to parenthood.

There were about seventy-five family and friends in the living room eating Jewish delicacies (a variety of smoked fish that would easily gross out even the most adventurous gentile), awaiting the ritual.

Lenny joined me a few minutes later. He was ashen, clearly shaken. Watching his boy's manhood compromised had obviously been too much for him.

"Is it over?" I asked, praying Jack had survived the trauma intact, other than the (hopefully) tiny, missing piece of foreskin.

"Yes, it's over. What do I do now?" Lenny asked, as he sat on the edge of the bed, placing his head in his hands.

"Don't worry sweetheart," I said, moved by Lenny's sensitivity.

"Don't worry? How can I not worry? I have to support us, and a baby, with half my income cut off?"

"How does Jack's foreskin getting snipped affect your income?"

Now Lenny looked confused. After a moment, he gained clarity.

"No, not the bris. Walter just called. The agency's dropping me."

Walter was his commercial agent. In truth, Lenny hadn't scored in a while, but to call a man in the middle of his son's bris to deliver that kind of news was a new kind of ugly.

We held each other and cried.

As with most dramatic shifts in life, Lenny's was based in need. To deal with the glut of comedians rising out of everywhere in the early to mid '90s, many of the old-timers who hadn't yet broken through were forced to be creative to continue making a living. Realizing that perhaps they weren't going to be the next Seinfeld or Shandling, they began writing for those who were. Comedy was a tight community back then, everyone knew everyone, and they all liked Lenny. Determined and hard working, he was soon selling jokes to the best of them.

At a gig, a couple of months later, Lenny ran into a colleague who was supplementing his income faxing jokes to *On the Edge*, a hot new show creating quite a ruckus. Michael Paar, the cantankerous and politically incorrect host, was whip-smart and funny as hell. A rebel, he openly loved hookers and pot, which made him naughty, sexy and highly watchable.

Lenny knew Michael from his stand-up days. After a few well-placed phone calls, he gained approval to submit material on a paid-per-usage basis. When on his very first day he scored four jokes in the monologue, he figured he was onto something.

From then on, he began each day with the newspapers, jotting notes in the margins as he drank his morning coffee. A few hours later, he'd usually have between twenty and forty jokes to submit. The head writer would call in the late afternoon to tell Lenny what he got on. Not a day went by without Lenny getting that call. After two weeks he was offered a retainer position, which guaranteed him a small weekly salary, whether or not he scored.

It was a prestigious political forum and even Samuel, Lenny's dad, was impressed. I think that meant more to Lenny than anything. His dad never thought much of stand-up comedy. A philosophy professor, he preferred more intellectual pursuits. *On the Edge* provided credibility in that world. Likewise, Cookie was a big Michael Paar fan. His libertarian politics were almost as right wing as hers. She was very proud of her son-in-law.

This new phase of Lenny's career gave him cred with his peers as well. Most of the comics we knew were struggling to make a living, competing for the few choice writing gigs and the ever-decreasing stand-up slots. Lenny was fortunate enough to be doing both, plus occasional commercials (thanks to hooking up with a new agent), stand-up spots on cable and corporate gigs. His money soared, as did the regularity of his jobs. It seemed subtle at the time, but looking back, his career shifted on a dime.

It was fantastic having Lenny home while he did his writing. Usually finished by early afternoon, it left the remainder of the day for fun. On weekends, we still traveled the road, doing the tourist thing by day and Lenny's club dates at night. We spent almost every minute together as a family in those early years. It was a rare gift for new parents. We appreciated every second of it.

About a year later, *On the Edge* was picked up by a major network and moved to Hollywood. That left Lenny in New York, hungry for another writing outlet. Soon after getting the news, he did a stand-up gig with Sheila, a comedian he'd known for years. A bit older, she'd had some "looked like she was gonna break big" success, but it never quite happened for her. Sharing the long drive upstate gave Lenny the opportunity to fill her in on the baby and his recent writing gig for Michael Paar. As he'd hoped, she offered to get his writing package to her husband, Marty, the head writer at *Holloran Hour.*

Within days, Marty offered Lenny a faxing position. As had been the case at *On the Edge,* Lenny scored immediately. In less than six weeks, he was offered a retainer—this time for his hero, Rob Holloran. The money was better than at *On the Edge,* but still a long way from supporting a family of three. Lenny continued performing and auditioning in addition to his daily writing.

It was one of the happiest times of my life. Married to my best friend, we had a beautiful baby boy, Lenny was writing for *Holloran Hour,* and he still got to be with us 24/7. It just couldn't get any better.

A few months later, Holloran was having his annual Christmas fete. An avid ice skater, he rented out a Manhattan rink for the party at the height of the holiday season. Marty casually mentioned to Lenny that he'd soon be receiving an invitation. Lenny had yet to meet his new boss and relished the opportunity. I was beside myself with anticipation.

We knew a few people that worked at the show and when, a couple of weeks later, they'd all received their invitations and Lenny had yet to get his, I pushed him to call Marty. Marty assured him it was on its way. Days before the party it still hadn't arrived.

I pestered Lenny to call again.

"You'll be on the guest list. Just come," Marty said, more than a bit annoyed.

EIGHT

JUSTICE

———— Attempting to skate with celebrities ————

It was a rare evening out for us without Jack. I was an excited, nervous wreck. The thought of a few hours in a room full of adults was thrilling enough, but anticipating being in the presence of Holloran left me breathless.

Going against Lenny's natural inclination to be exactly on time, I was determined to be fashionably late, so our entrance would go unnoticed. Little did I know we'd run into parking difficulty, which would further detain us.

When we finally did arrive, anxious and out of breath, the party was well underway. Dozens of revelers were skating and enjoying hot toddies outside. As we made our way to the entrance, I felt like we were approaching airport security without ID. Behind a long table, three interns were manning the guest lists. After a good nudge from you-know-who, Lenny tentatively approached the table.

"Lenny Blakeman plus one?"

The young man searched his list. Twice. Then reached for the others—meticulously scouring the pages.

"There must be some mistake," I jumped in, hysterically. "Lenny's a writer for the show. He's on retainer and works at home, that's why you don't know him. Our invitation got lost in the mail. Marty told him just yesterday that he'd be on the list."

Even I didn't believe me.

"I'm sorry, but I don't see your name." he said apologetically, looking more than a little embarrassed.

Thankfully, at that moment, Larry Pepper spotted us. Larry did warm up for the show. He and Lenny had worked together for years.

"Hey, Josh, this is Lenny Blakeman, a fine comedian and a new writer for the show. He's okay," he said, with a wink to the intern, while grabbing me around the waist.

"Sure, sure, Larry. G'head. I'm sorry folks."

"Don't worry, we understand, just doing your job," Lenny said sincerely, inhaling for the first time in minutes.

Larry escorted us in, heading straight for the bar. Man, did I need a drink.

In a sea of familiar faces, I recognized some from the show (Holloran loved to put his staff on camera) and others that we knew personally. A few guys in the Holloran band had played at my rock nights. A couple of them I counted as friends.

I turned to look towards the rink, and there he was. Wearing a baseball cap, skates, khakis, and a T-shirt, a light windbreaker was all that covered Rob Holloran on that freezing winter night.

I couldn't take my eyes off him. Even though we'd exchanged hellos years before at The Café, this was different. We were here as part of the team. His team.

Glancing over at the tables, I noticed Danny Robbins. We'd known Danny for years. He'd started out as a young guy with a lot of moxie, who very quickly parlayed it into success. He managed a couple of long established, highly respected and adored comedians. Chris Nicosia was originally one of his "yet to break big" talents, making better than decent money as a headliner, supplementing it with late night Manhattan gigs to keep him sharp. Chris's world changed a year prior while doing a coveted slot on *Holloran Hour*. Holloran loved him, and immediately signed him to a development deal.

Chris now had his own prime time show, which was enjoying marginal success in the ratings. It was still young, having only been on the air a few months. Not quite "must see TV," it had potential.

I wouldn't call Lenny and Chris friends per se, but they were cohorts who, I think, liked and respected each other. They were "friendly."

I'd met Chris a number of times at various gigs. He was shy, at least around me, but at our last meeting he'd been friendly and thoughtful. I was eight months pregnant with Jack. Chris had a daughter, about three years old. He and his wife were expecting another child. Parenthood is like a fraternity; have a kid and you're instantly a member. Chris was one of the first to welcome me in. He shared parenting tips and couldn't have been nicer. We were in a tiny Greenwich Village club, late on a Tuesday night. It was basically a no money gig the comics did to try out new stuff and stay working on off nights. Like everyone else, Chris was getting the usual $10. Here we were, less than two years later and he was verging on major stardom.

Lenny and I joined Danny, Chris and his wife Maria, congratulating them on his rising success. Then we caught each other up on what mattered most—our kids.

A short time later, Larry came bounding over.

"Want to meet the boss? Come on, I'll introduce you."

My breathing shortened. "Would you excuse me a moment?" I asked Maria, trying to sound calm. My heart and brain were racing.

We were only a few feet from where Holloran was holding court. Larry comfortably and confidently approached Holloran.

"Hey, Rob, I'd like to introduce you to your newest writer. Rob, this is Lenny Blakeman."

Holloran outstretched his arm, shaking Lenny's hand warmly and firmly. With a big smile, he said, "Nice to meet you, Lenny. Welcome. Thanks for all the great stuff. And who's this?" He asked, turning his attention to me.

"This is my wife, Andi."

I put out my hand and Holloran grabbed it in both of his.

"Hello, Andi. Thanks for coming."

"Thanks for having us Rob. What a great party."

At that moment, out of the corner of my eye, I caught sight of Marty, staring angrily in our direction. Was it my imagination? Paranoid delusion?

After a moment or two, Chris, Maria and Danny joined us. They seemed pretty starstruck and uncomfortable themselves in Holloran's presence. I offered to take a picture of them with Holloran. Quickly obliging, Holloran grabbed Chris on one side, Maria on the other. Was I crazy or did he wink at me?

"Would you take one with us, boss?" I asked.

"Sure," he replied, grabbing me around the waist and pulling me close. His other arm circled around Lenny. Chris took the shot. Holloran's arm lingered a second around my shoulder.

After doing a once around the room, saying "hi" to old friends, meeting spouses and future acquaintances, we had something to eat and ended up back with Chris, Maria and Danny.

I hadn't been on skates since I was twelve, and I was a better skater then. Lenny, on the other hand, knew his way around the ice. Leading me by the hand, he pried me away from the rail. We caught up to Danny, who was proficient, and Chris, who was holding his own.

Holloran came out for a spin. He skillfully and speedily made his way around the rink, smiling and waving along the way.

Was he glancing over at me? Nah!

Joining Maria off the ice, I took photos of Lenny, Danny and Chris. When Holloran skated up to them, I captured that as well.

No matter where I was, it seemed every time I looked over at Holloran he was looking back at me. I was definitely delusional.

Just before we were about to call it a night, Chris approached. "I'd sure appreciate copies of the photos you took."

"Absolutely. I don't think we have your address," I said, offering him a pen.

Chris hesitated, "Um... Danny, why don't you give Andi your card?" Turning back to me, he added, "He'll get them to me."

It was an awkward moment—the realization hitting like a bolt of lightening. The baby club had suddenly segregated.

A week or so later, I got the pictures. The best by far was the one of Holloran with Chris and Maria. Holloran looked so playful in it. There was an unmistakable twinkle in his eye. He seemed to be grinning at the photographer—holy shit, that was me.

I sent two sets of prints to Danny, one for him and one to pass on to Chris and Maria. Not a word came back—from either of them.

I've since come to appreciate that giving is not about thank-yous, but I wasn't as evolved back then.

Fuckers.

Called up to the show

Being a stay at home wife and mother suited me. Completely satisfied with our little family—at forty, I figured, three was what we were going to be. And I was just fine with that. At a girlfriend's bachelorette party, a psychic suggested otherwise.

"I see another child."

"A boy or a girl?"

"I don't want to say—just in case."

Just in case, *what*? She knew I had Jack, she'd already guessed that. So, I deduced, she must see a girl in my future. Why else would she not want to say?

When I got pregnant the last time, I knew it was a boy and was thrilled. When I lost the baby, all I wanted was that boy. Jack far exceeded my dream. I hadn't really fantasized about having a girl, since I was one. Once the psychic planted the seed of possibility, it was all I could think about.

Even though Lenny thought it was all nonsense, including her prediction about a writing project I'd undertake, I got pregnant the next month. When we found out I was carrying a girl, I signed up for a screenwriting class.

Just past the first trimester nausea, while spending a few days with Cookie at the beach, Lenny got the call.

Listening intently, he put his hand over the mouthpiece and whispered, "It's Marty—he's leaving the show."

"What does that mean? Are you still in?"

Lenny shrugged, still listening.

I gave him a nudge. Lenny mouthed, "He's recommending me as his replacement."

"HOLY SHIT!"

Marty had decided to leave *Holloran Hour* to write the great American novel. He'd had the job for years; we never imagined this could happen, let alone so soon. Lenny had been on retainer less than a year. The same day that he got the call from Marty, he landed his first on-camera, national commercial—playing Rain Man. It required he dye his blond hair black. Lenny left everything in the colorist's hands. It didn't dawn on him to ask, "Would you use a temporary dye, please?"

At his interview with Holloran three days later, nervous as a five year old on the first day of kindergarten, he couldn't help but notice Holloran staring at him. There was pale, white-skinned Lenny, with bright blue eyes and jet-black hair. He looked like Hitler.

After the interview Marty called.

"Holloran's got a couple more guys to see, but he liked you. I think you're in. He did say you looked kind of weird."

Holloran's a creature of habit. He surrounds himself with people he trusts and, maybe even more importantly, feels comfortable with. That's a very small group. He doesn't like change, dresses almost in uniform, eats the same menu daily, and only interacts with a very select, handpicked few. His staff are, for the most part, lifers, until someone dares leave or somehow loses favor. The cast of his inner entourage had barely shifted in the previous decade.

Everyone was anxious about Marty leaving and Lenny stepping in.

After two weeks on the job, Holloran called Lenny into his office.

"Have a seat."

Lenny nervously obliged.

After a long pause, Holloran said, "So how do you think things are going so far?"

Lenny felt like he was in a no win situation. If he said things were going well, he'd look like an arrogant asshole; if he played it down, and implied that things were rough, he'd look like a loser. So Lenny hedged his bet. "I think things are going okay... um... I see areas where I can improve, but I think overall it's going pretty well..."

Holloran interjected, halting Lenny's rambling. "Well, I think things are going much better than expected. You're doing a great job, Lenny; I really have no criticism. If there's one piece of advice I'd give you it would be to just relax a little bit."

After exhaling in relief, Lenny gave that his best shot.

Slowly they started to get comfortable with each other, which wasn't easy for either of them.

Lenny spent the mornings writing material and sorting through the hundreds of jokes submitted by the rest of the staff. He compiled a daily "best of," and dropped them off to Holloran mid-morning. Once Holloran checked his picks, Lenny had them put on cue cards. They had rehearsal at precisely the same time each afternoon. Just Holloran, Lenny and Sal, the cue card guy. It was a position of much stature, as only the three of them were allowed in that room. It was where Holloran was most himself—the good, the bad and the ugly. It could be an extremely stressful place on the days when Holloran was contrary to everything, but it was also a sacred ground, where very personal secrets were openly shared with a famous man that nobody knew.

Lenny was honored to be on the team. Unlike Marty, who was always "on," Lenny was low key, picking his moments to tickle Holloran when he found an in. He'd slip in a joke-joke or two, infusing dialects and impersonations, which he did about as well as anyone. He'd sneak in some magic, and recount stories of his life on the road—a past they shared in its heyday, although their timing was off and they never crossed paths. Holloran was a few years ahead of Lenny, but they knew a lot of the same people and Holloran loved hearing their tales. He was removed from the scene due to his celebrity and his self-imposed isolation.

As the months wore on, Lenny got to go out to a few dinners with Holloran and a very small group of handpicked funnymen. Considering that Holloran himself only did these dinners a couple of times a year, it was a big deal to be included.

When Sydney was born about six months later, we scheduled her arrival so that Lenny wouldn't miss a rehearsal. He knew Holloran wouldn't welcome an upset to his daily routine and worried about giving anyone else the "in." I was willing to be induced to lessen both their stress. The idea of avoiding another thirty-six hour labor wasn't lost on me either.

At the last minute the taping changed, too late to reschedule my delivery. We'd gone to extreme ends to avoid this very thing. Holloran had Pat, a senior staff writer and an old college pal, fill in, assuring Lenny it wasn't a problem. But Lenny feared doom.

Magnificent pink roses were delivered hours after Syd's birth, with a fun, thoughtful note from Holloran. I was euphoric to begin with, Holloran's attention heightened the deal considerably.

In spite of the effort, Lenny's fears were realized. Once Pat was added to the mix, he never left. Now that Holloran and Lenny had a buffer, neither of them had to try as hard with each other. So they didn't.

Holloran had a daily ritual of banging on the closet door when entering rehearsal. The guys occasionally tried to surprise him by stashing a guest in there. When Sydney was about three months old, waiting for the last possible second, we put her in there, bassinet and all, praying she wouldn't cry, while I hid in the bathroom. As Holloran approached to rap on the door, he stopped himself before anyone else had the chance. He'd obviously been tipped off, but it didn't matter. His genuine delight as he tentatively opened the door and beheld our tiny baby girl was clear. He softened like warm butter. Lifting her up into the air he cooed, "Hello, sweet Sydney. Hello pretty girl." It was a bonding moment for Lenny and

Holloran. Holloran continued to ask about "Sweet Sydney" until Marty resurfaced, after which, he never spoke of her again.

At one time, Marty was a young comic on the rise, giving it up for the honored position of being Holloran's conduit to the funny. It was a powerful post, one he took very seriously and complained about constantly. After a number of years, and more than a few gray hairs, Marty happily passed it on to Lenny, to pursue his dream as a writer of fiction. When the transition went off without a hitch, he began stopping by. And, whenever he did, Holloran distanced himself from Lenny. I truly believe it was Holloran's sensitivity to Marty's fragile ego and his desire to have his old pal around, more than it was a diss to Lenny. Marty was a trusted friend with whom Holloran felt completely comfortable. He could probably count on one hand the people he felt that way about. It was understandable that he appreciated the few who dared, and managed, to get close to him.

Even though Marty didn't want the job anymore, he didn't want anyone else to have it either. He began visiting the office more regularly. After some months, he was around a lot, and, maybe a year later, Marty was back on the payroll. According to the buzz, it was merely to entertain Holloran, who missed him. He got paid big bucks to come to the office a couple of hours a day for rehearsal. Once he did, Lenny was permanently excused from that task, and his private time with Holloran was drastically diminished.

When the gig was all Lenny's, we were at an all-time high. We were madly in love, the kids were thriving and we had enough money to stop worrying about it. We were living the life of Riley and we knew it.

Once Marty came back, the stress started taking its toll. First, Lenny was out of rehearsals, and then the dinners. He couldn't help but wonder if Marty would push him out completely. After a few years we got comfortable in our uncertainty.

There was still off-camera conversation with Holloran during commercial breaks when Marty had gone home, but they were getting less enthusiastic and, as time went on, chilly. Eventually, it was nothing but frost. That's when our world started to dim.

Mr. Big shot

It was a crazy life, but with the constant stress came perks beyond our imagination. About eleven months after Lenny started at *Holloran Hour* he found out he'd been nominated for an Emmy. It might as well have been an Oscar or the Nobel Prize.

At the Holloran Emmy party, we ran into Chris and Maria. I made no mention of the photos and neither did they. Chris was now a full-fledged TV star. Lenny was one of the only people in the room he knew from his salad days. We spent most of the evening in cozy conversation with him and Maria.

The following year, at the same event, an even bigger celebrity now, Chris was even friendlier, playful and complimentary. I'd finally lost the pregnancy pounds, taken up Pilates, and was in the best shape I'd been in years. Wearing a slinky snake print, low cut, figure hugging two-piece ensemble, both Holloran and Chris were vocal in their appreciation. It was food for the soul for this then forty-three-year-old wife and mother.

Some years later, while visiting Lenny in LA, we ran into Chris and Maria at a Christmas party thrown by Chris's television wife. It was a star-studded affair in a movie star environ—a huge home, with an enormous amount of property in Hancock Park, just this side of Beverly Hills. One corner of the grounds was set up as a children's paradise, complete with rides and clowns. There were tables and chairs around the pool and strolling waiters offering drinks and hors d'oeuvres. The celebrities, there with their own families, were amiable and accessible. Jack and Sydney were jazzed, meeting actors they'd enjoyed on the big and small screen.

While chatting with an old friend from New York, a little commotion caught my eye. There was a buzz around the back door. Chris and his entourage had arrived. It was early evening on a cloudy day, yet there were Chris, Maria and their children all wearing dark glasses.

Chris was, by this time, a bona fide superstar, earning more money than anyone in the history of television. But still. They just looked silly and, for the first time, he acted the part—aloof and unapproachable. Where in the past we'd discuss schools and the cruelty of aging, that day it was clear he didn't wish to be bothered. After quick introductions of the kids, we slinked away.

I suppose there's no way to achieve that level of success and remain unchanged. Who's to say that in that situation anyone else would've behaved any differently?

What about Julia? She seems to have remained grounded and lovely. Tom Hanks, someone else I admire tremendously, strikes me as so "everyman." Despite his Oscars, his fame and wealth, he appears to be the same as I expect he was before celebrity rocked his world. Of course, that's purely conjecture.

I admire Chris plenty. He's hard working, incredibly creative, innovative, talented and funny, funny, funny. Maybe he and Maria had a fight in the car on the way over like the rest of us mortals. Maybe they needed the glasses to cover their tears.

Or maybe I'm just a jealous twat.

Inside view from an outsider

When I think back, before the end, I believe Lenny and I mutually sealed our fate. In the fall of 2000, about a year before Lenny got... let go, he got a call from Lori—a young, ambitious go-getter producer for *Holloran Hour.*

"Interested in doing a freebie for the president after hours?" The opportunity to meet Bill Clinton, his political hero, and write for him, was a dream come true.

Celebrating her fiftieth birthday, Hillary was turning the occasion into a fundraiser for her senate campaign. Bill used his clout to enlist a passel of celebrities to perform. What Democrat with money wouldn't pay to see Cher, Tom Cruise, Robert DeNiro, Gwyneth Paltrow and Ben Affleck (back when they were a couple), Chevy Chase and Nathan Lane, plus, our most charismatic leader since Kennedy?

A couple of weeks before the event, Lenny's resume and press kit were delivered to Stuart, the head writer on the project. Before the day's end, he'd gotten the gig. An hour or two later, he found out that Marty was Stuart's partner on the project. He hadn't thought to bring Lenny aboard. Interesting, but not surprising. Marty had done a number of side jobs over the years, never hiring Lenny. Considering that Lenny was the person he felt most qualified to replace him at *Holloran Hour,* it seemed odd. But the bottom line is, that because of Marty's recommendation to Holloran, our lives were forever changed. I guess that should damn well be enough.

With some trepidation, Lenny went to the first rehearsal. As he expected, Marty virtually ignored him and his ideas. Fortunately, Stuart had no agenda and Lenny made his mark. Nathan's monologue ended up containing a load of Lenny lines, as did Chevy's and Hillary's. Stuart and he co-wrote a skit Bill himself did with DeNiro. Talk about a friggin' thrill.

Lenny was allowed a "plus one" for the big night. Upscale business attire was suggested, as most of the attendees were coming straight from the office. What was a housewife to do? I didn't own a little black dress (corrected immediately following the event), but I did have a black suit. Not feeling thin or confident enough to wear the skirt, I opted for the pants. A sexy top underneath seemed inappropriate for a meeting with the president, so I went with a hip, man-tailored INC crisp white shirt, buttoned up respectfully. When I arrived and saw the evening gowns, mini skirts, and peek-a-boob tops, I realized I'd misjudged. Feeling like Judge Judy in a sea of Pamela Andersons, I quickly undid a few buttons.

Lenny was given a seat at a table, while Stuart and Marty ran around backstage with walkie-talkies. Lenny was not given a VIP pass for the after-party that followed at the new, chic boutique hotel. Somehow, all the other writers had one.

As it turned out, the promoter of the event was an old colleague of mine from my rock days. He had an extra pass to the party, and a couple of seats in a limo with Nathan Lane to get us over there.

The show was a stupendous success; the audience was thrilled to be witnessing this historic celebrity-laden event. Even the participants were starstruck. There on the stage for the curtain call, lined up in a row, were Nathan, Chevy, Cher, Gwyneth, Ben, Tom Cruise, Bobby D and Hillary. Yet, no star shined as brightly as old Bill. The man had X factor out the wazoo. Amongst that line-up of super stars, all eyes were on him. He reeked of power, and that was damn sexy to everyone.

The ride to the party with Nathan was surreal enough, but the sights of the night kept topping themselves. In the lounge, Ben and Gwyneth were at the bar chatting with a bunch of privileged youth; Cher, still sequined and bejeweled, was sweetly accepting compliments from a fawning middle-aged fan; Hillary, in high spirits, was sharing a toast with a group of powerful supporters and there, in the midst of it all, was The Prez, holding court.

The reception was for the supporters who donated big money. Part of the thank-you was a photo with Bill and/or Hillary. As they were always a few feet and a world apart, it was usually one or the other.

There was a line of New York's elite waiting their turn to have an audience with the most powerful man in the world. Without speaking, Lenny and I drifted in step. Hillary had her own receiving line, not quite as long—made up of mostly serious politicos.

As we got closer, I noticed whomever Bill was speaking to had his undivided attention; they became the most important person in the room, for that moment. All eyes were on them, no matter where people pretended to look.

My heart was racing, my skin was on fire; I knew there was no way I could articulate any words of reason. As warm, smiling eyes welcomed me, I stepped forward, reaching out my hand. Our fearless leader took it warmly in both of his, pulling me to him. His left arm reached around my back as he outstretched his right hand to warmly shake Lenny's. All of this was happening as we were introducing ourselves. Somehow, Lenny had the presence of mind to mention that he'd co-written the sketch that Bill had done with DeNiro, to which President Clinton queried, "Did I do alright? Was I okay?"

"You were excellent, Mr. President," Lenny said, sincerely.

"What was your name again?"

"Lenny Blakeman, Mr. President."

"I'm gonna remember that."

We believed, with certainty, he would.

Lined up perfectly for a photo op, the shutterbug didn't miss his cue. Bill, on my right, was holding my hand in his, his left arm still behind me, resting provocatively very low on my back. Lenny was to my left, leaning in. Once the flashbulb popped, the photographer asked our names and handed me an official paper with instructions on how to retrieve the photo.

As we said our goodbyes, the President called after us, "Lenny Blakeman, good show!"

Standing a few feet away relishing the moment, I could've sworn I saw old Bill give me a wink. What a charmer.

Seconds later, we ran into Marty and Sheila. I'd met Sheila casually a couple of times at stand-up one-nighters and Holloran holiday parties. Some years older and very funny, her success had long since plateaued. As with many comics, in real life she was fairly serious. I always felt "less than" around her and Marty, and their dismissiveness toward me seemed to suggest they liked it that way.

Feeling a little smug that night, having just had a close encounter of the most intense kind, I had something that Marty and Sheila coveted. They'd arrived too fashionably late to get in the president's receiving line. Even though my tone was sweet and friendly, they were smart, and I'm sure they could sense my "nah, nah, nah, nah, nah." It was before I acquired a taste for humble pie and learned to savor its bitter sweetness.

For Lenny and me, the night topped off an all-time high of happiness, togetherness, excitement and fulfillment of our dreams, and, where I suspect, we overstepped our bounds. Not only did Lenny get the gig without Marty's knowledge or consent, he ended up writing a lot of the funniest stuff in the show, not the least of which was done by Clinton himself. We'd had an audience with the man, something Marty and Sheila hadn't managed, and the photographer who'd shot them with Hillary hadn't given them the official paper, so they couldn't even retrieve their photo. Marty was forced to fax me for the information. It was literally the first time in all the years I'd known him that he acknowledged my existence on the planet. (I don't think he used my name, even then.)

We added further insult to injury by using our presidential photo as our Christmas card that year, sending it to everyone we knew. Some unknown guy holding a cocktail appeared in our photo with the president and, unbeknownst to us at the time, Hillary was off to our right, so she, too, graced our picture. The caption read: "Happy Holidays from Bill, Andi, Lenny, Hillary and the guy on the left." At the Holloran Christmas party a few days later, where our card with Clinton was one of the hot topics, the tension between Marty, Sheila and us was palpable.

That was also the night (for the very first time) Holloran wanted nothing to do with me. There would be no smile, no hand kissing and no compliments. I tried to comfort myself thinking that it wasn't personal, that he was just in one of his moods, but he never warmed up to me or Lenny again.

His birthday was no exception.

Having caught sight of himself in an unflattering light one night (easy to do on television, which adds ten pounds to everyone), Holloran had taken control of his diet with the same discipline he applied to everything in his life. Even though he began eating the same small meals every day and structured his intake to an obscene degree, Holloran loved food. He rarely allowed himself to deviate from his healthy menu.

It had become a ritual for Christmas and birthdays that I'd try to surprise him with some of his favorite foods. Since he rarely went to restaurants, he hadn't been to a few of the best.

The first year I took a cab to Peter Luger's in Brooklyn. The steak and accouterments were without comparison. I'd pre-ordered the meal, telling them whom it was for—knowing that would guarantee it'd be the best of their already best. I timed it so I arrived at the studio just as Holloran was finishing the night's taping. See's chocolates, which I had expressed east, served as dessert. With his assistant's help I set out the meal and left. Moments later, Lenny's office phone rang.

"Why don't you and Andi come on down here?" Holloran himself offered. That was huge.

In his private dining room, Holloran, his executive producer and his assistant awaited us to join them in a taste. Another year, knowing he loved Japanese food and had never been to Nobu, I called my old friend, Drew Nieporent, formerly a manager at The Café, now a world famous restaurateur, soon to be a James Beard Award Winner. He helped me arrange a banquet that I again picked up by taxi and had set out just as the day's taping wrapped. Holloran raved about the meal for months afterwards.

My last foray for culinary pleasure was to have live Maine lobsters flown in one morning and delivered at lunchtime. Holloran had them taken to a local restaurant and steamed. Other than the requisite thank-you card written by his assistant, there was no other mention of it. I knew something was amiss. Holloran had always been a very gracious and appreciative recipient.

It didn't take long for the freeze to find its way home. Lenny was out in the cold, and it was following him everywhere. For the most part, Holloran was strictly business. On the occasional night when he could make him laugh, Lenny'd come home so joyful. Those nights were infrequent and dwindling. Marty was bossier and more condescending than ever. Lenny was feeling smaller and smaller. It didn't do much for his self-esteem or his temper. Being snapped at all day perpetuated the behavior at night.

The only comfort Lenny got was from the old Mary Jane and the computer. He'd amassed a huge email list of supportive fans he'd send jokes, political rants and "forwards" to. It became a thing to be included. The people who requested to be added to his list constantly amazed me: producers, performers, agents, executives and intellectuals. They'd pile praise and gratitude on Lenny for the daily joy. It was the only appreciation for the funny he was getting in those days, and he used it more and more like a drug to ease the pain and the disappointment. Losing ground with Holloran was killing his ego, his heart and his soul.

Didn't do much for our marriage either. I lost him. To the computer, the pot and the sadness.

NINE

SELF-DISCIPLINE

The upside of down

It's easy for me to blame Holloran and Marty for the damage to our marriage. But in truth, Mary Jane was the bitch that ripped us apart.

Soon after the Clinton party, my dad was coming to stay with us for Thanksgiving as he had every year since he and Roxlyn split. I was stressed.

A few years earlier, on one of his holiday visits when we were still living in Lenny's bachelor apartment, very late one night, long after my dad had gone to bed, we broke out the weed. Before lighting up, we put a towel under our bedroom door, sprayed the hallway with Lysol and, while standing on the radiator, hung ourselves out of the open window as we toked on a smokeless pipe (a smokeless pipe?). Feeling right at last, relaxing to some mindless movie on the tube, we were just about to fade off when we heard the bathroom door slam shut. (We only had one bathroom and you had to pass our bedroom to get to it.)

Surely everything was okay. We'd taken every precaution. No way my dad smelled anything. Shaken nonetheless, I had a fitful night's sleep.

In the morning while making coffee, Lenny still asleep, my dad was sitting at the kitchen table waiting for breakfast.

"I went to the bathroom in the middle of the night," he began.

Uh oh…

"There was a very strong odor."

I did what any good addict would do. Blamed Lenny.

"Dad, this is Lenny's house. He's a grown man. If he chooses to indulge himself, he owes no explanation to anyone, other than, perhaps, me,"

I might have convinced my dad, but I didn't fool myself for a second. I felt like the total lying dirtbag that I was for blaming Lenny.

Addict.

Ugly word. Uglier life.

Pot had freed me from myself. When high, I forgot I was "less than," scared, and unsure of myself. Marijuana was my great enabler. Under the influence I could be whatever I wanted to be—daring, outgoing and willing. Once I discovered that, I wasn't about to let it go.

It took me many years to realize that the pot that initially facilitated my power, eventually took it back, leaving me almost paralyzed.

I'd quit smoking grass numerous times over the previous ten years— when I was pregnant or trying to be, and when I was nursing the kids, but I kept falling back into the old routine. My smoking didn't have a big dramatic end externally, but I was dying inside, my self-loathing hitting bottom. I never believed marijuana was addictive, but boy when I tried to kick it... and I tried a lot.

Life had been pretty idyllic for a long time. I loved to smoke and laughed a lot during those years. For Lenny, it was his five o'clock cocktail, only he had it at eight, after work. For me, it was all or nothing. As soon as the kids were in school, I worked out, and then my day of consumption began. A few hits here, a couple of tokes there, jonesing in between. As controlled and anal as I was about everything, and I do mean everything, pot was the one exception. It controlled me and I hated myself for it. It was one thing when it was just us—but I felt like such a phony once we were parents. I couldn't look people in the eye. I was constantly brushing my teeth, washing my face, opening windows—it was exhausting.

In truth, I didn't even like being high any more; it just made me paranoid and complacent. What I loved was smoking—the smoke filling my lungs, inhale... exhale... relax. It was the ritual, the momentary letting go. The high had long since stopped working.

It was time to be a grown-up, not just pretend to be one. And even though I was pretty good at pretending, keeping it together was just becoming too much work. My self-hatred only left me for the moment after the hit. Within seconds, it returned more virulent than ever.

I had so many dreams yet to fulfill, so many unfinished projects. The more I procrastinated, the bigger the tasks became. And, the larger they loomed, the more impossible it became to even think about starting them. It wasn't that they were any big deal or anything; it just meant I had to get off the damn couch.

I considered myself an honest person, but I hid my addiction from everyone, including myself. Being wracked with guilt and shame didn't stop me from pinching pot from my closest friends if the opportunity arose. Not always, but sometimes. If I received extra change from a cashier, if they neglected to see an item in my cart, I gleefully made hay with it, suffering later for my lack of moral character.

I worked hard to convince the world, and myself, that I was a good person, but in truth, I was a liar, cheater, stealer.

I despised myself.

I was the mom with sunglasses on, even on rainy evenings. We had to leave the playground every hour or two so I could refresh my buzz. Our bedroom was my den of iniquity; the door always closed, the windows open. I was pathetic and knew it.

In sharp contrast, I was extremely attentive—overly so. I didn't let Jack out of my sight for the first fourteen months of his life, to both of our detriment. I was continually trying to control everything—my fear on parade.

I single-handedly saved the day, every day.

Addict thinking at its best.

By all appearances, I had it so together. Growing up with a working mom, we were always running out of toilet paper, substituting paper towels, napkins, whatever was around. The cupboards and refrigerator were almost always bare, just the necessities of the day on hand. To compensate, or overcompensate, no one in my home ever wanted for anything. There were backups for my backups.

Lenny and I owned our apartment, had money in the bank and no debt. We had two terrific kids; he had a dream job and was well-liked and respected. I volunteered almost full time, fund raising for the kids' public school. Our apartment was immaculate, thanks to an undiagnosed case of OCD. (Mental illness can serve a purpose.) The kids had a loving and structured life. I was organized to a fault with play dates, homework, bills, paperwork, errands and almost any responsibility—except living in reality. Beneath a façade of functionality, I felt shamefully guilty. Mommies aren't supposed to be stoned. Period.

With another Thanksgiving approaching, and my dad about to visit, I finally decided to just say "NO." No more Lysol, Visine, hiding in my bedroom, or making excuses to go to the store thirty times a day. Over forty and a grown-up, it was time to try to act like one. So, the night before my dad arrived, I smoked my last joint. I did it without help or fanfare; also, without joy or passion. It was a very un-dramatic bottom, not nearly as low as many, just the end of the line for this marijuana addict of thirty years. Driven by self-righteous indignation, I never wavered.

Lenny wasn't exactly seeing things my way. Unlike me, he could control his smoking, waiting until after work to indulge. He had a good job and was making lots of money; pot was the only thing keeping him sane—what with Holloran and Marty perpetually squeezing his nuts.

Now straight, I was his most annoying adversary of all. My nagging became incessant. The self-righteous crap that came out of me was astounding. I tried to badger, cajole, shame, plead, reason, any tactic I could think of. And, I thought of lots.

Lenny began trying. He'd quit for a few days, sometimes a couple of weeks. But, he couldn't make it stick. At my subtle-as-a-sledgehammer probing, he began seeking help. He attended Alcoholics Anonymous meetings and, when those didn't cut it, he switched to Narcotics Anonymous. Both groups tended to not take marijuana addiction very seriously. They'd suggest he come back when he had a "real problem." Some of them even used the "marijuana maintenance program" to keep them off booze and hard drugs. For the most part, they discouraged sharing on the subject, so Lenny kept his problem to himself. Naturally, he'd relapse.

We'd fight, he'd quit, go to a few meetings, relapse, and we'd fight some more. After a few months of that, we rediscovered Fay, my old therapist. Even though she had pissed me off, branding me an addict, she was right. She was always right. Bitch.

Fay's first order of business was to guide Lenny to Marijuana Anonymous. A newer, smaller fellowship, the meetings were held once a day and filled with kindred spirits of all ages and lifestyles, people you'd never suspect of having addiction issues—doctors, teachers, financial brokers and the occasional outlaw.

I white-knuckled my abstinence alone, too "holier than thou" to need help. As a result, I was miserable, taking my unhappiness out on my poor Homer.

Getting high since I was 13, I had no idea how to love without the buzz. I had no idea how to do anything without it. I begrudged Lenny his relief from the occasional joint or meeting, and tortured him for it. Our happy marriage began crumbling with my resented sobriety. Not exactly sobriety. I continued to have an occasional cocktail, as that was not my problem. I wasn't an alcoholic like the rest of those losers. I had no reason to give that up too. I never even considered it. But Lenny—he had a problem.

Driving us both insane, I rode him like a cowboy hanging on to a bucking bronco. Watching his every move, I waited for him to fuck up. He did not disappoint. He'd go to an MA meeting every Friday night, and stay straight until the next Thursday, his Friday. Holloran worked a four-day week. As his head monologue writer, so did Lenny. Every Thursday, after an excruciatingly long, two-show day/night, Lenny would wait until I was asleep and get high. Like clockwork, every Friday, our date day, he'd confess his digression during our weekly couple's therapy session with Fay there to buffer. After which, we'd suffer through an angry, silent late lunch, see a movie, and then I'd escort him to his Marijuana Anonymous meeting and wait outside.

For years, the thought of any "A" group (AA, NA, MA...) scared the shit out of me. I pictured a bunch of drunk junkies with sallow skin in some dark, dank basement, smoking nasty cigarette butts, drinking bitter black coffee from wilting diner take-out cups, looking miserable, white-knuckling sobriety and hating every fucking minute of it.

Each Friday evening, I'd sit in the hall reading some mindless magazine, listening to the laughter that would inevitably erupt in the room. I'd try to steal a glance before and after, to get a sense of what it was like in there, but the meetings scared me. And besides, I didn't need help. I was cured.

Week after week, Lenny would emerge a slightly changed man. After a couple of months, he started putting some clean time together and I began to have hope. One Friday night, for no apparent reason, I asked if I could go in.

The meeting leader approached us as soon as we got in the door.

"Hi, I'm Eric, welcome."

"Hi Eric, I'm Andi, Lenny's wife."

"How long have you been clean?"

"Nine months."

"Great! Would you qualify?"

"Qualify?"

"Tell your story. Your using story."

"My using story?"

"Yeah, what made you start getting high, what it was like the years that you did, why you quit, and what it's like now"

"Um, yeah, sure." I was terrified, but jazzed.

After a few 12 Step readings, Eric took the floor.

"Hi, I'm Eric and I'm a marijuana addict."

"Hi. Eric!" echoed back.

"And now to share her experience, strength and hope, please help me welcome Andi…"

Strength and hope? Hey, wait a minute…he didn't say anything about that!"

"Hi, my name is Andi and I'm… I'm… I'm a marijuana addict."

"Hi, Andi!"

It was the first time I'd said those words out loud. I let out a nervous chuckle. I was quickly put at ease by the group's energy and focus.

Beginning with my first hit of keef, I detailed my drug history and then told them about my dad's visit and my decision to quit.

"As for my strength and hope… well, in truth, I don't have any. That's why I'm here. Thanks."

I lowered my head in embarrassment and waited for the jeers. Instead the room erupted in applause. The easiest ovation I'd ever gotten.

The first person to speak was a woman a bit older than me, with short white hair, tanned skin, an athletic build and clear blue eyes.

"Hi, I'm Ellen and I'm a marijuana addict."

"Hi, Ellen!"

"Andi, welcome. Thank you so much for your honest and succinct share."

Some titters around the room.

"I related to so much of what you said."

As the meeting continued, they each thanked me for my brief, but relatable share. Ah, sweet validation.

I liked it.

One by one they told *my* story with self-effacing, brutal honesty. Their stories were my stories. For the first time in the nine months since I'd smoked my last toke, I remembered how to breathe, how to laugh.

An hour and fifteen minutes later, as the meeting concluded, they each came up and hugged me (totally weird—but kind of nice) and said, "Keep coming back!"

I had a feeling I would.

Once on the street, I asked Lenny what they meant about my brief share, and why they chuckled.

"A qualification is usually about 20 minutes."

"How long was mine?"

"Seven."

"Oh shit!"

I was shocked. A blow-hard, running short had never been my problem.

Unlike other 12 Step programs, where many have lost everything, in Marijuana Anonymous the stakes are often not quite so high. Although perhaps morally and spiritually bankrupt, potheads can usually maintain a façade of functionality—usually, not always. It's an insidious drug, as so many of us convince ourselves it's just a harmless, natural herb. The damage it does is often difficult to discern.

I wasn't really in danger of walking that road again, but I needed to figure out what drove me there to begin with. An unhappy mess that needed fixing, I quit because I was a mom and I was supposed to. Not because I wanted to. I still loved Mary Jane, but I felt shamefully guilty.

With the help of Fay and the Friday Night Marijuana Anonymous meeting, we began our journey to try to find our happiness without weed. Only there was none. There were relapses, broken promises, screaming, anger, disappointments, sadness, heartbreak and loneliness.

The big "L" was something I hadn't felt at all since I'd been with Lenny. I'd lived in loneliness as a child and through my first horrific marriage. When it reared its old familiar ugly head with Lenny, I was terrified.

We'd been happy for so long. Lenny gave me something no one else ever had, unconditional love. It was something I'd always dreamt about. Here was this wonderful, talented, funny man showering me with it. For the majority of our years together, I woke up in the morning with a smile, thanking God for my incredible good fortune.

With Lenny I felt connected, and that feeling was always with me. It was so scary when it was gone. Was it gone forever? Could we get it back? Was pot the glue of our union? Had we just run our course? Would we even like each other, seeing our true, un-enhanced selves? Fay warned that many couples that straightened out split up.

Perhaps it had nothing to do with any of that. Maybe it was simply Holloran and Marty working their magic, tearing us down piece by piece.

They huffed and they puffed...

We were planning our annual trip to LA; it was to be a second honeymoon, falling just a few days after our tenth anniversary. I'd suggested we renew our vows on the beach behind the Loews Santa Monica. Lenny was going to be wearing his tuxedo anyway, for the Emmys. It seemed like just the thing to re-kick-start our union.

Lenny's tux was still in style and fit him almost perfectly, despite his having put on a couple of pounds over the years. Nothing a tailor and some thread couldn't accommodate. I dug my knee-length, Pilar Rossi wedding dress out of hiding. It'd been dry cleaned, stuffed with tissue and was in remarkably good shape considering how much time had passed. The satin, blue-white, inch-thick horizontal pleats were, for the most part, still pressed and in place. I stepped into it, pulling up from my ankles, giggling as it enveloped my curves. As I began to pull up the zipper, which extended from the base of my butt, I was stopped almost immediately. No amount of Jenny Craig or Pilates was going to return my hips to my pre-mommy, thirty-something proportions.

I'd dieted and exercised like crazy prior to my wedding. The dress had started out a size 6 and, by the week before the wedding, after a month of Slim Fast, it had to be altered considerably. It was literally built around my body, which at the time consisted of a flat stomach and 36-inch hips. Tracking down the store where I'd bought it, I asked if it would be possible to restore the dress to accommodate my revised shape. Everything is possible for a price. My ego rebelled. For weeks, I considered what it would take for me to get back in pre-baby form. Realizing that nothing short of starvation and a scalpel could accomplish it, I finally abandoned the idea. If I couldn't fit into my damn dress, I wasn't going to take my damn vows. Second honeymoon, here we come.

We needed a break from the kids, our parents, the daily stresses and a chance to try to find fun. We hadn't had any in so long, I'm not sure either of us remembered how it was done. We still laughed and had some good times—but they were few and, frankly, not good enough. We were fighting all the time, about basically everything: the kids, money, Rob, Marty, time, money and, of course, there was also the marijuana. *His* marijuana, I should say.

On the morning of September 11, 2001, I was running around trying to get my arm through the coat sleeve of the trendy leather jacket I'd chosen over the comfy bomber that Lenny had brought home from the "free box." The free box was a treasure trove of mysterious wonders sent to Rob Holloran, which he kindly made available to the staff, on a first see, first grab basis. Lenny liked the free box a lot. So did I, the kids, our friends and even Jack's school. Swag is a beautiful thing. Barely able to move, I was already regretting my choice.

The *Today Show* was on as I added lipstick and a compact to my purse. CRASH went the plane into the World Trade Tower. *What the... ?* The pilot must have had a heart attack or something.

I'd pretty much stopped sleeping the first of September in anticipation of our trip. We were leaving the kids in the very competent hands of Mary, nanny extraordinaire, who'd been with us for years and two of these LA Emmy trips already. But those were just quick turnarounds. Cookie was going to be close at hand, bringing food and getting Jack to soccer. I knew they'd be fine. But how could I get through a week without my babies? Seven days without their sweet wet kisses ("Mommy, can I kiss you on the lip?"). The heady smell of their slept-on hair, the feel of their peachy cheeks; little fingers entwined in my own. I ached for them already and I hadn't even left the apartment.

I was wracked with guilt—all my failures rushing to the fore. The times I was more focused on my phone conversation with Aunt Maryann than on my baby wanting to share a joke; reading the newspaper when Jack wanted to play; leaving the playground to take a toke. When I yelled, lost my patience, or said something my mother would have said. And, shit! The time I pulled Jack's hair.

I can't believe I did that.

The horrible truth is, I did it again. Twice in seven and a half years is forgivable, isn't it? Especially if you add Sydney's three and a half years. That's only two times in almost eleven years.

There's absolutely no rational explanation or justification for my horrendous behavior.

I adore my children. Worship them. Kiss them millions of kisses every day, tell them I love them constantly, laugh at their jokes, applaud their dance, marvel at their writing, hang up their art, celebrate their brilliance and love them unconditionally. I hope that redeems me.

It doesn't though.

I can be a coldhearted, nasty-assed bitch when I'm not paying attention.

Reaching to turn off the TV, I snapped, "Homer, hurry up, the car's waiting." CRASH went the second plane. We saw it. Was it possible? Could two guys have heart attacks in the same hour, while piloting planes, in the same city, in neighboring buildings? The plane looked like it was headed straight for that building. *What the fuck?*

At that point, in my selfish little brain, all I was thinking was, "Shit, this stuff always happens in threes." My paranoid thinking was quickly overruled by our vacation plans and the Emmys. We grabbed the luggage and ran.

"The airport's closed," our neighbors shouted as we flew past. We jumped into our waiting car. *It's our second honeymoon, dammit!*

Driving east on 125th Street, which was bustling with morning commuters, we looked south and saw the smoke billowing through the air. At Lenny's request, the driver turned up the radio. "This just in, a plane has crashed into the Pentagon." We were yakking like mad, not really listening, and then we heard something about the White House.

The End.

It was time to go home. Something beyond terrible was going down. *This could not be happening!*

As we inched back west on 125th Street, a female reporter on the scene at the World Trade Center was calmly commenting on the current activity. Until she whispered, almost breathless, "Oh my God, it's coming down." Then shrieked, "The tower is coming down!"

Goose bumps are running down my spine even now, recounting it. At the time, it made my blood run cold. I will never forget the sound of her voice.

As the taxi pulled into our building's driveway, I jumped out, oblivious to the fact that it was still moving, and raced up the steps to Syd's preschool, conveniently located in the lobby of our building. I frantically recounted for the director the events to date; she'd been busy doing paper work and didn't know a thing. Hysterically, I raced on, "Get the children inside, now! We're being attacked." Conflicted, I left Syd in her care.

Impatiently waiting for the elevator, I tore up the four flights of stairs, bad knees and all, and threw our stuff down. Lenny had the car out of the lot and in front of our building just as I got there.

The one-mile ride to Jack's school was interminable. The streets were empty, the smoke still pouring northward from the south, the radio scaring the shit out of us. *What in the hell was going on?* Was this it, the end of the world? Would the nukes be flying, our children dying?

This was something I never considered I'd live to see. A radical in the late '60s, barely a teenager, I went to Progressive Labor Party meetings, protested the Vietnam War and marched on Washington. I sat in, survived riots, but it was nothing like this.

As we approached the school, I leapt from the car and raced to the elevator (I'd like to say I ran up the stairs but, frankly, I didn't have it in me at that point). Jack knew we were on our way to the airport to board an American Airlines 767 to LA. A thoughtless substitute teacher, who also knew, decided to share with the children that two planes had crashed into the twin towers. Jack asked if the planes were taking off or landing. Thankfully, the dumb-ass teacher guessed wrong. He took a little comfort in knowing that his mommy and daddy were leaving, not coming.

I can't imagine his fear, his terror. For two hours he sat there trying to push the horrible thoughts from his mind.

As the elevator door opened, I could see Jack sitting at his desk, head in his hands. I couldn't get my feet to move fast enough. His face registered surprise and relief in the seconds before I got to him. Grabbing him, tears pouring down my cheeks, I couldn't hold him tight enough. Feeling his confusion, I didn't let him go. I tried to compose myself so I wouldn't scare him even more. *Has he ever seen me cry?*

"Are you surprised to see me?" I said, trying to sound light hearted.

"Yes Mommy. I'm so glad," he said, as he buried his head in my shoulder and squeezed me hard.

"Whaddya hear?" I asked, trying to figure out how much he knew.

That's when he told me his takeoff/landing theory. Taking his hand, with a quick goodbye to his dumbass teacher, I led him to the elevator.

When Lenny saw us approach, he jumped from the car and scooped Jack up into the safe embrace of familiar love.

Getting into the car, we should've turned off the radio, but didn't. We couldn't. Stopping several times, we bought all the water we could fit in the car. I'd been grocery shopping the day before so we were okay with food. Arriving home, clutching Jack, we made a beeline for Sydney.

Mary had arrived and was watching TV when we entered, having just hung up the phone with my dad in Florida. She was unaware that we'd never made it to the airport and, now my dad, all alone in Lauderhill, was thinking the worst. For two hours I tried to call him, but the circuits were busy, forever busy. When I finally reached him, we both needed a drink.

Instead of a glass of wine at the pool bar at the Loews Santa Monica, Lenny and I shared a bottle of red at the small café on our corner. It was late afternoon, almost eight hours after the unimaginable. Five miles north of the World Trade Center, we watched in numbed horror as men and women, covered in ash and debris, silently walked past the café window, looking like costumed actors in a George Romero movie.

When the world fell apart, every minuscule part of the infrastructure crashed within. The reality was unknown, the fear so strong you could smell it. I was paralyzed. So was just about everyone.

Lenny was thankfully off work for the week. We were supposed to be vacationing, and losing another Emmy. How the hell was he ever going to be able to write funny again?

He knew how to do that, though. He was actually quite brilliant at it. Lenny's first official day on the job at *Holloran Hour* was the Monday after Princess Diana died. How do you figure out what's going to make Rob Holloran and America laugh after that? But, he did, doing it again a few days later when Mother Theresa died. Can you imagine your first week of work, your dream job, right arm to your hero, and you have to be funny with all of that shit going on?

It's an interesting thing with comedians. I've often found them to be very serious, depressive people, yet, they think in punch lines. There wasn't a topic or situation Lenny could not make funny. Except of course, the current state of our marriage.

Big on subtlety

Miss fancy pants, self-described mover and shaker, big shot promoter and publicist, hadn't had a real job in years. I was thought of as Lenny's wife, Jack and Syd's mom and, at the time, that was good enough for me. I had no idea when or how I'd ever re-enter Careerville when, based on a completely random happening, my life shifted on a dime.

It was after midnight when I sat down at the computer.

I usually hate those "Dear Friends" emails, telling of personal experiences, with little meaning to anyone other than the people involved, but in the last few days I've found the sharing of stories such comfort in this time of madness. Tonight, Lenny & I experienced something so unexpected, so extraordinary, I hope you'll forgive me this indulgence...

Dear Friends,

Tuesday morning, September 11th, Lenny & I were on our way to JFK to board an American Airlines 767 to Los Angeles. It was to be six days without the kids—a first.

We saw the two planes crash into the World Trade Center on TV. Not yet realizing the magnitude of the situation, or its cause, we headed for the airport, suppressing the nagging internal reminder that most tragedies happen in threes.

As the story began to unfold on the taxi's radio, the reality began to take hold. When the plane hit the Pentagon, we did an abrupt about face.

Realizing that Jack might have heard the news at school, we raced to pick him up, imagining that he'd fear the worst.

For two hours, he sat terrified at his desk, unsure if he'd ever see us again. He's been sleeping in our bed ever since, as I imagine many of your children are, as well.

Since Tuesday, we've been basically paralyzed in front of the TV.

On Thursday evening, the 13th, Sydney's school held their scheduled picnic. Thinking it dangerous and insane, we went in spite of ourselves. For the first time since the 11th, I felt almost normal. The weather was beautiful; laughing children and friends sharing stories surrounded us. I was so grateful we'd gone. Returning home, we read to the kids and tickled them until they screamed with laughter. What joy!

As soon as they fell asleep, we went back to the TV, the newspapers and the terror.

Our DSL had been down since the 11th. It was Friday by the time we figured out how to get on-line the old fashioned way. We'd gotten the same email message many times over, about a nationwide candlelight vigil, to take place that evening. You probably got it too.

Attempting to be casual, we asked Jack if he wanted to join us, moments before we were due to leave. He'd been so afraid of the bad guys since we foolishly let him watch TV with us those first few hours after the attacks. He opted for The Rugrats.

Improvising with two Shabbat candles in hand, Lenny and I headed down to the plaza in front of our high rise, at five of 7:00. Alone, we stood with a family who didn't have a computer, hadn't heard of the vigil, but were happy to join us.

Where were all our neighbors, so many forward-thinking activists?

Soon, two teenage girls came, lighting their candles as they joined us. A woman and her pre-teen son followed. Another neighbor stepped up, holding the hand of her little boy who was clutching a birthday candle, the wax burning his hand as he bravely kept the flame lit, because he somehow knew it was important. Soon, others joined until there were about fifteen of us. We stood quietly, holding our candles and our thoughts. One of the young women eventually spoke, articulating what we were all thinking— her surprise that we were so few in number—yet somehow she made us feel better about it. A gentleman then shared his story of loss while another told a miraculous tale of survival.

An elderly resident, pushing a shopping cart, told us of a group of people that had gathered on Broadway. As we moved towards the flickering lights, by the time we got to 125th Street we were about a hundred strong; all races and ages, headed we knew not where, but walking with purpose.

It was exhilarating and empowering to walk through Harlem feeling so welcomed. With every step, nods, smiles and fists of solidarity greeted us, as more of the community joined our group. The crowd gathered in front of the 126th Street Rescue Unit, which was missing three of its own. As we stood there raising our candles to the brave, a woman began singing "God Bless America." Everyone sang along. Despite being completely unmelodious, it was the most moving rendition I'd ever heard.

One of the rescuers spoke to us, telling us of his continued hope to save their men. He thanked us for our support and assistance. How humbling. I'd done nothing to help. I'd been paralyzed with grief and fear, while they'd worked without rest for days, trying to recover their brothers, and ours.

The crowd pressed on, down 125th Street. A civilian saluted us as we arrived at Fire Station Engine 37, Ladder 40. We were greeted by more than a dozen firefighters mourning the loss of one of their leaders. Young, strong and handsome, Lenny noted they looked as if central casting had handpicked them.

Singing the "Star Spangled Banner" while holding our candles high, we looked right into their faces all the while. One by one, we filed past the firefighters, each of us making contact with every one of them. I cannot begin to express how I felt, looking into their eyes, shaking each of their hands, and having the opportunity to say "thank you." I realized something I pray I never forget: In a world of celebrity worship, these less lauded are the true heroes; underpaid, under-appreciated saviors, working fearlessly day in and day out.

Amidst all this craziness, tonight, right now, I am reminded that life is for living. And sharing. Paralyzed no more, mobilized by the bravery of others, I realize the best thing I can do for myself, my family and for my country (of which I have a whole new appreciation), is to move forward, be normal again; my "fuck you" to the terrorists.

There's so much to be thankful for. Tonight, my neighbors, our firefighters and the rescue workers have gifted me with that awareness and given me the courage to be less afraid.

Love to you all,
Andi Blakeman

The experience was transformative, both in the living and the writing. As I typed, my energy soared. A cathartic release, my tears flowed for the loss of the brave and the innocent, also for the sense of community I'd experienced. Perhaps at the core, I was also crying because, for the first time in years, I'd written something that wasn't bullshit, allowing myself to express my thoughts and feelings without sensor or fear of judgment.

When I finished, without allowing myself time to measure every word, or have Lenny edit, I hit "Send All." It went to everyone in our email address book, all five hundred sixty-three of them.

I felt really good about myself.

A few seconds later I got a message saying, "There was an error in transmission." I hit "Re-Send All." Again I received an error message. I tried once more. On a lark, I decided to check the "Sent" box. My email had gone out after all. Only a couple of addresses had failed. The internet was new terrain for me. It was 2001. My inexperience bit me on my proverbial ass— five hundred sixty-three people were going to wake up to find three copies of my story in their inbox.

SHIT!

I'd sent it to everyone at *Holloran Hour*—everyone except Holloran, but that didn't matter. He'd hear. They'd all be laughing about it, about me, around the water cooler, first thing Monday morning. SHIT!

Within the next couple of minutes, I sent a follow-up.

"Hello, yet again,

I just realized my three failed attempts to send out my exceedingly long email actually succeeded. Guess you've heard my story a couple of times too many.

So sorry!

Andi"

I lay awake the rest of the night going over it in my head, sick to my stomach. Lost was the magic of the experience and the telling of it. I was left with my petty embarrassment. At around 7:00 a.m., I walked gingerly to the computer and hit "Receive." The wheel turned for what seemed like forever. When it stopped, there were 23 messages. My stomach was flipping, imagining the ridicule I was about to be subjected to—deservedly so.

The first email I opened was from a comedian friend of Lenny's we'd known for years, a guy I really liked and knew to be fairly cynical. DJ related his experiences since the 11th and his renewed sense of patriotism. He signed off lovingly, with more sensitivity than I ever would've anticipated from him. He hadn't even mentioned the multitude of copies he'd received.

Bill Young, a creative writing professor from NYU, thanked me for the sentiment and the writing. A second email from him eased me further. "Just call it 'repetition for emphasis.'" I was so moved by his encouragement and even more so by his compassionate understanding.

Next came this from Bean, one of my oldest and closest friends. "Well, it was very moving the **FIRST** time. However, re-reading it twice—making it thrice in all—and trying to find the differences, was a cruel trick indeed in these troubled times."

I was bruised to the bone.

Then this from Allison, an out-of-town friend we hadn't seen in years: "Thanks for your moving story from New York. Five of my family members were in the area that morning and, although each managed to escape physically unharmed, they all saw horrible things that will not soon be forgotten. However, it's reassuring to know New York is rallying in the aftermath of this madness and providing comfort to all its citizens."

A thousand kind words couldn't offset the pain of one slight. I wrote back to Bean. "I find it so interesting that out of, now thirty-eight emails, you were the only person to focus on the error rather than the sentiment."

I sent it off. Something I never would have had the nerve to do before.

Back came, "You're absolutely right. I'm sorry you didn't take the first few words as seriously as they were meant before I was callous. I apologize sincerely again."

A straight-from-the-heart apology from Bean, with no jokes. The 11th had surely changed us all.

The responses continued for days, reconnecting me with old friends and forging more meaningful bonds with current acquaintances.

That email, and more importantly the responses it generated, afforded me a new confidence—earned or imagined. It wasn't particularly well written, but in that moment, it was the impetus I needed to get moving. My words had inspired thoughtful responses from others. For the first time in a long time, I felt like my old self, not just someone's wife or mother.

I put my newfound energy into a campaign to bring the Emmys to New York. I felt sure and unstoppable—nothing like a little positive reinforcement for a starving, desperate housewife. There were so many New Yorkers scheduled to attend the Emmys. I figured they would feel as I did about flying at that time, having to leave loved ones for a silly awards show. (Silly, did I say silly?) It seemed to make sense for them to be bi-coastal, as they were originally done, and easy enough to accomplish with satellite remotes.

First, I contacted someone at the Emmy Committee who was sympathetic. He referred me to the producer and the head of programming for the network. Through Lenny's various contacts, I managed to get emails to all the pertinent people. I was fairly surprised to find that I seemed to be the first to voice the idea. Assuming the other writers from *Holloran Hour* would be equally interested, I pressed on. Not even a nominee, merely the spouse of one, it was a ridiculously ballsy move.

As soon as I'd made the calls, Holloran issued an edict that award shows were now inappropriate and *Holloran Hour* would not be attending, regardless of where it was. Was it directed at me? Or was that simply narcissistic delusion? In reality, it was probably just a big relief to him. He had complete disdain for fanfare. Holloran had disdain for almost everything. So little in life seemed to give him pleasure.

My quest wasn't about the awards (that's my story and I'm sticking to it). It was about carrying on, living—albeit cautiously.

Perhaps my email about the vigil, combined with my attempt to get the Emmys bi-coastal (which, coincidentally or not, did happen that year), contributed to Lenny's demise. Both events involved sentiment and Holloran was not a fan of it. And perhaps he was not a fan of mine anymore, either.

Hey, I'm lovely, remember?

———— I want patience and I want it now ————

It was four weeks to the day after September 11th when Lenny got the call from Lenore. To be fair, in the days prior to his expulsion, Marty assigned Lenny a tedious clerical assignment, cataloguing all the monologue jokes. Lenny couldn't seem to get it right. He was distracted. Hell, everyone was distracted. In the aftermath of 9/11 there was a steady stream of terrorist activity, bomb threats and anthrax scares—and that was just in our building.

He was doing his best, but it just wasn't good enough for Marty. He'd hand in the assignment and Marty would throw it back at him. Lenny would take another pass at it, but Marty was never satisfied. He grew increasingly frustrated with Lenny's attempts. In retrospect, perhaps he'd set him up for failure as a way to finally get him out of there, or maybe he legitimately couldn't comprehend Lenny's ineptness with such a menial task. Regardless, Lenny was a joke writer, a funnyman and a brilliant editor; clerical work was not in his job description, nor his forte, and should not have caused his undoing—no matter how lame the attempt.

Lenny kept it together after he was... f... f... fuck it, fired. He had almost ninety days clean and sober. After suffering a short relapse after 9/11, he was back on track.

We were straight, unemployed and scared.

The State Department issued its second warning that they strongly suspected terrorist activity within the next few days; they didn't know when, they didn't know where. Everyone was terrified, but Lenny and I were so afraid for our own personal, selfish reasons, we couldn't even begin to focus on the big picture—lucky for us.

I don't know if I've ever felt so awake, and I hadn't slept, really slept, in weeks.

The country seemed to be collectively sitting in wait, almost disappointed that nothing was happening. We were like pumped bullies ready for a fight.

Lenny and I, our future so uncertain, were smacked into living in the here and now for the first time in years. There's got to be an upside to everything and maybe that was ours.

There was anthrax all over the city and Lenny was out of work. The DSL was down, our computer kept bombing and the cell phone display wasn't lighting. I had broken my tailbone when a bus driver slammed on his breaks, jolting me down full throttle onto a metal rail. *Was mercury retrograde or what?*

I wanted to feel something other than hopelessness and fear—joy, just for a few moments—genuine laughter; things I'd taken for granted for so long. Was I ever going to smile again without my brow furrowed? I prayed so.

The day after the axing, Jack had been unable to sleep. I was at my women's support group—a gentler way of saying group therapy (another couple of words I used to choke on). Lenny was having a hard time putting the kids to bed. After much crying, and Lenny trying every funny voice and trick to try to comfort him, he finally got Jack to confide his fear. "Daddy, are we going to be poor?"

Karma is karma, neh?

Almost five months after Lenny's termination from *Holloran Hour,* seventy-two days of complete sobriety, about sixty Marijuana Anonymous meetings, a dozen or so couples therapy sessions, and a handful of serious job opportunities later, we were just starting to feel somewhat normal. Not really normal-normal, because Lenny was working at home and around all the time, but we were laughing again. The knot wasn't perpetually in my stomach anymore, and the future was beginning to look hopeful. Maybe there was life after Rob Holloran, after all.

Lenny had been working more since he'd lost his gig than he'd ever worked in his life. He was punching up scripts, writing treatments, selling jokes to comics, going on pitch meetings, job interviews, on-camera auditions, having strategy sessions with agents and trips to LA—all leading to what we hoped would be the next steady thing.

Each night, when we said prayers with the kids, we added, "May Daddy get a wonderful job in New York City." LA was looming large. Television writing jobs were rare to begin with, and after September 11th there were even fewer, particularly in the Big Apple. People were scared and speculation was limited. Nobody was taking chances and no one was moving. The few jobs Lenny had in discussion were for projects further on down the road.

As much as we wanted Lenny to be working again, we also wanted him to be with us. There was no way I was going to move the kids in the middle of the school year on a "maybe."

Lenny put a few weeks' work into a new show being developed and was assured a position if it got picked up, but *if* is a dirty word in show business. There was one "sure thing," but they weren't hiring for a couple of months. Even though Lenny was at the top of a very short list, it was little comfort as we watched the money continue to pour out of our checkbook. And, all "sure things" are subject to change.

At his agent's suggestion, Lenny took a trip to LA in early January, when things were slow and network execs had some time for meetings. There wasn't a specific job, but it was a chance to meet with heads of development who were always looking for people with ideas, plus a couple of producers with projects in their early stages. He also had a scheduled meeting with Patrick O'Neal, producer of *On the Edge*. Lenny had written for *On the Edge* when it was a brand new cable show in New York, prior to its entry into network, and its subsequent move to LA. It competed with Rob Holloran, which seemed fitting. There wasn't an actual opening, but they were anticipating movement soon.

All of Lenny's meetings went well. In fact, every meeting he'd had since leaving Holloran yielded nothing but positive response.

Home he came. We continued to hope for a job in New York, while anxiously anticipating a call from LA.

A couple of weeks later, the offer came. The money people were due to call on Friday. Our first reaction was jubilation; at last an end to the unknown. Respectability, a lateral move. We could hold our heads up again. The only job of its kind to open up in the past four months, and Lenny had nailed it. I was so proud of him.

Los Angeles.

The kids were in Manhattan schools we loved. There were friends and family, our co-op, and my invalid mother-in-law, next door; with Lenny as her much needed overseer. How could we possibly just pick up and go on a one-cycle promise? Television writers, at least those in the comedy/variety end, are only contracted for thirteen weeks at a time. The producers are obligated to let you know of their intention after nine weeks, with the assumption that it gives you four weeks to find a new job. Having just been through five months of hell, I said, "HA!"

During Lenny's first cycle at *Holloran Hour* he was so thrilled to be pleasing his hero that he focused even more intently on the job at hand, leaving me to tick off the days and weeks on the calendar. When nine weeks came and went without a word, I breathed deeply for the first time. When I mentioned to Lenny at the start of the tenth week that he'd made it, we celebrated with a night out.

After three cycles, you're considered safe—a really dirty word. A natural cynic, I continued to count weeks for four years. Ironically, I got lax only a couple of cycles shy of Lenny's termination. Somehow, being unprepared, having it so out of mind, made the blow that much more devastating.

Here we were again, facing another thirteen-week contract, on a show with a history for controversy, and the host, Michael Paar, pissing off the sponsors left and right. There'd already been speculation that when his contract was up at the end of the year, he wouldn't be renewed. But it was also assumed that there'd always be a home for him somewhere in respectable TV land. Assumed? Talk about a dirty word.

We knew we had to roll with it. There was really no choice. Lenny would go to LA alone. If he got through his first couple of cycles, we'd join him in the Land of La.

Just as we were beginning to get kind of psyched about the benefits of sunny California, the very day Lenny's offer was set to go down, there was a news flash:

"Rob Holloran is being courted to jump networks and replace Michael Paar, which could possibly impact Ken Powers, as well."

Was Holloran going to fuck us again?

A week went by. The unofficial offer from *On the Edge* was taking its time becoming official. It suited us. We were trying to buy time to find out if the show was going to get cancelled and if there'd be any interested parties to pick it up, if it did.

As the media speculated on Holloran's decision (he was on vacation and unavailable), our future was once again in his hands. The wait, for us, was interminable.

It was a good time to feel out those other offers, but they were buying time as well. "Let us know when the offer is firm. Don't sign anything until we talk."

Nothing is anything, until it's something.

I struggled daily with my resentment, going over and over it in my mind—trying to figure out what Lenny could have done differently at *Holloran Hour*. How might I have contributed to his downfall? Was Marty to blame? And even if he was, what weapons had we provided him to use in our defeat? It's interesting how I include myself in the failure. I certainly could have been part of it. I was outspoken and opinioned, openly disagreeing on "Holloran policy."

Maybe they took down the man to get to the bitch behind him…

Blowhard narcissist.

—— They made him an offer we couldn't refuse ——

As the country held its collective breath waiting for Rob Holloran to determine the fate of the competing networks, the offer came from *On the Edge*. The money was less than half of what Lenny had been earning at *Holloran Hour*. The expense of maintaining two homes, plus the cost of airfare every couple of weeks, made it a no-brainer. No. Period. It wasn't about ego, just survival. Even Lenny's agent, who wanted him working almost as much as we did (both for the money, but mainly so we'd stop driving her insane), agreed it was a terrible offer, suggesting he turn it down. So he did. We dodged the bullet.

Holloran got everything he wanted. More money, more headlines than the war in Afghanistan, and he got to look like a hero, again. Staying put, he'd rankled Ken Powers, one of the most respected journalists in American history, who had the slot directly before *On the Edge*. Holloran looked magnanimous by publicly stating that Powers deserved to be the captain of his own fate; yet, in the same sentence, he moaned what a difficult decision it was. He used the media to manipulate the spin.

Once Lenny's offer was official, his agent tried to use it as leverage with the maybes still left hanging. It might have worked if the timing weren't so bad. A month or so too soon, no one would commit. Despite that, Lenny and I had a certain confidence. If *On the Edge* wanted him, so would one of the others. If we just waited them out, everything would fall into place. We were able to breathe again, with LA not so imminent.

About a week later *On the Edge* upped their initial offer substantially. Hurray for Lenny. But, damn them. LA. Lenny had been out of a regular job for over five months; the severance was running low, his self-esteem even lower. There was no choice. He had to take it.

After twelve years of everyday living, loving and fighting, we were about to be separated by 3,000 miles, for what could turn out to be a very long time. There'd be weekends home, but Lenny was not a good traveler. He wasn't one of those "roll with it" kind of guys; he liked routine and was obsessed with getting his sleep. This was not a man who could hop a plane on a whim, change time zones, spend two days with a needy wife and kids, and be back at work Monday morning raring to go.

How the fuck were we going to do it?

It was a week before Passover and the yearly pilgrimage of my family to our home. They came from near and far—Nevada, Florida, the Bronx and West 86th Street. Most Jews say, "Next year in Jerusalem." For my mishpokhe it was always, "Next year at Andi's." My brother was jetting in from Vegas to be our houseguest for a couple of days, followed by my father arriving from Lauderhill and spending a week. The guest room was our office, and for the last five months especially, it'd seen a lot of action. Lenny and I were constantly strategizing for time in there, and now we'd both be displaced for Lenny's last ten days at home. Not only did we have to deal with our own anxiety, we were also going to host two neurotic men who lived alone all year. When they came to us, they wanted to spend all their time in conversation with Lenny, while I cooked, cleaned and served. They were lonely, and this was their time to be with family.

I felt tremendous guilt and shame that I couldn't open my home without reservation or complaint. Why wasn't I more generous of spirit? Why couldn't I be selfless?

When my brother moved to my mom's—pre-arranged, to accommodate my father's arrival, it took all of two hours for her to engage in a knock-down, drag-out with Jeff, leaving him phoning me at 1:00 a.m., ranting hysterically. Cookie laced into him when he was at his most vulnerable (a guest in her house, with nowhere else to go), pointing up his cheapness for not getting a hotel, and working on his already damaged self-esteem with reckless abandon.

Even though Jeff might have needed some tough love, there's a difference between tough and mean. Cookie seemed unable to differentiate the two.

We agreed he'd come back to us for one night while he made calls to secure another crash pad for the duration of his trip.

Lenny was days away from leaving home, Dad was on his way in, and we were all about to spend our one yearly visit together. *Damn it, did she have to start?*

——— I'll never eat lunch with my mother again ———

The mere mention of Cookie used to give me a stomachache. She critiqued, criticized, advised, condescended, sneered, judged and disapproved of almost everything I did; slamming me to the wall, causing me to withdraw and put on my armor—the two of us forever at odds. She'd ask, I'd withhold. She'd get annoyed, I'd get angry. She tried desperately to control everything and everyone. Being that way myself, I found it utterly intolerable.

I'd never consider being disrespectful or impatient with anyone else's mother, but with Cookie, I was a horror show.

When Jack was born it was a huge help to have her close. It was also a constant pull at my self-esteem, with her unending suggestions of how I could feed, clothe and hold him better. She'd mention that he looked thin—Was I sure I had enough milk to feed him? *No, I'm not sure. I'm scared out of my fucking mind that I'm starving him to death!* I suffered the nursing mother's nightmare daily. I would have done so even without her constant reminders, but with them, I was not only a fake, I was also found-out. No matter how good or strong I felt before her arrival, within moments in her company, I reverted to a defensive, angry child.

Cookie and I were one big, ongoing confrontation. We couldn't be in the same room for more than a few moments without engaging in combat. Our battle stations were always the same, Cookie on offense, flinging slings and arrows at my faults and failures—usually with a smile—and me on defense, lamely dodging the bullets with inappropriate, futile yelling and screaming—trying to convince us both that she was wrong.

What was I going to do about the Seder? Mom and Jeff couldn't be together, that was clear. As he was only in town for a week, his needs took precedence. He never got to see the kids, and she regularly did, usually to my detriment.

I was secretly a tad grateful for the war she'd waged with Jeff. It provided respite for me—a Passover of peace. There was little joy with it though.

How could I be such a shitty daughter and feel good?

I couldn't. I didn't.

When she entered our apartment the next day, briskly and square-jawed, with Jeff following behind, slump-shouldered and beaten, I knew what I had to do, but I also knew I'd have to pick my moment. We were silent as we drove to Sydney's gymnastics class. We all pretended Sydney was the only one in the car and directed our conversation to her. After arriving at the gym, I immersed myself in the newspaper I'd already read that morning. Jeff and I pretended to casually chat as we watched his niece perform extraordinary feats of courage on the balance beam. Cookie was busy leafing through the latest *New York* magazine, seemingly oblivious to everything. When Jeff took a bathroom break, I seized the moment.

"Passover's not going to work," I said matter-of-factly, trying to remain calm.

Cookie snippily replied, "You know I just don't think I feel comfortable staying for dinner tonight, then."

Well, duh.

The silence screamed.

Cookie made no attempt to reach out to Jeff, the troubled son she saw once a year, for a week.

At dinner that night, Cookie gone, Jeff wanted to talk about it. The more he did, the angrier at Cookie I became. I couldn't eat, couldn't sleep; I couldn't focus on anything else.

It wasn't enough to be free of her for Seder. I needed to be emancipated.

Tuesday came. Heading to group therapy, I knew I'd be taking up space in the room that night. Guided by Fay, for almost two hours, those generous women tried to help me sort through my feelings, sharing their stories of family frustrations. We made a pact to all focus on a group conscience at 4:00 p.m. over the holiday, hoping it would help us feel supported when we were most vulnerable.

I left empowered, but still unsettled. I'd allowed Cookie to massacre almost every holiday for me. Her constant suggestions made me a nervous wreck. Not to mention that she'd been flat out rude to Maryann at Thanksgiving dinner, going out of her way to not offer her a ride home. She created such a scene, that a beautiful day ended with everyone carrying a horrendous memory home with their doggie bags.

Even though I was relieved that this holiday would not be tainted by her overpowering presence, it wasn't enough. Jeff was suffering horribly. He longed for the maternal love he'd always craved. He never recovered from his childhood hurt when Cookie allowed him to live with Jerry instead of with us. Even though Jeff demanded it, he felt betrayed that she didn't fight for him—sort of a catch-22 for old Cookie.

I picked up the phone. "I don't want to get into a whole lotta drama, but I've had enough. I'm done."

Cookie pressed me for reasons. As I began ticking them off, I was getting more and more upset—so much for my resolve to remain calm. As she battled to defend herself, I abruptly cut her short.

"Stop! I can't listen to you anymore. You've been hurtful for too long. I don't trust anything you say. Your moral code is not up to my standard."

Oops. Even I realized that was ridiculous.

Before I could amend it, she said, "I'm ashamed of you."

Without letting her finish her thought, I hung up. Relieved at first, within moments I couldn't stop the flood of tears. As much as logic allowed, I trusted that I was undeserving of her shame, yet felt deserving of her harsh comment for my own thoughtlessness.

I left a shaky message for Fay, knowing it was the first day of Passover and she'd be busy cooking for her family. By the time she called back a little while later, I was starting to feel a bit better. She was harried, but listened to my brief recount of the conversation. As I got to the kicker, I began to cry.

"I know it's wrong, I shouldn't let it hurt. I should feel free, but all I can think of is that 'I'm an embarrassment.' Even though I know it's not true, it hurts like hell. That's exactly the way I've allowed her to work me my whole life."

Fay offered some comfort but she was understandably distracted, not her usual helpful self. I hung up, still a bit of a mess.

A funny thing happened while cooking my soup. The more I immersed myself in the task at hand, the lighter I got. By the time Lenny came home with my dad and the kids, I was smiling and happy. When I let myself think about the "I'm ashamed of you" line I'd start to slip, so I just didn't go there. I was actually able to control my thoughts. Holy shit, maybe the therapy thing was working.

I explained to the children that Grandma wouldn't be coming for Passover because she and Uncle Jeff had had a disagreement (ending with a knock-out, in the first round). Even though it was hanging over all of our heads, I had the most relaxed and lovely Seder I could remember. As busy as I was doing the cooking, serving and cleaning, Maryann helped a lot as usual, and there was no pressure for me to do it "differently" or "better."

The night seemed to validate that what I'd done was right. Or, so I told myself.

The kids continued their relationship with Cookie. When she'd call, I'd put Jack on the phone. Through him, we'd arrange times for her to pick them up. When she came, I'd escort them down to the lobby. When they returned, she'd buzz and I'd go down for pickup. There was no contact between us. It was uncomfortable, but liberating. Her noise in my head continued, but not at the same heightened level. My life was more serene without Cookie in it.

It took some time and a whole lot of work for me to discover that my real problem was actually me.

TEN

PERSEVERANCE

───── Stepping stone(d) ─────

Off Lenny went to LA, land of the young, hungry and surgically enhanced. I wasn't worried about infidelity. *Interesting*.

I was worried about sobriety—and, for the first time, my own. I'd been so self-righteous since quitting, determined to set an example for Lenny, that I never questioned my own ability to stay straight. I'd flushed so much pot down the toilet when Lenny was struggling, I was confident my resolve would never falter, until I had to face life alone. I still had the kids, but I hadn't lived without Lenny in almost twelve years. Loneliness was what drove me to marijuana to begin with; would it lead me there again? Months before, I'd found a long forgotten stash in an old wooden box. Without hesitation, I dumped it. Would that still be my choice?

I'd only started to go to MA to help Lenny. Somewhere along the way it became my salvation. Committing to step up my Marijuana Anonymous meetings, I began doing service for the fellowship, hoping it would strengthen my resolve. Not that smoking was really an option, but I needed support and a sense of connection.

"Working the program," means doing the 12 Steps. The Steps are tools for living which provide acceptance, hope, faith and, when practiced diligently, a modicum of grace. Ideally, the work is done with a sponsor. A sponsor is a spiritual guide who has already worked the Steps, continues to practice the principles and, hopefully, has some emotional recovery. We're advised to pick someone who has what we want. In most cases, that means someone with some serenity, a really good "tool box" and, hopefully, some joy. In the best of circumstances, a sponsor is a non-judgmental sounding board who guides the way through the Steps and helps navigate a better life. They listen to struggles, offering suggestions and solutions. It's a sacred relationship. Since they're addicts too, it can be far from perfect. Most rise to the occasion and even if they can't live the principles themselves, they can usually dole out some wisdom.

I couldn't help but notice that pretty much everyone had a sponsor except me. I found the Step discussions in meetings boring and tedious. People sharing their personal stories is what kept me coming back. I started taking away little bits-o-genius—delicacies for the mind and spirit. There was no shame, just raw, brutal honesty. It seemed the wisest and most serene people in the program were the ones who continuously worked and lived the Steps. I began to consider that perhaps recovery was more than just abstaining from pot and coming to meetings.

Since I'd quit smoking, there'd been little pleasure. I was convinced I'd never feel pure happiness again. There were lots of laughs at almost every meeting. People were finding their joy. I wanted to find mine.

I brought to my home group (the meeting I most regularly attended and felt most comfortable at) what I thought was a unique practice. Completely free of marijuana, I still had an occasional social cocktail. I didn't speak of it at first; it seemed irrelevant. Drinking was not my problem.

Many addicts are cross-addicted and must stop everything or endanger their sobriety. For me, one had nothing to do with the other. I had very little tolerance for alcohol; it made me sleepy and nauseous. I rarely in my life had more than a drink or two; it just wasn't my thing. More importantly, I could never understand consuming precious calories getting drunk when I could smoke and then eat food instead. The choice between a joint and a bag of chips or two bourbon and waters was a no-brainer.

For my first eighteen months pot-free, I continued to drink—at first, not realizing that I wasn't supposed to. I was a marijuana addict, going to meetings to stay free of pot. What on earth did that have to do with a glass of wine? Not being an alcoholic, I didn't understand the point of stopping. It made me angry. Just because a bunch of pothead losers were cross-addicted to alcohol, why should I change my life?

But I wasn't happy. I wanted what they had, and what they had was some happiness. They were working the Steps, they were being of service, and they weren't drinking.

Control freak that I am, I wanted to co-chair my home group meeting. That required ninety-days of total sobriety. My once-in-a-while drinking was preventing that.

Lenny suggested I adopt a "don't ask, don't tell" attitude as long as I stayed true to my own sobriety which, for me, meant abstaining from pot. But the program encouraged rigorous honesty. I hadn't lied about anything since being "in the rooms" (well at least, not while in the rooms) and I didn't want to start. Grudgingly, I was also learning that omission could be as damaging as a straight-ahead untruth.

Eventually bringing up my drinking to a friend in the program, I was shocked to discover that he shared the same secret. Feeling a bit braver, I began speaking of it at meetings, hoping to change the expectation for those of us whose issues were different. As each meeting is autonomous, I fought to change the requirement for taking chips (little circular plastic disks rewarding various periods of abstinence, that we coveted as if made of gold), and succeeded at the Friday night meeting.

With the ambiguous guidelines (there are no rules in 12 Step programs, simply suggestions), it meant that those of us who didn't have a problem with alcohol could remain social drinkers. The difficulty came in the example it set for those who perhaps didn't have that luxury. Without the discipline of total abstinence, they might, somewhere along the line, falter and fall back.

Was I being self-serving?

Fuck, yeah.

I attended a women's AA meeting a couple of times with a few other marijuana addicts. Susie, who brought us, was an alcoholic as well as a pothead, and had given up everything. She belonged there. Alyssa, still hooked on pharmaceuticals, and me, with my once-in-a-while cocktail, did not.

They told us, "You can't be high and sober at the same time." I couldn't hear that then. I was brazen, open about my drinking, unwilling to face the bigger ramifications that it potentially imposed upon the group. How insane not to realize that my callous admission that I could have half a margarita and put it down was a brutal smack in the face to the alcoholic women who could not. It condescendingly pointed out that there was something wrong with them. The fact that I was a marijuana fiend did not soften the blow.

After our third visit, they changed the rules and made it a closed meeting for alcoholic women only. Alyssa and I took it very personally. We knew it was directed at us. At the time it hadn't dawned on me that they were right.

I was incensed. How dare they deny another addict recovery? It didn't occur to me that my drinking was a painful reminder of what they longed for, yet denied themselves. They had spent the better part of their lives trying to believe they could be social drinkers, finally accepting they could not. *Who the hell were we, and what were we doing at their meeting, anyway?*

At the AA Writing Sober meeting, I just listened and kept quiet, figuring I wasn't hurting anyone. Tagging along with Lenny, I was hoping to pick up some pointers. The speakers were amazing. Writers all, they spoke as they wrote, with humor, intelligence and fierce emotion. Sitting on the sidelines was making me crazy. I could only share if I hadn't had a drink in the last twenty-four hours. No big problem there. The difficulty was that there was no way I was going to identify myself as an alcoholic.

Alcoholic or not, when Lenny left for LA, I realized that having a drink would be using booze to ease the weight of my loneliness. Even though there was no apparent consequence, nary a cocktail did I allow myself. The meetings were kind of ruining me for bad behavior. Not that having a drink is bad, fancying myself an exception... yeah, that.

After a lifetime of feeling like an outsider, I wanted to feel "part of." Motivated by the growth and progress of others, out of respect to them, and ultimately to myself, I made the decision that playing by the suggested rules was more important than celebrating my uniqueness. Having already fought the Herculean battle (quitting pot), I dropped my guard and surrendered.

Did it have to be during Passover, after a last drink of... Manischewitz?

Since drinking meant little to me, it wasn't that big a hardship to give it up. An added deterrent was watching others imbibe. The first few sips I coveted like hell. As soon as things started getting sloppy, silly and stupid, I gratefully swigged my seltzer. But I knew my sobriety was going to require constant vigilance. If I let my program slip, my cocky addict arrogance was undoubtedly going to convince me that I'm not an alcoholic, so why not enjoy a salty ice-cube laden margarita? Perhaps later, a nice little joint to cap off the night? And then I'm off...

What sucked the most was restarting my day count. What the fuck? Give up eighteen months of pot-free living and go back to Day 1? Is that what they meant when they said, "We will be humbly restored to sanity?" Humble? "Not I," said this addict. Whenever I announced my new day count I qualified it with my *real* deal—the one that mattered. The pot one.

I began my hungry and desperate search for a sponsor much the same way I did for a boyfriend when I was sixteen. I jumped at the first inappropriate fellow I found. The relationship lasted about five minutes.

A couple of weeks later, feeling very vulnerable on a cold Sunday night, a few hours after Lenny boarded a plane to LA for another three-week stretch, I was asked to share my story at a meeting.

Being a child of divorce, Sunday night meant leaving my attentive, loving father and my starting-to-be-cool older brother, and returning to the lonely, depressing reality of me and Cookie—she in her room, me in mine.

During all of my years with Lenny, that sucky Sunday feeling had gone away. I was rarely alone—never lonely.

As soon as Lenny went to work in LA, my Sunday phobia returned, intensifying tremendously on the weekends he came home and then had to leave again. On this particular Sunday, as we said goodbye, yet again, the sadness began to creep up my body. I tried to focus on my evening plan.

As I told my story, heads nodding in empathetic understanding, I felt validated and comforted. I wrapped up my share by venting my frustration at trying to find an appropriate sponsor: a woman with solid clean time and a mastery of the 12 Steps. I expressed my envy that Lenny had found just such a guy. He was working with Justin, who had an amazingly tolerant attitude. He accepted that Lenny was still drinking, applauding his marijuana abstinence as if it were the only thing in the world that mattered. Having slipped numerous times, it really was all that mattered. Justin just wanted Lenny to get through the tough part. The first ninety days.

In *What to Expect When You're Expecting*, new mothers are warned that, post delivery, it takes three months to settle into a routine and begin to feel human again. With both Jack and Sydney that was certainly true—the first weeks a crazy mix of hormones, sleep deprivation and excitement. When beginning a new job, basically the same wisdom applies. Initially, unsure of where everything is and how to budget the day, it seems to take a few months to adjust to change. Bill W, founder of AA, assimilated that. It is suggested that addicts attend ninety meetings in their first ninety days of sobriety to give the program a chance to work. It seems that those who do have a much greater shot at sober success.

After my allotted twenty minutes, one by one, the potheads began to commiserate. Justin, Lenny's sponsor, was at the meeting. He offered to work with me until I found the right woman.

The next day, I began working the Steps. The first Step asked me to accept my powerlessness and admit that my life had become unmanageable. My reaction was, "I'm not powerless; I'm *powerful*. There's nothing I can't do if I set my mind to it. Unmanageable? Ha! My life is totally together and always has been. I'm ambitious, organized, hard working and dependable. I've managed very well, thank you."

Clarity and humility come later.

As Justin guided me, I came to understand that the only thing I was truly powerful over was my next right action. I can't control traffic, Jack eating with his fingers (no matter how hard I try), Cookie's constant questions, the weather or just about anything else. All I can control is what I choose to do about them.

When something pisses me off, the Steps offer tools to work through it. Therein lies the rub: asking for help.

I'd never admitted vulnerability. Not ever. I knew all the answers, always had the solutions. When I didn't, I convinced myself I could figure it out. I'd fake it and then berate myself in silence. I was determined to never let them see me sweat. All my life I'd bullshitted my way through. I look at Sydney, who never lets anything unknown get by her without clarification. She questions everything—a word she doesn't recognize, an idea she doesn't grasp. She demands answers and then she retains them. That was so not me.

There was nothing I couldn't handle. I learned the hard way that weakness led to humiliation. There was no coddling from Cookie. Any sensitivity was pounced upon. Early on, I learned to suppress, to mask, to deny.

As has been proven to me almost daily, everything happens when it does for a reason. As soon as I finished the First Step, Cookie called. She wanted to talk. It'd been months since the Passover debacle.

I wanted to run, but what little recovery I had wouldn't allow it. I realized the only way I could trust revisiting those feelings was if Fay was present. Cookie agreed.

She and I had gone to see Fay once before when we were having a particularly hard time resolving a conflict. It got us nowhere. Cookie was defensive, rude to Fay and condescending as hell. Cookie's willingness to give it another whack was huge. It made me feel loved.

I called Justin, desperate for help. Cookie was scary. "Working the Steps means living the Steps, and this is a perfect opportunity to 'try it on.'" Guiding me through the First Step in regard to Cookie, he pointed out that I am powerless over my mother, but I am powerful over my reactions to her.

"Stay on your side of the street. Speak in the first person, say how you feel. Resentments, anger and pointing a finger will accomplish nothing. Use honesty, openness and willingness. Treat her like a queen. She's your mother, the grandmother of your children; listen to her. Respect her."

How the hell was I gonna do that?

As I rode the train to Fay's, I read *Life with Hope* (MA's guide for recovery) on the crowded New York subway. Every other word is marijuana and, although I'd admitted my addiction and had even begun discussing it with close friends, I was not quite evolved enough to want to share it with strangers on the train. I continued to read, trying as best I could to hide the pages.

As I exited the subway, I repeated the Serenity Prayer over and over in my head, a holy mantra.

God, grant me the serenity to accept the things I cannot change,
The courage to change the things I can,
And the wisdom to know the difference.

For months I said those words, but they held no meaning for me. Like reciting the pledge of allegiance in grade school, it was total lip service. Not this day. This day, they quieted the noise in my head and gave me strength.

When I arrived at Fay's, Cookie was already in the waiting room, intently reading *The New York Times* and trying hard to look focused. I nervously yammered some gibberish, excusing myself to the safety of the restroom. I repeated my prayer once more for good luck, before going off to face my dragon. Thankfully by that time, Fay had opened the doors to her inner sanctum and in we went, my mother to the end of the couch, and I to the armchair, as far away from each other as possible. *Could it have felt any more awkward?*

Fay began by stating some ground rules: "Stay in the present; talk about feelings not actions; try not to project the other's feelings, stay with your own."

Ready. Set. Go.

Cookie took the lead. Every time she started to talk, Fay interrupted and gently tried to put her back on course. It would've been tough stuff for anyone; it was murder for Cookie.

On and on, she defended. I listened.

Serenely.

I couldn't remember the last time I'd been in a room with Cookie and felt calm.

After the session, Fay took me aside.

"Who *are* you and what did you do with Andi? You were amazing in there. You really listened. Your mind and heart were open, I could see it on your face."

As time marched on, I slowly and deliberately continued my way through the Steps—until I got to Step 8.

"We made a list of all persons we had harmed and became willing to make amends to them all."

Shit! How the fuck am I gonna do that?

My sponsor reminded me, it was merely a list. Okay, I can do that.

Then I hit Step 9.

"We made direct amends to such people wherever possible, except when to do so would injure them or others."

No way, Jose´.

I started with the easy ones.

Syd and Jack.

I crawled into bed with them one night.

"I'm sorry for yelling so much and not being more patient. I love you both so much."

They hugged me, reassured me, showered me in kisses and apologized to me for being a pain in the ass.

Piece of cake.

Next was Lenny. That was a bit harder. I wrote out a list of all the things I wished I'd done differently and ran it by my sponsor. After removing a few "yeah, buts," she gave me the go-ahead.

Lenny was gracious and forgiving.

Snap. Nothing to this.

When I got to my dad, I had to do it on the phone, as he was miles away in Florida.

"Dad, I'm a marijuana addict."

"You're a what?"

"I'm a marijuana addict," I repeated.

"A *what*?"

I wasn't sure if the connection was lousy, or if he just couldn't believe his ears.

"*A marijuana addict*," I screamed, grateful I was home alone, praying no one was lingering in the hallway.

After I read aloud my carefully constructed letter, he thanked me and cried. So did I.

Continuing down the list, I returned money that had found its way into my sneaky little hands, and an inexpensive little turquoise ring I had stolen from my childhood friend when I was twelve—less for the piece of jewelry than for the happy life it represented. I didn't have her phone number, merely an old address, so I sent it with a letter of amends and explanation. I was anxious to mail it and shared about it at a meeting. The following Friday, as was pre-arranged, a group of a dozen or so fellows walked with me to a mailbox and were there to hold me up after I dropped the package in.

No word came back.

A year later I got a note.

"Andi, I had the hardest time finding you. Your return address was unreadable. I thank you for your letter. I wish I would have known back then that you wanted the ring. I gladly would have given it to you. I told my daughter the story. She now wears the ring."

Holy fuck!

Empowered by the generosity of spirit bestowed upon me, I called my brother, Jeff. We'd been at odds dating back to my earliest memories, worsening in severity in adulthood. After reading my letter, detailing all I regretted, he said, "You're right. It was all your fault." Ouch.

Not imagining that it could get much worse than that, I went to see Cookie.

"Ma, I have something I want to read to you."

"Alright, g'head."

"Would you mind sitting down?"

Facing her, I took out my carefully constructed script.

My hands were sweaty, my voice shaky.

"Dear mom, I'm a marijuana addict."

"You are? I know you've smoked some pot, but an addict?"

"Yes, mom, I'm an addict. I'm just gonna read this and then you can ask me anything you want, okay?"

"Sure. Sure." She looked as nervous as I felt.

"I'm sorry for judging you, disrespecting you."

I'm not sure I needed to say any more. I think I had her at "I'm sorry." Two words I'm not sure I'd ever said.

As I continued through my three pages, accounting for every lie, theft and misdeed, I sobbed. Cookie, eyes watering, looked more vulnerable than I could ever remember seeing her.

When I got to the end of my missive, Cookie rose and came towards me. I stood awkwardly, unsure of what to do next. My mother threw her arms around me. It had only taken forty something years but, with my apology to her, a lifetime of anger, pain and resentment was neutralized.

Lastly, there was Ellie, my mother-in-law—what to do about her? After years of ignoring me by choice, she was now bedridden and uncommunicative, my long-held, deep-seated resentment towards her now a shameful memory. For Ellie, any woman who came between her and Lenny was a threat, and treated as such. I'd made the mistake of taking it personally.

With letter in hand, I went to her bedside to read my apology. She was more alert than I'd seen her in ages. She looked directly into my eyes as I sat down next to her. I held her gaze for maybe the first time ever and smiled. Her eyes responded. I began:

Dear Ellie,

It is unfortunately too late for me to make true peace with you. I regret not having gotten to this sooner.

I'm sorry for not trying harder with you, being more patient, understanding and accepting. I wanted you to be who I wanted you to be. I unfairly judged who you actually are.

As I read, I looked at her as much as possible. I'll be damned if she wasn't paying rapt attention over the drone of the television that played twenty-four hours a day. I fought back tears, embarrassed by my emotion, moved beyond description. I'd never felt even remotely connected to her before.

I thank you for taking such good care of Lenny, loving him and sacrificing so much for him. Your generosity has made our lives so much easier. I hope to better honor and respect you, and the decisions you made to make that possible.

I'm sorry that I didn't do more when I could have made your life more pleasant and that I was not more giving in every way. I admire your strength, humor, intelligence and devotion. I'm so sorry I failed to do better.

With love and respect,

Andi

A lone tear streamed down her cheek. I took her hand. Was it my imagination or did she give a gentle squeeze?

What a gift to apologize—and to mean it. They say the miracles come as we work the Ninth Step. Nothing could be more miraculous than the feelings that stayed with me after that experience. Was it too little too late? I pray not. I hope I gave Ellie some comfort that day. I know that I chipped away a small piece of my self-loathing by doing the right thing—which, I very slowly began learning, is so much more important than being right.

Being a marijuana addict is one of the luckiest things that has ever happened to me. That's some crazy-ass shit, but it's true.

A recipe for living

After every visit, the first few days after Lenny left for LA were excruciating. Even though we'd been driving each other insane over career stress and getting sober, once he left, things fell into a whole new perspective. "You don't know what you got till it's gone…"

Marijuana Anonymous meetings and the kids were my only saving grace. Knowing their needs were greater with Lenny gone, I recommitted myself to them. I began giving them the attention they deserved without the commotion of our marital woes. Lenny and I had been so busy trying to comfort ourselves (rather than each other) in the midst of our failing relationship—making half-assed attempts to heal it—but the therapy was getting us nowhere. We really weren't present when we were with the kids. We were both distracted—he on his computer, me on mine—trying to fill a hole that technology couldn't provide. We were anxious, and most of the time, arguing. Screaming is more like it.

Things slowly changed. The house was calm. When Lenny and I spoke on the phone, it was usually happy, loving and thoughtful. Not only were we seeing our relationship in a new light; so were the kids. I could tell they had a new sense of security through all the uncertainty. As young as they were, they knew mommy and daddy were laughing, being silly and loving each other. We started a countdown on the calendar until Lenny's next visit home. There were many daily phone calls and emails. The anticipation grew as we ticked off the days.

The night before the first visit, we were all so excited, none of us slept a wink. The following morning I dropped the kids off at school with the promise that daddy would see them soon. Racing back home, I sat on a bench in front of our apartment building, turning the pages of the newspaper, absorbing not a word. I kept looking down the path, glancing at my watch and fussing with my hair. After about twenty minutes, in the distance, I saw his familiar silhouette in the shadow of the sunlight.

Smiling shyly, I sauntered slowly towards him.

"Hey Homer, good to have you to home." It was one of my favorite lines from one of my favorite movies, *My Favorite Year.*

"Hi Marge. Come 'ere."

We hugged, tightly. Then we kissed—a real, wet, open-mouthed kiss. It'd been a long time since we'd shared one of those.

Since we'd quit smoking we'd become so disconnected emotionally and physically. I'd never had a relationship with a man, straight—not to be confused with a "straight man." I didn't know how to be intimate without pot. I'd made love sober over the years, but I'm not sure I was ever really able to relax and enjoy it without the great uninhibitor.

What was once so natural and effortless now seemed foreign and uncomfortable. When I stop eating carbs, I stop craving them. How sad that sex works the same way for me—sort of. In truth, I missed it a lot more than I did a damn baguette. It wasn't really the craving that dissipated; it was the confidence to see it through. We were still best friends, but just as the daily stresses had taken their toll on our intimacy, it was going to take work to get it back. We hadn't put in the effort. We whined about it, or at least I did, but we didn't do all the little things it takes to keep the fire burning for the long haul. It was easier, less uncomfortable, to not. We'd talked about it and thought about it but, basically, we'd been on one l-o-n-g hiatus.

What the fuck is up with marriage? Romance killer.

Fay had given us tasks to try to help us get back on track—play backgammon naked—stare into each other's eyes for five timed minutes— act as if. We tried each once. It felt weird, so we stopped.

Sydney's class was in the pre-school playground just behind me. Lenny snuck up to the fence, calling out to her. She ran to him as if in slow motion, her little legs taking so long to cover ground. As she neared the fence, Lenny reached over and swooped her up in his arms. As they hugged, I felt the tears stream down my cheeks. After kissing her a dozen kisses, he placed Syd back over the fence. I was afraid she'd go nuts, but she skipped off happily to her friends.

He was exhausted, having worked a twelve-hour day prior to traveling through the night. After an hour or so of catching up, he collapsed in bed for some much needed sleep. I probably should have joined him, having not slept myself, but I had so much caffeine in me, sleep would've been impossible. I also knew that if I lay there with him, I'd never let him sleep—yapping (sadly), rather than seducing. Not for lack of wanting, just uncertainty at how to initiate it.

I kept sneaking into the bedroom, so grateful to see his naked body wrapped beneath the sheets. I was determined not to let this opportunity to love slip away.

Hours passed. As scheduled, Mary picked up Sydney from school and brought her home. Unable to wait a moment longer—we only had forty-eight hours, I sent Sydney in to wake him. Tip-toeing quietly to the side of the bed, she flushed as she touched his shoulder and whispered, "Daaaaaddy." Lenny stirred ever so slightly. "Daaaaaady…" He pulled the sheet away from his face, opening his eyes. A broad smile flashed across his face as Lenny hoisted her onto the bed, turned her upside down and tickled her into a frenzy.

"Marge, would you mind making me a cup a coffee? I feel like a train hit me. Maybe that'll help."

"Sure, Homer. Want a bagel?"

"That'd be great," he said, with a wink.

We were flirting—over Jew food and children.

I sent Mary to fetch Jack, knowing that he'd be disappointed that it wasn't Lenny, but hoping his excitement would forgive all.

Hearing the elevator door open and footsteps running down the hall, Lenny opened the door, lifted Jack, and flew him over his head. Lowering him to eye level, they drank each other in as tears flooded their eyes.

It all started to make sense: the divine purpose. Lenny and I had been living in hell. Even with Fay and Marijuana Anonymous, we'd been unable to get over ourselves and get back to loving. We owed Holloran and Marty everything. If Lenny had stayed at *Holloran Hour,* we would've continued our descent into resentful disconnect. The isolation Lenny endured at that job was never going to go away. Having to run everything through Marty, where once he'd had a direct line to Holloran, battered his self-esteem. It was a bad situation that would've kept getting worse. The only thing that would've improved was the money. Lenny had been due for a huge bump the following September. Try as I might, I couldn't seem to let go of my resentment of that friggin' loss.

———— Revert to saved ————

Mercury had been retrograde for almost a month, a time when extra caution is advised with communication and all things mechanical. Astrologers specifically advise to back up computer files.

An avid paranoid, I usually copied files daily; feeling rather smug, I defied logic and ignored good sense. Now that I had a 12 Step program, I figured I had divine protection and began to slack.

Following my post 9/11 email and Lenny's expulsion, I began to write. At first it was a rant, railing against Holloran. I needed to get it out. I showed it to Lenny and he encouraged me to continue. About fifteen pages in, it started to feel like a book.

Prior to a recent visit to LA, I'd copied what was now my manuscript to disk, making another copy upon arriving back in New York ten days later. That was seven weeks and thirty-six pages ago.

As I sat down at the computer on my two hundred and fourth straight day of writing, I decided to change the title page. While erasing the current cover, unbeknownst to me, I also erased the entire volume. I had dozens of versions, but while trying to correct my mistake, I also copied over the most recent backup. I knew Mercury was retrograde. For weeks I'd meant to back up onto disc and had even tried, that very day but, as luck (or Mercury) would have it, my disc drive was on the fritz.

A woman had come to the writers' meeting two hundred and five days prior. Ramona had been a homeless, toothless junkie. Losing everything and everyone, she ended up in jail, penniless. Less than three years later, she sat before us having just returned from the opening of her first film, an independent feature based on her life. *How the hell did she manage that?*

"AA and five minutes a day."

Ramona had made a deal with herself to commit to that. She stuck to it, making regular meetings, working the Steps and five minutes of daily writing, which often turned into twenty, sometimes an hour, or maybe three. Knowing all she'd committed to was five minutes made it manageable. She never felt overwhelmed.

I'd heard similar advice before, to break the work down into small increments. I just wasn't ready to listen. On that day, to that woman, I was. So inspired by her miraculous turnaround, I figured if she could do it, just maybe…

Surely I could manage five minutes a day. But, I knew from years of dieting, that unless I had to step on the scale in front of a witness, I wouldn't be successful. I needed to be accountable. On my own I was still a cheater, even if now I was only cheating myself.

Lori, another regular at Writing Sober, generously agreed for me to email her daily with my time and page count, which, on many days, ended up being not much more than the bare minimum. But, no matter what, I managed to write at least five minutes every day, without exception. The only thing driving me some days was the "daily weigh-in."

I spewed my day count at Writing Sober for the addicts on 96th Street. Each week as the alcoholics announced their sober days, I did as well. Only mine had nothing to do with substances or abstinence. Actually, it did. Had I still been using, I never would have put together a week of daily writing. Sobriety was enabling me to finally see a dream through to its end. "Hi, I'm Andi. Today I have one hundred sixty-seven days of writing every day." It always elicited titters of laughter, some days, applause. Paying it forward, I hoped to share Ramona's methodology.

In the two years prior to my post-9/11 epiphany, I'd written fewer than fifty pages. Often, I skipped days, weeks and, occasionally, even months. Within my first year of daily accountability, I'd almost tripled my output.

The discipline inspired me in other areas of my life as well. I began keeping a day count for dieting and exercising but, inevitably, got only a few days in before I was back to square one.

There was nothing altruistic about my writing day count. It was purely ego driven, but as a housewife and mother who hadn't earned a penny in years, it was a way for me to feel viable. If along the way it helped motivate someone else, I'm sure it was offset by those who thought I was a self-righteous asshole.

Here it was, a damn Mercury retrograde, and I'd let my guard down and was careless.

In a panic, things went from bad to worse. There was still an opportunity to "Revert to Saved," which would've undone my change. Instead, not realizing my entire manuscript was gone, I hit "Save." I did the same thing to the older version. As I began working, returning to page 338, where I'd left off the day before, I noticed that my side scrollbar was large. *Way* too big for a document with hundreds of pages. Still not getting it, I figured I must be doing something wrong. Again and again I tried, finally going back to the previous version and trying there. My hands started shaking; I broke out in a cold sweat as I realized I'd lost seven weeks of writing. Thirty-six pages. Many of them were shit, but damn!

Our computer guy came with no guarantee of rescuing the lost words. Seven hours later he aborted the mission. The pages were gone, lost forever in the cyber abyss. Eventually, I realized with clarity and certainty, that I was meant to begin those pages anew. They sucked. Finally admitting it was a relief, although it took time and a shitload of meetings to get to that. There's a reason for everything. Turn, turn, turn…

I'm obsessed with horoscopes and all the crap that goes with them. My mission is always to prove them wrong when they're negative and try to help them along when they're positive. When I was doing stand-up and promoting, I asked a psychic if I'd be successful. She said, "It could happen, but not in the Page Six kind of way." That wasn't what I wanted to hear. Within two months of that reading, I was on Page Six. A few weeks later, I was on it again. I wasn't famous or anything—but I wasn't going to let the negativity win.

Likewise, when Mercury's retrograde, I defy it to harm me. It's cautionary information I use to be on my guard but, sometimes, I just tell it to go fuck off.

That psychic also said that something amazing would happen to me, something huge. "Not winning the lottery, or anything like that. A once in a lifetime dream come true." For twenty-five years I've waited. "Was that it?" Nah, not big enough. "This?" I choose to believe that one day it'll happen, whatever the hell "it" is, and I'll know without a shadow of a doubt that that was it, because it'll be so damn BIG.

A pony?

Ch-ch-ch-ch-ch-ch-ch-changes

When *On the Edge* folded, we rolled the dice, rented a beautifully furnished townhouse in Sherman Oaks and figured, if nothing else, it'd be a great place to spend a two-month family summer vacation if work didn't happen. Gratefully, it did. Within a week, Lenny landed a new gig.

Working for the show that followed *Holloran Hour* (which, ironically, was owned by Holloran's production company) spoke well for Lenny and for Holloran. *Really Late* was hosted by a smug Holloran wannabe that I just didn't get. But, a job is a job. Coming off the heels of *Holloran Hour* and *On the Edge*, it wasn't a lateral move. There'd be no Emmy nominations. In fact, Lenny was warned that it was a minus credit. The show had no critical acclaim, no cred in the business. But it was a union gig, and that was worth its weight in benefits gold.

While Lenny was at work, the kids and I were prisoners in the immediate community. I didn't drive. I had my license, but I used it for identification only.

When I was sixteen, I hung out occasionally with Josh, twenty-six, a head shop owner from the Bronx, who kept the bong filled and the patchouli oil flowing. I liked him a lot, and sometimes "that way," but he was too old and too serious. He kind of scared me.

Just after buying a brand new Datsun, he invited me out for a spin. It was a spectacular spring Saturday. We passed a joint, sang along to the Dead and left the city behind. Two hours or so later, on a remote country road, he pulled over.

Opening his car door, he said, "Andi, you drive."

"What're you crazy? I just got my permit! I haven't even started driver's ed yet."

"Don't worry. I take full responsibility."

I'd never been behind the wheel and here we were on a winding mountain road. I was stoned, therefore brave, so when he prodded again I said, "What the hell." Nervous at the outset, I quickly relaxed. Soon, I had my left arm hanging out the window, drunk with the new independence. The sun was shining, the radio blaring Sly and the Family Stone. All was right with the world.

About a half hour later, Josh leaned over to check the gas gauge as we passed a Texaco.

"Pull in here."

A bit tentative, I was trying to decide which pump to pull into. I was nervous, knowing I was going to have to judge the space carefully for the first time. Josh decided to take matters into his own hands. Without a word, he grabbed the wheel. My foot was still on the gas. I'd already begun pulling into the left island; Josh was taking us to the right. There wasn't time to adjust. I slammed on the brakes, but it was too late. We nicked the cement divider pole. Shocked silent, at first all I felt was panic. How could I pay for the damage? Would all the money I'd earned working weekends at Ski Stuff for the past year cover it? And, if it didn't, where would I get the rest? Josh hadn't bothered with collision insurance on his brand new car.

Just as I was remembering his assurance that I wouldn't be responsible, he was forgetting.

Head in hands, he began moaning, "My first new car."

He may have been ten years older than I, but, in that moment, he was behaving more like a ten-year-old whose favorite toy was broken.

"I'm sorry, Josh."

"Ohhhhhhhhhhhhhh," was all he could manage.

With that he got out to look. On the right bumper was a big old dent. Josh resumed moaning.

I began to get angry. He was acting like it was my fault, alone—like he had no hand in it. I didn't ask to drive his car. He insisted. He said he'd take full responsibility; only he sure wasn't acting like it. He offered no words of comfort. No words at all—he just moaned.

"Josh, I'll pay for it," I said, knowing full well that he should be footing the bill. I was just a kid. He was a businessman. So what if his business was selling hookahs in the Bronx?

Getting back behind the wheel, he mumbled, "We'll split it."

I could tell he thought he was being more than fair. I thought he was being a dick.

We drove the two hours back to the city in silence, him brooding about his misfortune, me furious at mine. As he pulled in front of my apartment building, we awkwardly said goodbye. He didn't get out of the car. God forbid he should have to see that dent again. "Let me know what I owe," I said, closing the door behind me.

A few hours later, I was lying in bed listening to Jefferson Airplane's Surrealistic Pillow, contemplating my fate. I hadn't asked for this burden, yet here it was upon me. It was his fault. He said he'd be responsible. He shouldn't have taken the wheel out of my hands. I may have been unsure of myself, but I'd have driven so slowly and carefully, I wouldn't have hit anything if he'd have just let me be.

The phone rang.

"Hello?"

"Hi, Andi."

It was Josh, sounding even more morose than when he left.

Not in the mood for a further guilt trip, I asked, pissily, "What's up?"

"I'm in the hospital."

"WHAT?"

Had I driven him so crazy he'd checked himself him? Was the accident so traumatic that he'd had a heart attack? He was only twenty-six.

"After I left you, I was so upset and distracted that I had an accident. My car's totaled. I'm in the emergency room."

"Are you okay?"

"They're about to release me. I just have a few scrapes and bruises.

Thank goodness he couldn't see me. Exhaling, I unwittingly... smiled.

There'd be nothing for me to pay for now. The dent on the right fender was bupkis compared to the smashed-in front-end that brought the headlights in to meet the dashboard.

But pay I did. I developed a crippling driving phobia that day and was reminded that trust is for fools. And, karma is friggin' karma.

Still a slave to my fear, I basically hadn't driven in almost twenty-five years. Forced to get a car senior year in college in small-town Tucson, in time I learned to relax and even enjoy it. Do anything every single day and a certain comfort will most assuredly set in. Moving back to New York City a year and a half later, I immediately sold my car (*drive in Manhattan?*) and didn't get behind the wheel again, except for that one day on the film set. I was panicked. Frank and Lenny both had standard transmissions, so I used that as my excuse but, in truth, it was fear keeping me down.

Fortunately, there was a beautiful pool at our place in Sherman Oaks, where we made fast friends with a lovely Croatian family with two boys close in age to Jack and Syd. We spent most of the summer soaking in the pool with them. On the days they were busy, the kids were bored and cranky and so was I. It was a brutally hot summer and the half-mile walk to the mall was often unbearable. I tried to sweeten the pot with ice cream and See's Candy, but that got old really quick.

Evenings were our saving grace. Lenny got home in time for dinner. I occasionally cooked, but we usually ate out, needing the change of scene. After dinner, we'd go for a drive up Mulholland. It became a nightly ritual we all looked forward to. Having lived apart for months, we savored every moment of family time.

As the end of summer neared, the kids and I readied to return home and helped Lenny settle into a lovely apartment in Studio City that would better serve his solitary needs. The rent was a fraction of the townhouse; it had a gym and a very well populated pool, filled with people in the business who would, hopefully, alleviate some of the loneliness Lenny was sure to feel.

Returning to Manhattan, unsure of the future, we held hope that a gig in New York would open up. Moving west was not an option. The kids were in great schools, and I'd already committed to chairing the annual school fundraiser.

On a two-week hiatus, Lenny helped us transition back into New York life. When he left in early September, we were all brokenhearted. Silently, I cursed Holloran and Marty for dividing our family, blaming them for our fate. My resentments were the poisons I was feeding myself, to kill them.

During the next ten months, Lenny came home during every hiatus, and we traveled to LA whenever school allowed. It was no way to live. No way to be married. No way to be a parent, or a child. All the cell minutes and emails in the world couldn't make up for the missed school plays and lost Little League games or the empty place in my bed.

Lenny wasn't comfortable at *Really Late* as he was never quite sure where he stood. For the most part, the staff was a boys' club of young up-and-comers who drank beer and shot hoops. Lenny did his work and went home. Office politics, as always, eluded him.

West Coast Marijuana Anonymous fellows kept him connected and social. His close college chum, David, had moved out to LA years earlier, plus a lot of his comedy road buddies had relocated, hoping for their big break. Lenny acclimated to his new life.

We decided we'd keep the status quo and wait for the right gig at the right time, before doing a 180. Besides, there was Lenny's mom, Ellie. Even though she had an amazing caretaker, and Lenny's dad, Samuel, visited her regularly, we were still handling her finances and dealing with things as they came up. There was also our apartment, which we owned, and had no intention of selling or subletting. We'd put a lot of money and love into renovating it when Jack was born. It was the only home the kids knew. Having spent my youth always being the new kid in town, I was determined it would be different for them.

By spring, things took a dive south at *Really Late*. Pressure mounted, and Lenny felt certain he was on double secret probation. He began to sweat his fourth thirteen-week pickup. Determined to guarantee it, he threw himself into his work with renewed resolve. It consumed his every thought. One fateful day, while working through a joke in his head, he didn't pay careful enough attention as he made a left turn. Out of nowhere, a car came speeding towards him, running the yellow light, plowing into the passenger doors.

In New York, on the phone with a friend in LA, I got a call waiting beep. It was 11:30 a.m. my time, 8:30 a.m. in LA. At first, all I heard were moans.

Then slow, slurred, "M a r g e..."

The panic set in immediately. "Homer, what is it? What's wrong?"

"A c c i d e n t."

"When? Are you OK?"

"J u s t n o w... d o n' t k n o w... c a n 't m o v e. C a r' s g o n e."

"Gone?"

"T o t a l e d ."

Before I could formulate my next sentence, an unfamiliar voice was on the line.

"Hello. This is Officer Thomas. To whom am I speaking?"

"Andi Blakeman. Is my husband alright?"

"We don't know yet."

"WHAT DO YOU MEAN YOU DON'T KNOW YET?" I screamed, filled with a whole new level of terror.

"We just arrived. So far, Mr. Blakeman has not been moved."

"Not *been* moved? You mean he can't move himself?"

"We don't know yet."

"YOU DON'T KNOW YET? Is everything still attached? Can't you ask him to move his limbs?"

"He's in shock, ma'am."

That makes two of us.

Three thousand miles away and I had no idea if Lenny was simply stunned, or gravely injured. Officer Thomas was not very reassuring.

Suddenly, I remembered Ilene on hold.

"Officer, I'm in New York. I have a friend on the other line in LA. Where are you exactly? Maybe she could meet you?"

"I think you should have her meet us at St. Luke's. The ambulance just arrived."

I hadn't known Ilene long. She'd been an interim sponsor for me the previous summer. When you're in a 12 Step program, you're never alone, never without resources. The bond is solid as a rock.

As soon as I brought Ilene up to speed she was, without hesitation, off to the hospital. I breathed for the first time.

Clicking back, "Officer Thomas, are you still there?"

"Good news, Mrs. Blakeman. He seems to be able to move everything. He's standing now."

The tears exploded.

"Can he talk to me?"

Still sounding shaky, but a lot less scary, "Marge…"

"Homer, I can't believe I'm not there. I'm so sorry. Are you okay?"

"I need to get to work."

"Are you NUTS? Two minutes ago you couldn't move. You have to go to the hospital. Ilene's on her way. She promised to stay with you and be my surrogate."

Lenny barely knew Ilene. I could tell he wasn't comfortable.

"Do you want me to call David?"

"Yeah. Thanks, Margie."

An hour later, Ilene called me from the hospital. Checking in with the doctors, she asked all the right questions, even held Lenny's hand. David got there a little later and I could hear a bit of calm settle into Lenny's voice.

Gratefully, other than a concussion, a bunch of bruises and soreness everywhere, Lenny had come away without any permanent damage. Judging from the photos of the car, it was a freakin' miracle. Ordered to bed rest for the remainder of the week, as much as Lenny tried to protest, his body could not join the fight.

The next day, the show sent an intern with food, magazines and treats. David and Ilene saw him through the worst of it.

My frustration at not being there, of not being able to offer physical comfort and support was palpable. With that was also a sense of relief. I didn't have to deal. When I hung up the phone my life was normal. I didn't have to look at the wreckage. My day went on as scheduled. Tip-off number one that we had lived apart too long.

By the time summer rolled around again, everyone was not so subtly suggesting that it was time for the kids and me to relocate. We ached to do just that. Lenny had left *Really Late* to become head writer/producer on a new show starring cult legend Bill Plant. Bill was a young, wild and crazy guy. I'd never really gotten him. Maybe I was just too darn old. I was shocked when Lenny interviewed for the gig and came back incredibly impressed. It seemed Bill was smart, very funny and had a great vision for the show.

The kids and I arrived a week into the run. Receiving rave reviews and good ratings, it looked like they had a hot one on their hands. Lenny hadn't served as head writer since *Holloran Hour* and, this time, he got to do so without interference. He thrived. I'd never seen him so happy professionally. There was plenty of aggravation to be sure. Work is work. But Bill respected and trusted Lenny; it was a much-needed elixir.

Lenny handpicked a small staff of writers he respected and enjoyed. Treating them as such, they, in turn, killed themselves to please him. Lenny's true gift is serving in that capacity. A great "room runner," he's never fired anyone, and no one's ever quit under his charge. He laughs freely, validates good ideas, and is a master conductor of the funny, always able to orchestrate to a perfect crescendo. Bring him a good idea and he'll turn it into a great one. His capacity to sculpt the perfect joke, bit or piece, is masterful.

As unlikely a match as forty-something Lenny and barely-thirty Bill were, it worked. It looked liked a sure thing, especially when the critics began comparing it to early Carson *Tonight Shows*. Everyone was certain it was the real deal, destined to last for the long haul.

Wanting to believe, I was ready for a change. Burnt out on fundraising, having spent four months a year doing it 24/7 for the kids' school, I'd had enough. Sleeping alone had completely lost its charm. The initial trade-off of not having to share the remote, turn off the light, open the window, put down the toilet seat and pick up the socks, had lost its import. Snoring, bed hogging, blanket robbing and all, I wanted Lenny every night. That's what I'd signed on for and what we'd shared for over eleven years before this insane arrangement began.

We were all snuggled into Lenny's Studio City, one bedroom apartment, grateful to have almost three months together ahead of us.

Lenny was working crazy hours trying to get the show off the ground. We visited the set often. There was a tremendous air of optimism, with no dissenters. Everyone was pressing us to make the move. It was a magical summer, but my gut nagged, nonetheless.

At the beginning of September, the show welcomed its first hiatus. The four of us headed back to New York the next morning—a Saturday. Lenny had a two-week break. We welcomed the opportunity to have a week of family time before the kids started school, and then a much-needed week for Lenny and me to focus on each other. Even though we knew we were about to face another separation, we also felt, for the first time, that there was an end in sight. As soon as the show got its inevitable renewal, we'd commence charting our course.

On Monday morning, at barely 9:00 a.m., the phone rang. Stella, Lenny's agent was very matter-of-fact.

"The show's been dropped. Effective immediately."

"What show?" I asked, completely not getting it.

"Bill Plant's show." Silence.

"Come on Stella, they still have a month left on their run. Bill just had a planning dinner with the head of the network. *At the guy's house.*"

"They've decided the show's too expensive to produce and not right for their demographic."

I continued to defend it. What was I doing? Stella hadn't pulled the plug. It was a huge loss for Buckley-Shapiro as well. The agency produced the show, and both Bill and Lenny were their clients. They were taking a big hit from this too—but they had other balls in the air. For Lenny and Bill, it was their only ball.

The old, all too familiar knot began rapidly taking shape in my stomach. Uncertain, I made my way to the bedroom, not sure if I should wake Lenny or let him get one last good night's sleep.

I just couldn't suffer it alone another minute.

"Homer. Homer."

"Huh? What? What time is it?"

"It's 9:15."

"Can't you let me sleep?"

"I have something I need to tell you."

The urgency in my voice had impact. He sat up.

"Stella just called."

"So?"

"The shows been cancelled, effective immediately."

"What? *What*?"

As with me, he'd never considered that anything could bring Bill Plant down.

"I had the same reaction."

Without contracts, the majority of the staff were screwed. Lenny would at least get four weeks severance. His salary was at an all-time high. The money would go a long way, but still. What now?

I crawled into bed and we held each other. This shit never got easier.

Stella began making calls. The new fall shows were already under way. In variety, openings happen sporadically, with hundreds of writers scrambling for the few available slots. Lenny's credits pretty much guaranteed him an interview. He'd gotten almost every gig he'd gone up for. Why was I so panicked?

Because we had two kids, two apartments, a ton of bills and no idea what the future held.

As the pressure and fear began to take shape for Lenny, it was time for the old, "How about you?" (Meaning me.) "If you got out there, you'd make a fortune in no time. You're smart, capable and hard working."

That panicked me even more. I hadn't been out in the work force since pre-pregnancy. Now in my late forties, my recent credits were "mommy" and "fundraiser." My resume, yellowed with age, listed a slew of rock 'n' roll venues, not exactly bait for my current situation. I could barely stay up until midnight anymore, let alone begin my night then. That time was gone anyway. Rock clubs no longer enjoyed the frenzy of the '80s and early '90s.

With no idea how to apply those skills to the world as it now was, I did what any terrified housewife would do. I defended my position to the death.

"Who'll take care of the kids? We only have Mary twenty hours a week. What if they get sick? By the time I buy the clothes, pay Mary full time, we'll be left with almost nothing. I'll be in an entry-level position wherever I go. I'll be lucky to come out ahead."

"No matter what you do you'll climb the corporate ladder in no time."

"Corporate ladder? I don't want anywhere near that."

Having promoted the talents of others for years, I wanted to focus on myself. From managing rockers and Lenny, to raising kids and money for their schools, it hadn't been about my own aspirations since my stand-up days. When I was pregnant with Syd, I gave it a first whack.

As my tummy swelled with new life, my whole being seemed focused on creation. Writers Boot Camp guaranteed that if I came in with a premise line, did all of the assignments, put in at least four to six hours a day, in six weeks I'd leave with the completed first draft of a screenplay. Seemed impossible, but I had little to lose other than the dough. A full-time wife and mommy for the prior five years, my creativity had been limited to Halloween costumes, themes for school fundraising events, an occasional contribution to the funny and my very s l o w moving manuscript.

With focused passion that I'd forgotten I possessed, I threw myself into the task. My instructor was enthusiastic and supportive. When, at about three weeks in, we began to read aloud from our work, I became increasingly encouraged by the reaction of my fellow writers. They laughed in all the right places, gasped when appropriate, and gave me hearty applause upon conclusion. (It was an easy crowd. We were all vulnerable, seeking acceptance.)

At the end of the six weeks, we sent our first drafts to an unknown professional, who would evaluate our work. The teacher who'd been guiding us would have no part in the process. They believed an impartial opinion would be of more value. Made sense.

Cocky, confident, I was sure I'd written a witty, moving little screenplay that any actress in her right mind would be thrilled to star in. They say write what you know. I centered my film on the romantic triangle of Lenny, Barry and me. The story always garnered laughs and rapt attention when I told it.

Lenny took a pass before I turned it in. Other than pointing out a couple of flaws and adding a few killer jokes, he left it intact. Never one to appease where writing was concerned, with his approval, I was sure I had a winner.

After sending my screenplay off, I was busy casting the film in my head when, about a month later, I got the letter.

"Dear Andi, Please call Lance at your convenience to discuss your screenplay."

At my convenience? I raced to the phone, anxious for the certain praise and approval I had coming.

"Lance please."

"This is he."

"Hi, Lance. This is Andi Blakeman. I received a letter today that you've read my screenplay."

"Um, okay, let me get my notes."

I could hear him shuffling through papers, lots of papers. Lance had obviously read quite a few screenplays.

"Okay, here we are. Right. To be honest Andi, I didn't think your depiction of the comedy world was very accurate. I do a little stand-up myself and I didn't feel you had a realistic vision of that world."

"Huh?" Was about all I could manage. I was in shock. Down to my solar plexus.

He continued, "I also felt that the three main characters were too 'written.' I didn't believe they were real people."

He now had my total attention. "Lance, how old are you?"

"Twenty-four, why?"

"And how much stand-up have you done?"

"I've been doing it for about six months or so."

"Lance, my husband was the head writer of *Holloran Hour*; I've been in the comedy world for the better part of ten years. Two of the three main characters you describe as 'unreal' are my husband and me."

I don't remember anything he had to say after that. It didn't matter. The fact that he was twenty-four, knew nothing of life or comedy made no difference. I had empowered him to be the teller of truth. I took the piece of shit, threw it in the bottom of my drawer and never looked at it again.

With no intended purpose to return to LA, Lenny stayed with us. It was the first time he'd gotten to sleep in his own bed, for more than a week or so, in almost two years.

The LA apartment was sparsely decorated and inexpensively furnished. A futon served as bed and sofa. A cheap table and chairs doubled for eating and working. He had an old 19-inch television, a boom box for a stereo, and a fake tree to warm the place up. There was no coffee table, easy chair or DVD player. None of it terrible, except that Lenny had worked his ass off for years and had acquired some nice things, but they were all 3,000 miles away from him. Now he was finally getting the chance to enjoy them, but he couldn't.

At first we tried to savor our precious time together. We went to movies, restaurants, and lots of 12 Step meetings. Together, we picked up the kids from school, shopped for groceries and went on weekend excursions to visit friends.

Very quickly, the panic set in. There were a few interviews, but not many. Once again, it was fall, not the best time to be looking for a job in television.

After a few weeks, Lenny got a gig in New York. We were gratefully relieved, even though it was a short-term commitment. A pilot for a cable network, it would keep Lenny home and employed for the next thirteen weeks, with the possibility of a pickup.

We decided to keep the LA apartment for the time being. Most of the work would undoubtedly be out there.

For the next year, Lenny job-hopped from one project to another, thirteen weeks here, another thirteen there. With the exception of about two months all told, the work was all in New York. In May, when Lenny landed a gig as head writer for an American version of a successful British variety show, his third New York job in a row, he decided the time had come to give up the place in LA. The kids and I couldn't have been happier.

For Lenny it was a mixed blessing. Although happy to be home with the kids and me, his folks, and his Bose surround sound stereo, he genuinely missed LA. Having lived in this Manhattan enclave for forty years, he was ready for the change that the West Coast provided. His closest childhood friend, our upstairs neighbor, had recently moved to Maine. I could tell Lenny no longer felt he belonged in New York. California sunshine, swimming, driving and the creative guys he'd been working with, called to him. Living in New York full time was no longer part of his plan.

— When a door closes, a window opens. Don't jump. —

Just prior to beginning the gig in New York, Lenny took a two-week job in LA, using the time to pack up his West Coast apartment. Donating the futon to charity (mostly so he wouldn't have to deal with moving it), he stored the smaller stuff with different friends around town. He had the car shipped east, but he was determined that one day he'd return.

No sooner had he gotten home and started the new job when it fell apart. Within two days he was released. The host, gay and British, without ever meeting Lenny, hired him and fired him, deciding he wanted one of his own. Gay? British? Gay and British? *Who the fuck knows?*

Was tumult to be our destiny? I cursed Holloran and Marty, blaming them for this uncertainty we were forced to continue living with. If only...

Lenny's thirteen-week contract was paid in full and we were good, at least for the summer. He spent the time putting projects together, developing a few show ideas and taking meetings.

By fall, another short-term project with potential presented itself in LA, just before we had to dip into our savings. Lenny was hired as head writer for a pilot for a new cable comedy show. The executive producer, Zack, had worked on *Holloran Hour* for many years before Lenny had come on board, and was another of its casualties. Lenny had always wanted to work with Zack. They'd met a few times and had exchanged war stories.

Wrapped in high hopes, there was a lot of optimism that this show had a genuine shot to get picked up, as long as the pilot scored.

Smack in the middle of the two-month commitment, a call came about a possible opening at *Nightlight,* starring Lou Randa. This was the call we'd waited years for.

I'd always felt that Lenny and Randa were of like sensibilities. Aside from having the same astrological sign, they shared a similar dark side. Lou hid his from mainstream America, but we remembered it well from his early stand-up. No one could churn out jokes like Lenny, and Randa did more of them nightly than anyone on TV.

Since he was already in LA, renting a room in a guesthouse, Lenny extended his stay and did a trial week with Randa. There were three positions available—in itself a miracle, as the show was known to have little to no turnover. Things were changing over there. Even those with years of seniority were being reevaluated. Two of the positions were for entry-level staff writers. Neither Lenny's experience nor his salary quote made him eligible for those. There was also a position for a senior field producer, which meant producing short films.

Not his area of expertise, having had only limited experience producing pieces for Bill Plant, Lenny wrote up dozens of ideas while still working on the pilot, awaiting the days prior to his weeklong trial.

In mid October, the live pilot showcased, exceeding all expectations. The buzz was strong that it was sure to be picked up. As head writer, Lenny was given a great deal of the credit. It was a terrific high note on which to be leaving. Fairly certain he'd be offered the return position, he had a self-assuredness walking into *Nightlight*. As usual, he thrived under pressure. Lenny showed up at Randa confident and ready to prove himself.

His trial week there went well. Lenny got a number of jokes on; one was even picked up by the morning shows and appeared in the next day's newspapers. Placing a "drop-in" (a thirty second, filmed, "visual" joke Randa did nightly in his monologue), he also scored approval for a field piece, and added his spin to an ongoing regular segment, that killed.

Another writer, Mike Armour, was trying out the same week as Lenny. They'd worked together previously. As much as they were friends, the competition was fierce. The show had already tried out about a dozen writers, and there were still a couple more to go.

Lenny arrived home cautiously optimistic. We were fairly confident that no matter what, he would land one of the LA gigs. I was certain it was going to be Randa.

A couple of days later, while grocery shopping with Cookie, my cell phone rang. "I just got a call from Mike. Randa offered him a writing job."

My stomach sank.

"Mike doesn't have your credits or your salary quote; this has nothing to do with the position you're up for."

I said the words, but my stomach ached.

The next few weeks were a nightmare. As the days passed and the call didn't come, Lenny became convinced he'd lost his opportunity. Midway through the third week, Renee called. Renee was Lenny's LA agent. She was green, but eager. She was also good friends with Bob, *Nightlight's* head writer.

"Bob wants you to come out and do a second week."

It wasn't exactly the call we were hoping for, but it was a shot. If given the chance, I was convinced Lenny could prove himself. He'd gotten almost every gig he'd ever been up for. There was no reason to believe this would be different. Yet the fact that Mike was already on staff was a bit unnerving.

Lenny's second trial week went even better than his first. He shot his first remote and a lot of his stuff made it to air. When the week ended, a couple more pieces he'd written were scheduled to be shot the following week, in his absence. He left having done what he set out to do.

Lenny caught an earlier flight than planned, hoping to get home in time to tuck in Syd and Jack. He needn't have bothered. Due to crappy weather, his plane was delayed. Lenny's dad, Samuel, always early, had come to pick him up. He'd been circling the terminal for almost two hours in the rain by the time Lenny made it to the curb. I reached him just as he got in the car.

"Homer, thank heavens you finally landed. You must be exhausted. How's your dad?"

"Falling asleep."

"What?"

"Relax, I'm driving."

"How're you?"

"Tired and not in the mood for this shit. It's fucking pouring, and there's so much traffic I can't get out of the damn airport. Oh, I got the job."

"You *what?*"

"Renee got the call before I landed."

"Congratulations, Homer. You earned it!"

"Thanks, Marge. Do you believe this?"

"It's great!"

"The money's shit. Guild minimum."

"You can't take that."

"Renee's insisting."

"What's she—nuts?"

"She said there are hundreds of qualified writers willing to do it for this."

"But, they want you. If you don't value yourself, why should they?"

Perhaps, if we didn't have kids, if I was working, if Lenny didn't have the experience and the credits, then maybe? The show was in the power position, but my guts were screaming, "Hold your ground."

We had to factor in Lenny taking another place in LA, starting all over with furniture, shipping the car cross country yet again, and, living apart—the most devastating price of all. If we didn't at least come out ahead financially, it hardly seemed worth it. *Or was it?*

It was the most prestigious institution in variety TV, dating back to the '50s, garnering more and more strength over the years. Cookie, Si, Jerry and Samuel's favorite show, it was a parent thrilling gig. But when we crunched the numbers, it was going to cost Lenny money to work there.

Jumping into manager mode, I started to bark figures and reasons, getting Lenny all worked up. We were both yelling—mad now, building a case. In an instant, there on the rain-slicked Grand Central Parkway, Lenny forgot he was driving. A nanosecond later he drove over one of those triangular highway dividers. Hard.

BAM. Flat tire. It was 9:30 p.m., pouring rain and freezing cold. Poor Samuel just wanted to be home in his warm bed, and Lenny was missing yet another opportunity to kiss his kids goodnight.

They managed to drive to a gas station a few miles away. Unfortunately, gas was all they did; flat tires were not on their menu. Calling AAA, Samuel was told, because of the weather, it would be a while. *A while? What did that mean?* Try as he might to replace the tire himself, it was pouring and Samuel's trunk was not equipped for the job.

I wanted Lenny home. He wanted to be home. There was something to celebrate. *Or was there?*

As the minutes turned into hours, many phone calls later, Lenny's frustration mounted. Thank goodness his dad was with him. He remained unruffled, soothing Lenny each time his anxiety soared.

At 12:30 am, Lenny arrived home—drenched, cold, hungry, tired, pissed off and pleased. It was nice to be wanted. Period. After three years, this was his greatest validation since Holloran's rejection. We allowed ourselves a few minutes of triumphant joy.

The next morning he called Stella. Stella had been Lenny's senior agent since the beginning. A bigwig at Buckley-Shapiro, Stella handled major celebrities, the huge moneymakers. Because her kids went to school with ours and we had a social connection, she'd always been willing to do more than just oversee Lenny's career. Whenever there was a negotiation, she rolled up her sleeves and jumped in there.

I had a friendly rapport with Stella and I think I had her respect. I volunteered for our kids' schools, spearheading the gala, which raised hundreds of thousands of dollars over the years, something her career did not allow her to do. I suppose she felt indebted in some small way. My fragile ego needed that, as a non-earning mom. It by no means made us equals in my mind, but it enabled me to at least approach her.

To our relief, Stella was in total agreement that Lenny should hold out for more money.

There was a bit of phone tag back and forth for the remainder of the day. By evening the deal was done. Stella had gotten every dollar and benefit possible from the network moneyman.

Since *Nightlight* was an institution, stable, even in showbizland, we decided the kids and I would make the move west as soon as school let out in June. We knew it was a huge risk. Lenny was stretching his wings, stepping into a new arena. Even though we were both confident that he was up to the challenge, there were so many variables. There was a large, competitive, writing staff vying for limited screen time, and a little added caveat. Bob, the head writer, made clear, in no uncertain terms, that he wasn't convinced Lenny had what he needed. Lenny was basically on probation. Bob had wanted someone with extensive field experience. The problem was that the field guys he found weren't the best or the funniest writers. He decided to gamble on Lenny, and hope that his writing and his funny would translate to polished produced pieces.

Bob encouraged Lenny to not make any drastic changes until he was sure things would work out. *When would that be exactly?* He was relieved the kids and I were remaining in New York, for the time being.

Starting a new job is scary enough. Add to that working in one of the most established institutions in the annals of television, going through its first major staff overhaul in years, and cap it off knowing you're going in as a big fat *maybe*. Sounded like a recipe for...

Failure was not an option.

No sooner had Lenny made his deal, when it was announced that Lou Randa would be stepping down when his contract expired, three-plus years down the line. Shades of *On the Edge* all over again. Only three and a half years is three and a half years—a lifetime in network television. If Lenny got to ride that wave, it was quite all right with us. All we really had to think about at that moment was getting past the first renewal.

Because television writers work in thirteen-week cycles, there's little to no time to get comfortable. If you're lucky enough to get a renewal, you're back on trial for the next cycle. Perhaps there's a week or two, post-notice, to breathe. Most contracts stipulate that, by the ninth or tenth week, "no news is good news." If you get *the visit* or *the call,* hopefully you're sitting down. Say goodnight, Gracie. Lenny had ten weeks to reinvent himself and win Bob over.

Piece a cake.

The Great Whodini

I was abruptly awakened at 2:20 a.m. on Halloween morning.

"Marge... Marge... hey Margie, I need you to look at something."

"Look at something? *What are you crazy?* I'm sleeping. Or at least I was."

The room was dark, save for the light streaming in from our bathroom around the corner. I could barely make out Lenny's silhouette. As my vision adjusted, I saw he was holding a towel around his leg, almost exactly at my eye level, which was comfortably flat on my pillow. Not yet grasping the situation, yet sensing there was some cause for concern, I softened.

"What's up?"

"Tell me if you think I need to go to the hospital..."

He now had my total attention. "What happened? What's wrong?"

"Come into the bathroom, I'll show you."

Lenny was hobbling as he led the way. His back was to me as he opened the towel. He turned. There was blood everywhere. As my eyes adjusted to the light, I saw that Lenny's leg just above the knee was slashed, his skin and guts splayed open like a vagina.

"Oh my God. Oh my God. You need an ambulance, NOW!"

"Calm down, Marge, its no big deal. It doesn't even hurt."

"No big deal?" I shrieked, running down the hall towards the phone.

The next thing I knew I was grabbing the wall, rising from the floor, my head hurt and my lip was throbbing. There was no time for me to worry about me. But, I was feeling really shaky, the room was spinning and I was sweating. So, I ran to get an ice pack for the back of my neck before grabbing the phone. *Man, did I feel faint.* I have no tolerance for blood or vomit that's not my own.

"How'd it happen?" it finally dawned on me to ask.

"I was trying to cut the bottom out of a sneaker for a levitation trick. The box cutter slipped and I sort of cut my leg instead."

"Sorta? Whadda you, shitting me? Fuck that damn magic already."

Lenny had always had an interest in magic and did a number of tricks proficiently. A year earlier, a very successful magician had approached him about writing a pilot for a television show as a vehicle for his unique talents. Lenny and I went to catch his live act and were blown away. We worked on the pitch together and came up with what we felt was a great concept. The show never happened, but Lenny's passion for magic went through the roof. He became obsessed with it, spending every possible moment buying trick after trick and then learning and performing them for anyone who was game. He couldn't get enough. Magic was the only distraction that worked. It took Lenny's mind off his career lulls, filling the void, giving him focus and purpose. I'm sure my own insanity over our uncertain future, which manifested in nagging control mania, nicely fed his addiction. He spent hours online, on the Magic Café, conversing with other magicians, instead of with me, or the kids. It was not only eating his time, but lots of money too. I resented the hell out of it.

I called 911.

"My husband cut himself with a knife. His leg is sliced open and he's bleeding like crazy! Please hurry!"

Hanging up, I made my way to the scene of the crime. There, in the den was Lenny's old sneaker, now quite bottomless, with hundreds of tiny pieces of rubber strewn everywhere. The box cutter sitting on yesterday's *New York Post* was covered in blood.

"Asshole." I muttered.

Moments later, the police arrived.

"Please step outside, ma'am."

I was in my PJs, which consisted of a pair of old flannel bottoms and a t-shirt, which age had softened like silk and made almost completely transparent. I really didn't want to go out in the hallway with the police, and have the neighbors privy to our business or my tits.

"Won't you come in?" I asked sweetly. Police scare me.

"In a moment, ma'am. We'd like to talk to you first."

"But my husband's bleeding to death!"

Lenny, holding the bloody box cutter, ambled past me towards the kitchen.

"Hello, officers. Thanks for coming so quickly," he said, smiling.

"This will only take a moment, ma'am. Please step outside."

Shooting Lenny the look of death, I obeyed.

"What happened, ma'am?"

"Well, my husband's a magician. He was cutting out the bottom of his sneaker for a trick, and he kinda sliced open his leg."

"When the incident occurred, were you fighting?"

"No, I was sleeping. Catch us another time," I said with a giggle.

They weren't laughing. They were staring at my face and neck. I licked my lip and thought I tasted...

"Can you tell us why you're holding an ice pack?"

"When I saw the wound I felt faint." I said, sensing I had something to fear.

"Why are you bleeding from the mouth, ma'am?"

I touched my wet, throbbing lip, and blood dripped down my finger. Recalling grabbing the wall, it suddenly hit me. "I think I might have passed out a little on my way to the phone and hit my lip on a picture frame on my way up."

Just saying this line, made me realize it sounded... like a line.

Then it hit me. They thought Lenny had punched me in the face and I'd stabbed him in the leg. I began to laugh. If only I would've thought to show them the floor of the den with all the little pieces of rubber and Lenny's "magic" sneaker.

Although clearly not completely satisfied, they allowed me to re-enter my home. Lenny was down on his hands and knees, cleaning blood off the kitchen floor.

"What are you doing?" I shrieked, before remembering I was under scrutiny.

Even injured, Lenny's OCD and my perpetual intolerance were right at the fore.

One of the officers took Lenny into the living room to get his side of the story while the other stayed with me, giving me the once-over about twenty times.

I guess they decided we were telling the truth because, when the paramedics finally arrived, the cops allowed them to tend to Lenny and ready him for his trip to the ER.

Jack and Syd, now awake, were wondering why there was so much commotion in the middle of night. Thankfully, Lenny's leg was already bandaged and a lot less scary.

Always the sensitive soul, Jack started to cry.

"It's nothing. Maybe a few stitches—don't worry," Lenny assured, giving him a hug.

As the policemen and paramedics made their way with Lenny to the elevator, he was already doing tricks—taking great delight in entertaining his receptive new audience.

"Next Halloween, you might wanna try carving a pumpkin," cracked one of the paramedics.

"So that's why they call it trick or treat," countered his partner.

"Everyone's a fuckin' comedian," I muttered, as I closed the door. Making my way to the kids room, I was relieved to see that Jack and Syd were already asleep.

I should be too, I thought, as I approached my bedroom. I noticed Lenny's bloody pajamas lying on the floor in the doorway. Scooping them up, I dropped them in the hamper, and grabbed what was left of his sneakers from the middle of the room.

"Pig!" I said, heading to the hall closet.

Passing the den, I caught sight of the gazillion little sneaker bits still littering the floor. I couldn't stop myself. I began picking them up, piece by piece. My hands full of dead sneaker, I lumbered to the kitchen and dropped my wad in the garbage. I opened the pantry and grabbed a Hefty cinch sack and a jumbo bag of Cheetos. Wrestling with the cellophane, I couldn't budge the damn thing. I reached into the sink, snatched up the bloody box cutter, ripped into the cheese puffs, shoved a handful in my mouth, shook my head and muttered, "Fuckin' addict."

ELEVEN

AWARENESS

———— Be careful what you fish for ————

Back in LA, Lenny embarked upon his new job with passion, vigor and anxiety. The two new staff writers were being eased in, supported and shown the ropes. He was on his own. Dazzle or die.

Lenny asked Bob where he should focus.

"Drop-ins (very short filmed pieces), desk bits (done by the host in the studio) and field pieces (short films done on location)."

Lenny first targeted drop-ins, as they seemed to be a baby step to where he needed to end up. Initially, a tremendous challenge, he wasn't having much luck. Before long, he found his groove and was scoring regularly.

He continued to try to do everything else, as well. When Bob sent around writing assignments, Lenny worked tirelessly, producing almost tenfold what the other writers were turning in. Almost nightly, he was successful.

Before long, he got his share of desk bits on. Field pieces continued to elude him. Lenny was expected to cultivate his own talent pool, but Bill Plant, his number one resource, was already working with Bob as correspondent for the show. Even though Bill trusted Lenny more than anyone, he was off limits to him. Each field producer had his own talent. There was no sharing, no matter what. Lenny suggested a number of comics he knew. Bob kiboshed each one.

Continuing to write his ass off and get a lot of shorter stuff on the air, it culminated in a series of mock commercials utilizing Randa. They were dark, not at all the usual tone of Randa's pieces. The spots were very controversial. The producers were skeptical. Then they aired.

They were a huge success and became a running gag for a number of weeks. Randa loved doing them and the reaction was surprisingly strong, especially from the cynical staff.

Thirteen-week contracts, the bane of my existence, are like lying on a bed of nails. By the ninth week, the discomfort is palpable. Nervous and fearful during periods of non-productivity, even when scoring nightly, there's no guarantee. As exciting and glamorous as show business is, the perks come at a high price. There's no security, ever. Writers have held gigs for twenty-plus years, but there are also those who have lost them after as much time. Some come and go after a cycle or two. It's hell on the talent, and their families. When writers land a dream gig, they usually can barely believe their luck. Aware of the potential lack of longevity, they often try to stay low key, inevitably shouting it from the rooftops, as payback for the shame and heartache of the last cancelled show, the previous dropped contract.

Thick skin does not suffice. One needs armor.

On the first day of Lenny's tenth week, Bob called Renee.

"Lenny's doing a fine job. He's being renewed."

A few days later he had Lenny into his office and told him the same thing.

Encouraged by Bob's words, Lenny took it as an endorsement that he could make life fit into his plans rather than the other way around. He wanted to write. He wanted to do running pieces with Randa. He wanted to focus on the sure things.

Feeling strengthened following his pickup, the accompanying "good job," and the nightly successes, I decided it was time to consider making a plan. We'd been bi-coastal for three out of the past four years. Enough was enough.

Into his second cycle, Lenny continued to gather strength, getting nightly short pieces on. Randa seemed to really enjoy working on them, and encouraged Lenny to come up with more.

Things looked good.

Lost in transition

I'm fine as long as I know what's in front of me. As soon as that shifts, I'm fucked. Change is a bitch I don't welcome.

How many cycles before we should commit and move to LA?

After years of bi-coastal daydreams, the thought of leaving New York produced sheer terror. I stopped sleeping, stopped eating. Showbiz, coupled with sobriety is not for the fainthearted.

You can't move a family 3,000 miles without doing your homework. Where would we live and, more importantly, how would I find the right schools? After devoting myself to that quest since becoming a parent, I wasn't about to drop the ball. A public school advocate, private schools weren't an option, as much for me as for the kids. There is little to no diversity. Ooh baby, it's a white world, a rich, white world, with no basis in reality. Even if money were no object, I didn't want the kids segregated from the mainstream, where we belonged. Although we'd enjoyed a few prosperous years, we were middle class folk at our core and would always be so. I never felt smart enough, rich enough or good enough around "those people." Even though Lenny, a Dalton graduate, was one of "them," he'd been on full scholarship and got booted out senior year for some teenage shenanigans. His outlaw status humanized him in my eyes.

Studio City felt comfortable, urban and kind of like home. But the middle schools were awful. There was no way that would work.

I'd need a car. I'd have to drive. *Drive?*

Upheaval. Unknown. Uncertainty. The "Us" were getting to me. Leaving a bedridden mother-in-law, helpful mom, our home, our stuff, incredible public schools (that were so hard-fought to get into), our friends and family, not to mention New York itself... *shit!*

In a city of asphalt and cement buildings, our windows overlooked trees, flowers and playgrounds. Friends and neighbors gathered in the plaza out front, whenever the weather allowed, as our children played. It was the best of all possible worlds.

From NYC to the Land of La; a place where the car you drive and the body you have mean more than your spirit or your soul.

On the upside, it meant we'd be together, living daily life as a family. That trumped everything.

California had always been my dream. First sidetracked by my high school sweetheart, who'd had other designs. We compromised on

Tucson. As was so often the case, my decisions revolved around the man in my life.

After college, again coveting LA, and an acting career, my then boyfriend Frank, soon to be husband, dreamed of New York. Somehow, I got talked into returning, even though it was not at all what I wanted for myself.

Twenty-five years later, the dream was about to become a reality. Only now it was my nightmare.

Packing up the kids and heading west was to be no easy task. There was Lenny's mom to consider. Now completely dependent upon her caretaker Maria, what would happen to Ellie if something happened to Maria? Aside from paying the bills and doing her banking, everything else I did was basically handled via telephone. Would a few miles affect that? With Citibank also in LA, it seemed doable. But there was the psychological factor. Even though my father-in-law, Samuel, still visited Ellie regularly and handled the shopping that Maria couldn't manage, he was eighty-four. What if something happened to him?

Chilled by the icy silence when I mentioned we were "looking," when she said goodnight, I could hear the panic in Maria's voice. I'd assumed she knew the move was imminent. You know what they say about ass-u-ming.

How long can a husband and wife sleep not just in separate beds, but states? When is it enough that the only touch felt is that of the telephone against your cheek? Who was going to show Jack how to improve his batting stance and help Sydney learn to ride a two-wheeler? How many Little League games, school plays and award ceremonies can a daddy miss? What is the consolation for months of goodnight kisses blown from 3,000 miles away?

Despite the painful realities of leaving, there was no choice. We had to do it. We all ached for each other. It was just so damn scary.

Years ago, when my marriage to Frank was becoming increasingly intolerable, he told me he would wait me out. He knew how badly I wanted my stuff: the apartment I'd found, my step-mother's paintings, the antique furniture I'd had since my youth, wedding presents, knickknacks. Almost everything we'd amassed had come from my clan. He threatened he'd make it so unpleasant for me, I'd eventually leave it all behind to be free. He made good on his threat. It took time, but eventually the pain of staying did become bigger than the fear of leaving. Here I was again.

So many things terrified me: driving, roller coasters, rats and the unknown.

Taking risks was never my strong suit. My horoscope was screaming that my courage would be rewarded with a happier life. But change always freaked me out. Try as I might, I almost always ended up doing the same old thing, the same old way. Yet when I dared to stray, to take a risk, I was almost always delighted with the result.

Life was overwhelming. My dad's undiagnosed Alzheimer's was kicking into a higher gear. Unaware that his memory was compromised, he didn't remember forgetting. Totally unwilling to seek help of any kind, every time a crisis arose he promised to see a neurologist, but quickly changed his mind when the moment passed. Knowing he'd one day follow Ellie's path without resources or support was terrifying. Jerry lived in Florida, hundreds of miles from family, with no close friendships to speak of. He'd made no provision for his future, refusing to discuss it. What little money he had was rapidly diminishing. He'd even sold his burial plot for some quick cash. His drastic mood swings made him difficult before the Alzheimer's set in. Combined with it, he was a scary handful.

By early April, the time to hesitate was through. If the kids and I didn't make the move during the summer, if we waited for another renewal, it'd be too late to make a cross country move before school restarted. We'd have to wait another year, and then some.

We knew no matter what, we had to keep our New York apartment. Like the Three Bears, we didn't want anybody sleeping in our beds. Subletting wasn't an option, because then we couldn't come back when we wanted to. This was showbiz. No matter how good things seemed to be going at any job, there was always the threat of cancellation and expulsion. What if, on a dime, life changed again as it had so many times before? What if the next job was in New York? As hard as it was to find the right place in LA, in New York, it's next to impossible.

There was also Ellie, who might require our presence, Cookie who desired it, and all of us needing to maintain the connection.

Besides, Lenny had grown up in the Gardens. It was the only home Jack, Syd and I, for that matter, had ever known. I'd never spent even half as many years in one place before. Our next-to-Harlem haven was home.

During spring break, Jack, Syd and I flew West. Matt, a cool and patient realtor, took us around to check out schools, houses and neighborhoods.

The market was insane—at an all-time high. Houses that were, a year before, totally unreasonable were now completely out of reach. When we crunched the numbers with a mortgage broker we realized there was no way we could swing buying in LA and eat. Maybe we wouldn't starve, but it seemed crazy to be working a big gig and live poor.

Renting made sense for a multitude of reasons. We'd not be tied in to a neighborhood, a school or an investment. What if the kids hated it? What if the house didn't end up feeling right? And, God forbid, what if the gig didn't last? If we hated LA, we could cut and run. If the job didn't pan out over the long haul, we wouldn't have a messy extraction. *Right?*

Lenny was anxious about our moving. He still felt insecure about his job, yet understood we couldn't spend another year apart. The kids couldn't handle it anymore and I could no longer bear witness to their unhappiness. So, Lenny agreed to white-knuckle us coming, as I white-knuckled leaving.

Two more times that spring, I went out to LA and Matt and I searched for the ideal rental. With the best public schools top priority, coupled with a minimal commute for Lenny (after three years apart we wanted to maximize family time), we settled on a sleepy town just north of the city limits.

We needed to commit to the lease by June 6th, the school board needed to know where we'd be living by the tenth, but Lenny wouldn't know about his third renewal until the twentieth. Boy, did my stomach ache.

Dead Man Writing

Moving across the street is a pain in the ass. Moving across the country is a freakin' nightmare—especially with one foot remaining behind. You can pull a muscle. What to take? What to leave? Other than clothes, some toys, books and a few personal items, we left our New York apartment almost completely intact. I believe I left whatever sanity I possessed there, as well.

I was so single-minded of purpose in my desire to do right by the kids that I didn't really consider what a shocking transition it would be for me. I'd like to say I settled into my new life gracefully. I'd *like* to say.

With my driving phobia in high gear, I had to face getting a car, immediately. I was terrified to drive, get lost, pump gas, break down, have an accident—lions and tigers and bears, oh my! I had yet to drive on an LA freeway; the mere thought of it scared the shit out of me. Living in the foothills ensured that I would not be able to avoid them for long.

I'd been checking Craigslist constantly for weeks, making loads of calls and looking at countless unsuitable messes. Lenny wanted me to get something cheap in case we had to cut and run. I wanted a sunroof, and a new enough car to ensure that I wouldn't be breaking down. Opting to lease after a futile, exhaustive search, it was the safest move—a new car, almost nothing down and reasonable monthly payments. The downside was the three-year commitment. Lenny was freaked at the prospect. I insisted we have faith; if things didn't work out we'd find a solution. It didn't make sense to me that we'd go through all that we had to be together, only to fail.

From the Upper West Side of Manhattan to the foothills north of LA, I did not yet have a clue that we were doing a 180. We went from a totally urban life, surrounded by mostly two-working-parent families, challenged by finances, politics and daily stresses—to Mayberry—more like Stepford. The "perfect" homogeneous environ: white, wealthy and Christian.

Seemingly the only Jews for miles, we later learned there were a few others, but they were hiding. Not a synagogue in sight, nor any African Americans; there were very few Hispanics, or other people of color. The only ethnic infusion was Korean, with a touch of Armenian sprinkled around. The neighborhood was as white as freshly snorted blow.

After years in New York progressive schools, this new world was shocking. Back home, the children were encouraged to think outside the box. They were never "wrong." Here there was one right answer, period. Back home, they embraced cultural diversity and learned to have a social conscience, but did not learn multiplication tables or proper grammar. This school was more rigorous academically, but every kid traced the same exact picture.

Back East, there was an open door policy for parents where we often sat in on classes, had lunch with our children and shook hands with their teachers when we checked them out at the end of the day. Here, the kids were dropped off out front and parents were not allowed in unless it was pre-arranged. The gates were locked, yet the kids were released at the end of the school day without supervision. It took some getting used to.

In theory, living as a family again should have been heaven on earth, but in reality—Oh, Nelly. The years of extended separation had taken their toll. Lenny, acclimated to being on his own, without obligation to anyone other than himself, got used to doing what he wanted (magic), when he wanted (whenever possible). I'd come to enjoy ruling the roost, controlling everything without question—a regular Mussolini, running the show without interference. I interrupted his solitude—he, my well-oiled machine. Bossing him around like a mommy was not very sexy. We'd forgotten how to be man and woman, husband and wife.

Added to that, Lenny was perpetually worried about the roof caving in. Bob was increasingly distant. Surviving his second renewal conditionally, Bob made clear he needed Lenny to focus on the bigger picture and not concern himself with anything else. Yet Randa wanted to do more of the regular runners with him, plus Lenny continued to receive the writer's daily assignments and couldn't ignore them. He worked overtime to ensure that he completed them, while giving ample energy to getting field pieces approved. He was finally given the go-ahead to work with an independent film character actor who was offbeat, to say the least.

Everyone hated the guy. (Ironically, a short time later he landed a regular role on the hottest sitcom on television.) The piece flopped. Lenny was determined to right the situation, but sensed doom. He was anxious all the time. In fact, he never really relaxed at that job, ever. He was brought in on a maybe, and it hung over his head for his entire tenure there. While accepting kudos from the rest of the writing staff, he was never confident that he pleased Bob, and his was really the only vote that counted.

It was three weeks before my fiftieth birthday. Cookie and Si were due to fly out to visit and take care of the kids, while Lenny and I spent some much needed time having a playdate of our own.

Renewal number three was overdue. No news is good news!

Lenny was anxious but didn't want to rain on my parade. Nor was I about to let him. My fortieth birthday party had been cancelled when Ellie went into the hospital suddenly. We hadn't celebrated a birthday of mine in a big way, well, ever.

For years, we'd talked about going to Paris for my fiftieth, but now that we were in LA, it seemed too far a trip without the kids. We settled on Vegas. We both loved the nightlife, gambling, luxury and good food. I booked a suite for five days at The Venetian.

Sydney had a birthday party to attend, her first since moving West.

"What should we get her?" I asked, heading to the local shopping strip.

"Something Roxy."

"Roxy, who's Roxy?"

"Not who, what!" Jack added, exasperated. My increasing lack of coolness increasingly annoyed him.

"Okay, what's Roxy?"

"Really cool clothes and stuff. They sell it there," Syd said, pointing to a surfer shop, just down the street.

As I pulled into a vacant parking space out front, my cell phone rang. Lenny's face appeared on the screen.

"Are you sitting down?" Almost a whisper, his tone dead, he added, "I don't think I have to say any more."

Deafening silence was pounding my eardrums. Nausea overtook me.

"What happened?" I asked, not really wanting to hear the answer.

"Bob just came in, closed the door, and I knew. He said because he'd be on the road for over a month in February, he needed someone with more field experience to hold down the fort. Said it had nothing to do with my writing."

"Come home."

I'd said that once before. I'll always remember where I was when Kennedy was shot, when the planes hit the towers. In kind, I'll never forget the moments when our lives crashed. Memories of the Holloran horror came flooding back. I had the same sick, hopeless, world caving in feeling that I did then. It never gets any fucking easier.

Lenny ended up not getting home for hours. Packing up his office, he said a few guarded goodbyes, then bid adieu to his childhood dream. Somehow, despite my gut, it was simply not meant to be.

Determined to keep it from the kids as long as possible, I sleepwalked through the rest of the day. Thank goodness I had program. My sponsor offered some suggestions that helped keep me moving. Namely, keep the faith. When Lenny finally arrived home with boxes in tow, I tried desperately to transfer some strength and hope.

That evening he had a brainstorm.

"I still have two weeks left on my contract. Rather than just give up, what if I offer to do one more field piece?"

After checking with Renee, who concurred, he placed a call to Bob. Lenny and I held our collective breath.

"I'll have to check with business affairs and get back to you tomorrow. That's what I love about you, Lenny, you never give up," Bob chuckled. He was the only one laughing.

The next morning, Bob gave Lenny the thumbs up. His self-induced return to the scene of his shame had Lenny feeling like a convict readying for his lethal injection. Most of the staff treated him as they always had. Others clearly avoided him or seemed overly friendly.

For the next few days, Lenny sat at his computer without a break, constructing the piece. He had a dragon's fire fueling him.

The shoot, that Friday, filled with the usual frustrations, yielded some terrifically funny footage. Lenny spent the entire weekend pulling "selects" from the tape in order to ready it for the edit that was sure to be extensive and grueling. The kids and I weighed in on our favorite scenes. With few exceptions, we were in agreement.

Was there enough there for a killer piece?

On Monday, Lenny painstakingly labored over the first edit, getting the hours-long footage down to fifteen minutes. He brought it home and we got in bed to watch. Our mutual anxiety immediately eased with my genuine continuous laughter.

Sydney and Jack joined us for the second viewing and they roared with delight. Perhaps Lenny was saved.

Afraid to hope, we did anyway. On Tuesday, he showed the rough cut to Bob, and Mark, the editor. Holding his breath, Lenny exhaled as laughter soon filled the room. Bob made some suggestions, leaving Lenny to make the final cut.

One of the other writers told Lenny he'd overheard Bob say, "It looks like Lenny saved his ass."

We were cautiously optimistic.

After making all the changes Bob suggested, Lenny brought the final cut home. As the kids and I watched, there was silence.

"What happened to…" "Where's that great…"

Bob had had Lenny edit out the funny. We tried to have faith that he knew best, remaining nervously hopeful when Lenny brought it in to the office the next morning.

Lenny put it in Bob's hand and returned to his office, trying not to make eye contact with anyone. Just in case.

A couple of hours later, Bob called.

"I thought you did a good job, so did Valerie (the show's director), but I'm afraid I have to let you go. I'm sorry Lenny."

Lenny had worked through his two weeks severance. Nine months he'd worked like a madman, scoring bits nightly, and it was still not enough.

Two homes, two kids, two cars, and no gig.

Happy fiftieth birthday to me.

Wandering Jews

I'm convinced there's nothing crueler than losing one's mind. Especially in the early stages, when you're aware it's happening.

Alzheimer's had touched our lives with the subtlety of a sledgehammer. It began with Lenny's mom. Just prior to my fortieth birthday, she broke her hip. In her late seventies, she was put in the hospital for an extended stay. Weighing less than eighty pounds, she was far too frail to manage on her own. Her first night in the hospital, she spoke meekly, making no sense. We chalked it up to the anesthesia. The next evening she was bolder, again speaking mostly gibberish, uttering disconnected thoughts. We couldn't follow her. She was frustrated and angry. We were worried sick.

By the third evening it'd progressed to almost violent agitation at our inability to understand her. Ellie's doctor assured us it was "sundowning," a common occurrence with the hospitalized elderly. Outside of their usual environs they become confused and disoriented as the sun sets. The sooner they return to their homes, the better.

That's when we decided to bag my fortieth birthday party. It didn't seem like a time to celebrate.

From the hospital, she moved to rehab. It was weeks before she came home. She was never the same.

Ellie had always repeated herself. Her world had gotten small since Samuel had left her. Nonetheless, he and Lenny remained the focus of her life. Any news regarding either of them filled her head and left little room for anything else.

It became increasingly concerning when she began asking the same questions immediately after receiving the answers. At first we mistook it for her not listening. It became apparent soon enough that although there was a time when that might have been the case, that was not the issue anymore. Ellie could no longer hold a thought for more than a moment or two.

It progressed to her wandering off and forgetting her way home. Neighbors and local security guards were finding her with increased frequency, blocks away, confused and aimless.

As with many seniors who live alone, TV was Ellie's company. It was always on. In no time, she forgot how to work the remote control. Initially, she would call a few times a day. Within weeks, it was hourly, until it escalated to incessant. No sooner had we slowly and deliberately explained the procedure (through clenched teeth), than the phone would ring again—Ellie, with no remembrance of the prior call.

Patience was never my strong suit. If I'd had some recovery then, perhaps I could've done better. As it was, I was frustrated and awful. Since Lenny was working most of the day, the brunt of the calls fell to me. It was nearly impossible to do anything without constant interruption.

After a few months of living as tech support for Ellie, she had a stroke and needed care. A nurse was brought in to help with her immediate needs; she never left. Our burden was lifted, but for all intents and purposes, Lenny and Samuel lost Ellie forever.

Other than the Alzheimer's, she was remarkably strong and healthy, despite weighing less than eighty pounds. Unable to move her legs and rarely leaving her bed, except for an occasional moment of clarity, she lived in a world we could not enter. It was heart wrenching.

Losing track of his keys, uncertain as to whether he had turned off the stove, repeating the same story, my dad was always absentminded. In recent years, he only ventured North once a year for Passover. I'm ashamed to say I hadn't been down to Florida since visiting him in the hospital years earlier. I used the kids as my excuse.

Even though I spoke to him on the phone daily, the change in him was subtle and hard to discern. Initially, I found myself answering the same question numerous times. Then there were increasing tales of missing things, getting lost and forgetting important occasions, like birthdays (even his own).

It didn't become alarming until Jerry came for his yearly visit a few Passovers back. As was his custom, he misplaced things, blaming it on not being in his own home and not having room to properly unpack. The amount of time he spent searching is what became cause for concern. He'd go into his room to check a baseball score and would emerge an hour later in a sweat with a furrowed brow. When I'd ask what was wrong, he'd mumble that he couldn't find his money, keys, yarmulke, whatever it was at that moment.

It was happening with increased frequency. Every couple of hours, he'd disappear, reappearing sometime later, agitated. Nobody thought much of it except me. Having been through it with Ellie, it was all too familiar.

I tried to bring the behavior to my Aunt Rose's attention. She'd have none of it. In fact, she gave me a good what for for even suggesting such a thing.

The phone calls throughout the year became repetitive and frustrating. The following Passover, during his annual visit, I returned home with the kids to the smell of gas overwhelming the hallway. As I made my way down the corridor, I was filled with dread as I realized the odor was emanating from our apartment. Jerry had made himself a cup of tea and left the burner on. A breeze from the open window extinguished the flame, allowing the gas to leak for hours. Fortunately, he'd gone for a long walk, and no one on the fourth floor had lit a match.

Following that trip, he returned home and couldn't find his keys. He searched everywhere he'd been, finally calling a locksmith. No sooner had the lock been replaced than Jerry found his lost keys in his pants. A few weeks later, he lost his checkbook. After turning his apartment upside down, he stayed up all night, showered at dawn and waited for the bank to open. He cancelled the missing checks. Days later, finding the lost checks, he wrote them out and subsequently bounced them all, forgetting he had cancelled them.

On the morning of my fiftieth birthday, all I could think about was Lenny's unemployment and the fact that, for the second year in a row, Jerry had forgotten my birthday. Jerry forgot everything. Why did I take it so personally? Perhaps because my brother Jeff asked for my address on the big day so he could send a card, and Cookie gifted me with a piece of jewelry that I'd always hated, "from her collection." She did make more than good, a couple of months later, treating me to a gorgeous pair of diamond earrings. But on that day, I sat atop my pity pot throne.

Lenny was kind enough to sleep in. I got to take Jack to Little League practice at 8:15 after spending the night before trying to restore all of our lost computer data, thanks to a crash caused by his magic magnet. *That damn fucking magic.*

Lenny bought a lovely birthday cake—only it was cookies and cream for the kids, and chocolate for Si. I preferred vanilla. *Can you hear the frikkin' violins?*

The week in Vegas was somber. Lenny and I tried hard to have fun. We managed here and there. A few days shy of Halloween, one of the smaller hotels had set up a series of haunted houses in their parking lot. From the entrance, where a zombie collected the money, to the exit where a chainsaw wielding "Jason" chased us to our car, we screamed in horror and delight. For the most part, the wicked unknown and painful recent past overshadowed our attempts at fun. Every dollar we spent reminded us of our uncertain future. We talked about making love, but didn't extend the effort—the chasm between us, ever widening.

Expectations are the building blocks of resentments. I know this. Yet, it's never stopped me. Left wanting, I sabotage my happiness. Seems like every year for as long as I can remember, the shit hit the fan right before my birthday. This was a chart topper.

My last birthday party was for my twentieth, a surprise party I orchestrated myself. Pathetic. My twenty-fifth was overshadowed by my first wedding two weeks later. All well and good, it was the best party I'd ever been to (despite the fact that the marriage sucked and Frank and I split up the week after my thirtieth birthday).

I harangued Lenny into throwing me a fortieth birthday party. He made the calls, and then, a week before the big day, Ellie fell and broke her hip. That ended that.

My forty-fifth came and went. Just before my forty-sixth there was 9/11 and then, a few weeks later, Lenny lost his job at *Holloran Hour*. Not much to celebrate that year. On my forty-seventh birthday, Lenny was in LA and I was in New York. For my forty-eighth we were busy recovering from the recent demise of *The Bill Plant Show*, and my forty-ninth came and went when there was no news from Randa after Lenny's first trial week.

There was always a compelling reason to put off celebrating, not spend money and feel really sorry for myself. *Poor fucking me.*

When we moved West, we met a fabulous couple who lived in our neck of the suburban woods. Like us, Kyle and Georgette were sober. Unlike us, they had been for almost half their lives. Fun and generous, they invited us for a welcome BBQ, kids and all, and gave us a tour of the neighborhood, with tips on the best shops and restaurants.

I initiated future social contact, something I rarely did. We went on a few double dates, always having lots of laughs and easy conversation. On one such evening, my fiftieth birthday came up.

"I was supposed to have a party in New York. Clearly that ain't gonna happen." Cue violins.

Georgette jumped in. "We'll make you a fiftieth."

"Get out. We just met."

"Absolutely. Our pleasure."

For the first time in my adult life, someone else took control. All I had to do was show up. What I usually did for others was now being done for me. Maybe fifty is the charm.

The party redeemed all. There was a houseful of friends, some of whom I'd gotten to know over the years while visiting Lenny, others I'd met since our move months earlier. I was overwhelmed by the affection my new friends showered on me, and the kindness of my hosts, who welcomed near strangers to their home on my behalf. As an added bonus, a close friend from New York happened to be in town for business. His presence at the party linked me to home.

The knot in my stomach was ever-present, but I felt loved and cared for. What greater gift than that?

Happy, Happy Birthday to me—or *are you still busy feeling sorry for yourself, old hag?*

—— Fear and clothing, living in Los Angeles ——

Weeks turned into months, and the months mounted. No jobs, nary an interview, zilch, nada, nothing. How was it possible in the land of television for there to be no jobs for a writer with Lenny's resume?

Magic and a new passion for mentalism saved him. *He was mental all right*. Obsessed with the distraction, he invented a trick and, with a partner, began selling it. It was pennies, but for a while it kept him sane. It allowed him moments away from his worry, until it consumed him, and then there was little time for anything else. I suppose that by focusing so intently on reading other people's minds, it allowed him to escape from his own.

To his credit, he didn't smoke pot, but he didn't seek help either. A "dry drunk," as it's called, a non-using addict without program, is almost worse than one actively imbibing. Without a substance to dull the pain, we feel it, but are void of solutions that the rooms provide. I'd stepped up my meetings to the other extreme and was gone almost nightly. We were on complete disconnect.

Lenny had a few side projects he continued to work on with various partners. He plodded along, sans his usual passion. Classic depression soon set in.

Jack was struggling too. Socially, he was always challenged; shy and self-critical, he was slow to warm-up. He couldn't bring himself to make a first move, remaining on his own until someone else basically commandeered him. Once comfortable, he could be bossy and opinionated—an interesting dichotomy. On the one hand fearful, on the other loaded with self-will—me all over. I prayed he wouldn't succumb to my fate.

Lenny and I watched with concern as Jack mirrored our insecurities. What if Jack tried weed? Would he not experience the same relief we had? Would we be able to convince him that it wasn't worth the damage it would inevitably cause?

Each day, Jack came home from school despondent.

"Do you know what it's like to eat lunch alone and not have anyone to play with at recess?" He'd ask, his eyes filling with tears.

My heart breaking, I'd think, *"YES!"* As I remembered my own misery as Cookie moved me from school to school, which forced me to make new friends, over and over again.

Not wanting to feed his pain, I'd say instead, "It'll get better, just give it a little more time."

Eventually, it did. Jack hooked up with a couple of other new boys at school, then found his way with a few of the old-timers. A seemingly interminable process, I vowed to not change neighborhoods again. I prayed I could keep that promise.

But could I? How long would we last with no income other than unemployment and our expenses now including two of everything? Surprisingly, Lenny was the one who wanted to cut and run. Mr. LA was shook. The man who, just one year before, insisted he had no desire to ever leave, wanted out. His confidence, understandably, was at an all-time low. He figured if we cut our losses and went back to New York, eliminated our big LA rent, my new car and a shitload of other expenses, we could wait out the work draught in our mortgage-free New York City co-op, with our paid-up old Camry, until the tide inevitably turned.

And then what?

It was fear talking and I knew it. Lenny was done with New York. Other than Ellie and Samuel, there was nothing left for him there.

That was not the case for me. I missed our comfy-cozy home filled with a lifetime of stuff. I missed Cookie, Bean and Maryann. I ached for my regular meetings and the fellows I'd trudged the road with. I longed to walk the streets of Manhattan, running into people I knew, no matter where, no matter when. And the food; man, I missed the food.

And yet...

I held firm. A lioness protecting my cubs, I was not about to shake up the kids' world again. We had ripped them from their roots, removed them from everything comfortable and familiar we'd built for them for years. To what end? Now that they were finally settling in, we were going to yank them back? And for how long? The work would inevitably be in LA.

We can't cha-cha with our kids.

In spite of my longing, I had this sense that I was in LA for a reason. I wasn't sure what, but something was beginning to feel right. After months of living on the fringe, I'd developed a few genuine friendships. Immersed in the local Marijuana Anonymous fellowship, I was savoring its strength and finding my place. My sponsor was here, in the flesh. I'd heard her speak at a meeting on one of my early LA visits, when Lenny first started working out here. I called her the next day and "proposed' to her a few weeks later. Asking someone to sponsor you is kind of like asking for someone's hand. You vulnerably put yourself out there and risk rejection. Hell, sometimes they say "no." It's happened to me more than once. Ouch.

After years of working with her long distance, via phone and email, I got to share a meeting and a meal with her every week.

I discovered Al-Anon. Addiction wasn't my only issue—attempting to control the world and everyone in it, was right up there. The comfort Al-anon afforded me made all of the recent hardships manageable. Learning to address and care for my needs, I realized that being in the wild, wild, west was one of them. I was compelled to stay, convinced that we didn't come all this way, go through all the tumult, just to fail and return home with our tails between our legs.

Something had to give, damn it!

TWELVE

LOVE

Hope for the holidays

We returned to New York mid-December for vacation. There is arguably no better time in Manhattan than the weeks before Christmas through New Year's. I was thrilled to be in the thick of it.

Lenny and I had written a show a few years earlier that focused on our struggles with marijuana addiction, our relationship and our subsequent attempts towards recovery. When we first submitted it, Lenny's agent felt we didn't stand a chance in the scripted hour-long world with no previous credits in that genre. She also felt the subject matter was too small. Pot wasn't "sexy" enough.

We watched *Weeds* make it to air two years later. Even though it was a straight comedy and took a very different approach (ours was a dramedy), our concept no longer seemed as original or groundbreaking, but I was more determined than ever to be heard.

Once Lenny's new agent, Greg, came into the picture, he shared our vision and began sending us out.

Our first meeting in LA, just prior to our trip East, was a disaster. Nervous and unsure of myself, the network "suit" we met with had no interest in me, giving all of her attention to Lenny. Didn't do much for my confidence.

Our second pitch went much better.

During our vacation in New York, the city was in the midst of a transit strike. With Cookie's help, we managed to get to the meeting at a cable network that specialized in women's programming. That was not what we had to offer, but they listened to us with interest as we tried to make the round peg fit in the square hole. All in all, it was a really good meeting.

Undeterred, I pestered Greg to get us into the networks where I knew our show would be better suited. We never got to the exact right person, but I learned how to pitch.

That same trip, Lenny met with Lori, the woman he'd worked with at *Holloran Hour* who'd hooked him up with the Clintons. She was now in development at a cable station. Originally a music network, they were veering into celebrity pop culture entertainment. Lenny pitched her a show that was right in that wheelhouse. Lori was receptive, encouraging him to get back to her with any other possibilities.

Almost immediately, I had an idea. My years in rock 'n' roll provided fertile ground. Combining many of the elements that contributed to making my nights a success, I restructured them to work for an hour of prime-time programming. Lenny agreed my idea was sound, but discouraged me from calling Lori until his show had been given due consideration. Waiting a few days, I again pleaded for his blessing, which he eventually, reluctantly, gave.

Nervously putting in the call, Lori, with whom I'd socialized at Holloran company parties, was open to hearing my pitch. I hadn't even put it on paper, figuring I would see if she was even remotely interested first. She was, advising me to flesh it out, put it in print, and get back to her after the holidays.

I called Brian, who'd been my jam master for years during my club days. We met in a coffee shop and brainstormed on my concept.

Lenny and I indeed had a little hope, just in time for the holidays.

Hold on, let go

As soon as we'd arrived in town, Lenny and I went to see Ellie, having been warned by Maria that she was not as we'd left her five months prior.

At first, it was all too familiar. The ever-present, unwatched, blaring TV, the hospital bed in a not quite upright position, the smell of A & D ointment (for years a sweet association with my babies—now, a painful reminder of the cruelty of aging), and there, slumped over, toothless mouth agape, the shadow of what was once my mother-in-law. Her eyes were closed, her hands limp and her nightgown askew, revealing sagging skin and jutting bones.

There was no response whatsoever to Maria's prods to stimulate her. No matter how much we needled her about my being in the house (never her favorite person, this son-stealer), or how many times Lenny repeated, "Ma," there was nothing. Not an eye flicker, a cheek twitch, not even a finger wiggle, to the tickling of her palms.

She had rallied so many times over the years when everyone counted her out. I believed that this too would pass.

I'd sometimes wondered over recent months if this living was merciful. She had no joy. Not from coffee, once her life's blood, chocolate, her passion, which she could no longer digest, or from Lenny, her beloved, no longer recognized. She was lost in the abyss, unable to communicate whatever was in her mind and heart. *There had to be something going on in there, didn't there?*

I was not the only one to have those thoughts, yet I was wracked with guilt.

We stood to gain.

For every subway ride Ellie took in the pouring rain, freezing cold and blinding snow; for every thrift shop dress, hand made hat and passed down coat she wore; for every discount coupon can of food and days-old bread she ate—penny by penny, dollar by dollar, she had saved a worthy sum.

She'd sacrificed, denying herself life's simple pleasures, while Lenny and I ordered take-out.

Lenny visited her bedside every day praying for a miracle. Not praying really. Hoping. Lenny didn't pray; he didn't believe in prayer.

Being the child of intellectuals was sort of like being raised by wolves. Life was wild—laissez-faire. There were no formalities or social graces. Say what's on your mind, do what you want to do when you want to do it, and never worry about what anyone else thinks. There was no God, no spirituality—no comfort. Debate and lofty argument ruled the day, for sport and challenge.

When Nurse Campbell came later that week, telling Lenny in no uncertain terms that it was the endgame, time to make final arrangements, he desperately sought escape and soothing. *Where to get it?*

First he tried a beer. Total sobriety had eluded him for any length of time. Years free of pot, thankfully, he didn't consider that option.

When the spirits didn't move him, he called his sponsor; the program was always a last resort for Lenny. It was easier to remain an outlaw, true to his roots, if he didn't buy into any group. It was a convenient way to not commit, accept fallbacks, without being accountable. Yet, when there was immediate need, the program was always there to catch him. He'd never needed it more.

Gary, Lenny's sponsor, suggested that he make his peace with Ellie. Following his advice, Lenny sat at her bedside and took her hand, composing himself as best he could.

"I love you, Ma. Thank you for all that you've done for me, always. Please don't hold on for me. I'm well taken care of. It's okay for you to fight if you want to, but don't do it for me."

He repeated those words, again and again through his tears. He didn't really want to let her go, but he knew for her sake he had to set her free.

He came home broken.

The next day he phoned Riverside Chapel, where all Manhattan Jews eventually end up. It was the worst call of his life.

As the days passed, I was sure that Ellie had once again dodged the bullet. Lenny and Maria were not. They were both on deathwatch, certain of the inevitability. I was visiting that river in Egypt. *What else was there to do with this?*

Christmas and Chanukah were fast approaching, the first time I could ever remember them falling on the same day. Eager to make this holiday as normal as possible for the kids and for Lenny, Maryann and Bean were coming over, as they had every holiday for years. They were my oldest friends, godparents to the kids.

Maryann says that family is an accident of birth. She and Bean were no accident. I chose them. Bean and I went back almost thirty years to college. He'd been through everything with me, and everyone.

Cookie and Si were coming over as well. We'd all spent enough occasions together to feel at ease. The awkward years forgotten—or at least forgiven—I was looking forward to it.

Cookie and I had long since repaired our relationship; in fact, it was better than it'd ever been. Thanks to my ongoing recovery, my Ninth Step amends, and a little maturity, I truly appreciated my mom at last. We hadn't had so much as a cross word in a couple of years.

On Christmas Eve afternoon, as was our tradition, I cooked the biggest shrimp Citarella had to offer, chilling them for dinner. Sydney and I baked cookies as we did every year. For some reason, first thing in the morning, I also put on a big pot of chicken soup. I wasn't going to serve it the next day. I had so much to do and prepare as it was. Why had I set myself up for the extra work?

I had Lenny take a container of broth over for Ellie (she hadn't had solids in a long time), and another with chicken and noodles for Maria. Later that night, I called her.

"I'll send over Christmas dinner about six tomorrow, okay?

Maria's voice was flat, emotionless. "Okay." She never mentioned the soup—very unlike her.

"Are you mad at me?" I asked. *Because it's always about me.*

"No, I'm not mad at you," she snapped, sounding exasperated. "I'm just upset."

At the time I thought she was being a touch melodramatic, sensitive soul that I am. It wasn't until later, when I reflected on what it might be like to sit and watch someone slip away (someone she'd spent almost every moment with for years), that I began to understand and empathize.

Christmas morning was hectic as I stuffed the pre-brined organic Murray's turkey. After prepping the chestnuts and the vegetables, I set about cleaning the house. Singing along to holiday music playing continuously throughout the day, I joyfully attacked the business at hand.

I was so grateful to be home, in my favorite pajamas, with all of my stuff. I admired my kitchen, fully equipped with everything I needed— unlike in LA, where we had a hodgepodge of thrown together cheap junk. I rarely cooked anything of significance in California as a result.

Our holiday meal was as joyous as any. We lit the menorah, exchanged gifts and ate for hours. After dinner, I prepared a plate for Maria, and Lenny took his leave to deliver it. I was busy doing the dishes while everyone settled in to talk and digest.

An hour passed. I had just set the coffee, cookies and chocolates on the table when Lenny returned. He was as white as a slice of Wonder bread.

"Ellie's breathing very heavily; she's struggling."

"Is she eating, Homer?" I touched Lenny's shoulder awkwardly, not knowing how to be physically comforting to him anymore. I wanted to, I tried, but it was so much less than was in my heart.

"The soup you sent her yesterday was sitting on her dresser barely touched. Maria's was still unopened."

That explained why she hadn't mentioned it. Her mind was obviously on other, more pressing things.

Dessert and the festivities kindly distracted Lenny. As was our custom, we concluded the evening with a game of Trivial Pursuit. Once everyone left, we cleaned up, got the kids to bed, and headed off to sleep ourselves well after midnight.

I was startled awake at 5:21 a.m., by pounding at our front door. It took a minute to wake Lenny, who was lost in deep, needed sleep. Clumsily, he headed down the hall, crashing into the wall on his way.

I could hear voices but couldn't make out the words. Dreading what was coming, I slowly put on my slippers and followed Lenny's path. He was just closing the door.

"Ellie."

I ran to him. He began to sob.

"I'm so sorry, Homie."

No matter how sure you are that death is coming, there's no way to prepare for it. Not really.

"Maria's been trying to call us."

When we moved to LA, we'd taken our New York bedroom phone there with us. Forgetting, as was our custom, once we closed our bedroom door there was no hearing the telephone.

I went to the answering machine and pressed play.

Maria's voice was flat and haunting. "It's over. She's gone."

Lenny, now all too awake, dressed deliberately, in no rush to face the un-faceable.

Sydney and Jack were standing frozen in the entrance to their room. As Lenny reached for the door, they snapped out of it long enough to run to him with kisses of comfort.

Touched so closely by death for the first time in their lives, they were frightened by the intensity of their own feelings. Seeing their daddy cry was the scariest part of all. As Lenny slowly walked towards the elevator, Sydney, Jack and I called out in unison, "I love you, Daddy." "I love you, Homer." There wasn't a dry eye in the hallway.

Jack and Sydney came to bed with me. Not yet 6:00 a.m., it was too early to get up, yet there was no way to sleep. I waited a few minutes and then called Lenny.

Maria had already contacted the funeral director as she'd been instructed. It was early morning, the day after Christmas. Ellie's doctor was required to pronounce her dead before her body could be removed and brought to the funeral home. Only Ellie's doctor was on vacation. It took dozens and dozens of phone calls over the next couple of hours trying to enlist the covering doctor, checking with the funeral director to see if he had heard from him, and trying to wake Samuel. Like us, he was far from the nearest extension when he slept. I called repeatedly for hours until I reached him. At least it kept me busy.

Poor Lenny sat with Maria in the living room of Ellie's apartment, painfully aware that he was but a wall away from his now deceased mother. He couldn't bring himself to go in to see her. Maria and Lenny ended up sitting there together for four hours until they finally got the okay to call 9-1-1.

From there, Lenny followed the ambulance to Riverside Chapel.

Being an only child at a time like that was unmerciful.

For two hours, Lenny sat alone in the funeral home with his grief.

Lenny's childhood friend, Roger, upon hearing of Ellie's passing, ran to keep him company. A more generous act did not exist in that moment. The passing years and the thousands of miles did not, in any way, separate their souls. He arrived just after Lenny identified the body. Thank God for him.

The mortician asked Lenny if he wished for a rabbi. Unsure, he looked to me.

No matter how much of an atheist Ellie claimed to be, she still celebrated many Jewish traditions. I felt that she should leave this Earth with divine guidance. *What could it hurt?*

Rabbi Resnick was vacationing in Boca. The chapel provided an unknown substitute.

As is Jewish custom, the funeral was scheduled swiftly. There was just enough time for Ellie's nephews, her last remaining blood relatives, to make the trip from Florida. I was anxious about Sydney and Jack seeing adults, especially their dad, so emotional. But such is life—death, a harsh reality.

For so long, Ellie had been bedridden—her memory, but a memory. She'd existed, not lived—unable to move without assistance, completely non-communicative. The funeral brought her back to life.

There was a bulletin board at the front of the room where we pinned photos of her as a girl, young woman, wife and mother. There were pictures of her laughing, smoking and arguing. The most moving was one I'd never seen before of Ellie as a young nursing student. She was in her teens, without make-up, a kerchief tied around her blond hair, so young, full of promise and purpose. She was striking.

The rabbi was the first to speak. Not knowing Ellie, his opening remarks were forgettable. Lenny followed and, although fearful of being unable to hold it together, he was never more riveting or funny. He shared

Ellie's hardships, then extolled her triumphs, her loyalty and devotion. Saving the best for last, he recounted her feigned scolding for one of his many boyhood pranks. In perfect Ellie, German-accented English, he spat out, "Ach! Lenny make fire!"

The room erupted. In that moment, Ellie was right there with us—the Ellie we all knew, but had forgotten. Our memory, tainted by the seemingly endless bedridden years, was now restored.

As each of Ellie's friends and family eulogized her, she continued to become revitalized. I felt far closer to her in death than I had in life. What a painful revelation.

Samuel's wife, Cherie, asked to speak. I thought it completely inappropriate that the woman who romanced Ellie's husband away should pay homage to her, but Cherie, a devout Buddhist, could not have been more humble. She used her time to publicly apologize to Ellie for ruining her life. It was extraordinarily brave. I think Ellie would have approved.

The entire service would've given Ellie more happiness than almost anything she got to experience in life. She was revered, admired, adored and respected. Publicly. She was the center of attention, the guest of honor. How long had it been since that was the case? If ever.

At the end of the service, Lenny asked if anyone else wished to speak. I was moved and felt so compelled.

I wanted to say out loud that, although she'd never much cared for me and we didn't really get along, I was so grateful to her. I benefited from her life as much, if not more, than anyone in the room. Because of her, I met the love of my life and had Jack and Sydney, my most precious gifts. Because of Ellie, Lenny and I were saved from the hellish financial fear of the prior few months. Her lifetime without was now providing us a future, with. Her thriftiness was going to enable us to sleep knowing that we were safe until the next job came, even if it took its damn sweet time arriving.

I wanted to acknowledge publicly that even though I'd done so much less than I could have for Ellie, I did apologize to her, hopefully before it was too late for her to know. I wanted to talk about the chicken soup. About it being God's will that I made it on that hectic Christmas Eve. Ironically, the last thing that passed Ellie's lips was made with love, from me.

I quickly searched my motives. Did I want to speak for Ellie? Did I have something to add that hadn't been covered? Or was it for me? So that I could feel better—be witty, clever and remembered?

In Ellie's honor, I did the most grown-up, unselfish thing I've ever done. I said nothing.

———————— **And the beet goes on** ————————

In January, back in LA, Lenny and Tom (his sometime writing partner) got the go-ahead to do a live pilot. The premise was a 12 Step program for people addicted to show business. Putting together a wicked cast of funnymen and one woman, after a few meetings, the girl dropped out. Having already campaigned to join the cast if they did a subsequent performance, sight unseen, at Lenny's recommendation, Tom agreed for me to step in—nepotism at its best.

I hadn't been on stage in eighteen years. The rest of the cast were all stand-up comics, currently working, with years of experience under their belts. *What was I thinking?*

After writing my "share" I felt a bit more confident, especially after Lenny laughed in all the right places and added a great punch. If I could just get through it without showing my nerves, perhaps I'd be okay. There was little time for rehearsal; after just one meeting with half the cast, there we were.

Originally, Tom had assured us that he and his agent would fill the seats. A couple of days before the performance, he asked for help. There were only a few reservations to date. I didn't want to invite friends, remembering my stand-up days and what a disaster that could be. And after eighteen years, shit!

I did it anyway.

As we sat there in the dark, a packed house and three cameras rolling, the long forgotten thrill and fear took their place in my stomach. Utilizing a new resource, I silently repeated the Serenity Prayer again and again in my head. By the time it was my turn to take the spotlight, I charged, like a bronco released at the gate.

It took a moment or two but, as soon as I got my first laugh, my insecurity subsided a bit, taking a back seat to my long repressed passion for performing. Man, it had been a long time.

After a few lines, I dared a peek at the audience. The entire first row were our friends from Marijuana Anonymous. *Holy shit!* I felt the old panic begin to take hold, then willed myself to imagine it as a real meeting. That helped me stay in the moment.

The biggest laugh I got was an improvised response to Tom after he slammed me. My adrenaline hadn't pumped like that in a long time. I felt like a desperado housewife, ignored and unloved for years, sharing her first illicit kiss with a young lover—scary and thrilling. (I vaguely remember that feeling.)

The response afterwards was encouraging and exhilarating. No one in the room, except for Lenny, had ever seen me onstage or knew that side of me. A far cry from the mom I'd become. For a few moments, I was the Andi of old—daring, foul and fun. *Man, I'd missed her.*

At the same time that the pilot was happening, two "sure thing" jobs Lenny had in his pocket fell through. A new opportunity opened up out of nowhere. After a couple of interviews, they made an offer. It was awful, but it was on the table.

Assured by his agent that the deal was undefined and could be elevated to worthy, Lenny went in and began working. What was described as a part-time job ended up being two eighty-hour weeks of thankless work. On the third week, he was told by his agent not to return until the deal could be renegotiated. Two months later, he was still waiting.

Simultaneously, Bill Plant got a deal on cable. Lenny was sure this would be his ticket out of the depths. When he learned weeks later there was no place for a writer in the small budget, all hope was lost. The dark overcame him. The bottom finally sank its teeth in. Denial was gone. Finally, Lenny woke up. He sought help. Doing something he'd never done in his life, he prayed.

As if rising after a winter's hibernation, he was starving and determined to satisfy his need. Now single-minded of purpose, Lenny did everything he could to turn things around with a conviction I hadn't seen in him since those last two weeks at Randa.

Karma came through. Out of nowhere, not one, but two jobs he'd been hoping for opened up. Additionally, a new show was announced, seeking a head writer.

While all that was going on with Lenny, I'd written up the pitch for Lori. Her enthusiasm grew. For the next two months she came back with a number of suggested revisions, which I immediately set out to address.

After two months without a commitment of any kind, new inside info surfaced that Lori's network had another similar show in development (previously unmentioned). I got ants in my pants.

Frustrated that I couldn't get a definitive answer from her, I decided to reach out to Timothy O'Rourke. Lenny had worked with Tim at *On the Edge*. They shared a passion for magic. Even though Tim was a "suit," he was an open and down-to-earth guy. I'd met him only once at a surreal Hollywood Christmas party we'd attended a couple of years back. In a sea of weird, he was warm and friendly, chatting with me about parenting.

Currently, he was the senior VP of Televised Productions, a large syndicator with a great track record. I felt no fear reaching out to him, as he'd made me so comfortable at that very intimidating social gathering. Some people are like that. Without pretense or self-importance, they can be delightfully accessible.

I emailed, reminding him of our connection, and asked if he'd be willing to hear a pitch. I received an almost immediate response.

"I don't take pitches, but I'll find out who to direct you to."

Within a few moments, he'd emailed me back with his colleague Jason's phone number and a nod of good luck.

More than I'd hoped for, I wasn't prepared to make the cold call. Emailing Lenny's agent Greg, who'd been acting as my agent as well, I asked him to make the call. Greg felt I should do it. *Of course he did.* Shit! I wasn't even a client. Not really, not at all. I was simply his client's wife, whom he'd sent on a couple of pitches for Lenny's sake, not mine.

Thanks to being a big old pothead in recovery, I had tools to deal with fear. With my sponsor's help, I talked it through.

I made the call.

Nelli, Jason's assistant, was expecting me and made it easy. It was a Tuesday. She gave me an appointment for that Friday. *So soon?*

Trying to decide how to dress was torture. As I had for the pitch meetings, I opted to go "young and successful." That translated to jeans, a long-sleeve, button-down, Banana Republic, fitted, black shirt and a good amount of hip bling—my mainstay.

Almost a half hour early, I pulled into the underground parking lot and tried to meditate. I didn't quite pull it off, but it worked enough to at least slow my breathing down to the level of "not quite racing."

Jason met me in the reception area and led me to his office. Rather than sit at his desk, he pointed to one of two armchairs at 90-degree angles to each other.

As I began my pitch, he built on it.

Before I'd finished, he said, "I can't believe this isn't on the air already."

Whew… acceptance. I allowed myself a breath.

"I know. It's crazy, isn't it?"

"A no-brainer."

For the next almost-hour, we riffed on my idea, sharing my vision. He was the warmest, coolest and most passionate corporate guy I'd ever met.

After he told me I'd hear back from him the next week, I tried to remain hopeful when I didn't. As the following week progressed, my hope began to diminish when a "Just checking in," email to him went unanswered.

On Friday, I awoke at 6:00 a.m. My Inbox contained *Variety Headlines,* as it did every morning— my private conceit that I was in the business.

There was news that Lori's network had greenlit the show that was competing with the one I'd been shopping. *Shit!*

Despondent, ready to give up, I called my old jam master, Brian, who I'd brought on board to work on the project. We composed an email to try to convince her that she should still do our show.

Cyberspace is an amazing thing. As I hit "Send," I also "Received." As my email of despair (masquerading as a congratulatory boast of confidence and compatibility) to Lori was going out, coming back at me was an email from Jason.

"Call me. I have good news."

Afraid to assume, but unable not to, I raced up to Lenny.

"Wake up, Homer. Wake up!"

"What? What's wrong?" Lenny asked, alarmed, shaking himself awake.

"I got an email from Jason. He said to call him, he has good news."

"You think?" I asked, seeking validation.

Lenny smiled. I ran to make the call.

"What took me so long?" I said, calling five minutes after receiving his email, hoping to get a chuckle.

"What took *me* so long," Jason responded apologetically. "Sorry I didn't get back to you sooner."

It had only been two weeks. Lori had kept me on hold a whole lot longer.

"It's a go. We're optioning your show. Is Greg your agent?"

"Uh.... yes... he is." I stammered, hoping that were true.

"Business affairs will be calling him later today."

"Thank you, Jason!" I blurted out amidst a bunch of gibberish of which I have no memory.

"We're going to be talking a lot, Andi, fleshing out our pitch."

There are moments in life when I've known I'm creating my own history. Even if the outcome is a long way off, and certainly not a given, I can sense that the journey I'm embarking upon is a life changer.

This was such a day.

I couldn't think. I wanted to scream the news to everyone I could think of who was rooting for me, and especially to those who weren't. *Where was my program now?* I felt twelve, and acted about as maturely. I hadn't had any professional creative success of my own in so many years. To say I felt the need to compensate would be a gross understatement.

All I knew in that moment was that I had to get off the phone so I could start bragging immediately. I abruptly ended the call and ran to Lenny.

After we hugged and jumped up and down for a while, I called my mother, my father, my brother and just about everyone else I could think of. Whomever I couldn't reach, I emailed. Humility eluded me when I needed it most. Was it too many years living in the shadow of others, or just a good excuse to be obnoxious, narcissistic Andi?

Most everyone was happy for me, or at least seemed to be. A few friends in the business couldn't hide their disdain. Who the hell was I to get an option only a few months after arriving in LaLaland?

I bit my lip and called Bill Plant. To Bill, I was just Lenny's wife. I was nervous to approach him, but he'd sold a few shows over the years and I valued his input. Very gracious, he offered sage advice.

"I probably cost myself a number of projects by insisting on what I wanted. I've learned to be a team player. Be liked. Get in the door. That's my advice to you."

Bill encouraged me to call his manager, Richard, and ask his opinion. Just as we were hanging up, he got a call waiting beep from Richard.

"I'll fill him in. He'll be expecting your call."

I called my old friend Mark, first. Now wildly successful, the comic he represented was a huge TV and film star. Mark was set for life.

Always cautious, Mark was, for some reason, competitive with me (even though he'd left me in the dust more than a decade ago). More to the point, I was competitive with him. Despite our yin-yang, he'd always, in his way, believed in me and given me a number of opportunities, dating back to my Comedy Shack debacle. He was abrupt, a bit patronizing, but he offered some wisdom about what to prioritize. As usual, he was right.

Next I checked in with Sarah, who'd been my lawyer back in the day. She was a trusted old friend and Jack's godmother. We hadn't talked shop in years, our conversations usually centered around family life. She, too, offered guidance.

Finally, I called Richard. He immediately put me at ease.

"I don't know exactly what this is about, but I want in."

We'd met backstage at Bill's show a couple of times and had chatted amiably. He liked Lenny. A family man himself, he was nice to the kids. Without telling him the specifics of the pitch, I brought him up to speed. I hadn't told anyone anything about the show itself, other than that it was a music reality show. In a town of quick turn-arounds, I trusted no one. Paranoia strikes deep.

After all the input, my head was spinning. Mark thought the credits were most important, Richard preferring I fight over "Created by;"

Sarah thought, "Executive Producer," was more important and wanted me to protect "the back end." In my eagerness, I made a few missteps almost immediately.

Finally I thought to call Greg, who was surprised, but trying not to show it. We discussed strategy. I guess he was my agent.

"What do you think about reaching out to Lori and letting her know I have an offer?"

"It might be wise to wait until you actually have one," Greg pointed out. Ouch.

What if it was all a joke? What if Jason was just messing with me?

I called Timothy, who picked up the second his assistant announced me. "Congratulations, Andi. I found out last night. We've got to celebrate."

I was, at last, a somebody.

—————— Proud of my humility ——————

Even though I'd written for the past five hundred and thirty-one straight days and three plus years intermittently before that, I was finally, sort of, legit. I felt I could at last call myself a writer without looking over my shoulder to see if anyone was giggling behind my back. No longer invisible and in Lenny's shadow, people (other than mommies) took my calls, asked my thoughts and paid attention to my answers.

We knew we still had to sell the thing. Nonetheless I felt like a player.

In my first development meeting with Jason, Brian, my jam master, teleconferenced in from New York. Joining us was Bruce—our new producing partner and Kelly, the "suit" overseeing our project. Following a brief round of introductions, I re-pitched my vision.

Brian and I had lofty goals. We hoped to avoid a cheese fest of C-list celebrities and sub par performances. The experts in the room patted us on our proverbial backs, while advising us to be ready to lower our sights.

The tasks were divvied up. Bruce was to pursue possible alternatives in the show's structure, while attaching talent fell to Brian and me.

As soon as I left the meeting, I sucked it up and called Bill Plant. Describing the show to him, before I could even ask, he offered.

"Sounds cool. Count me in." *Love him!*

In less than an hour we had our first celebrity. Flying, I called Brian, Jason and Bruce. We all reveled in the news.

Lenny had been working on a package for a new talk show starring sitcom star Erin McDonald. He threw himself into the task at hand. Where most submissions were between three and five pages, he churned out twenty-five. The response was instant and effusive. Lenny's agents were confident he'd get the gig. Things finally seemed to be turning around.

After months of so much nothing, we couldn't help ourselves. We started talking—to our parents, our friends and even the kids. We were sure our stars were changing. It wasn't about bragging, it was about redemption. Surely the gods and our peeps knew the difference.

We were happy, laughing again. We even spent a little money frivolously.

We knew life was about to change. We could feel it.

From there to here

Driving Sydney and Jack to school one magnificent spring morning, I realized, "I like it here. Life is good." The hard-boiled, big city, New York loving me, was being won over.

Life was easier. Jump in the car and you're there. No foul weather to contend with or overcrowded subway trains, everyone so stressed and overworked that there is little time for fun. There's an ease, a relaxed calm that permeates Los Angeles. *Sedation?*

Sydney was happier than she'd ever been. Embraced by a circle of best friends, she went from one playdate to another, and it required little effort. In New York everything had to be so carefully orchestrated with nannies, schedules and transportation difficulties. Not so here. Finally challenged academically—she was thriving.

Jack, shy and slow to integrate, had settled in with more friendships than he'd ever enjoyed back home. His confidence continued to build with his growing independence. Once reliant upon me to schedule and organize his life, he had taken control, and as a result was much happier and self-assured. Plus, there was baseball twelve months a year. For Jack, there was nothing better than that.

Lenny felt at home. Connected to a slew of writers, magicians and comedians, he was tapped in. LA was where the work was, even if it had temporarily eluded him. Thousands of miles from Manhattan, he was freed from staring into Ellie's empty window.

As active as I was in the kids' school back home, I never really felt part of the PTA scene. I didn't here either, but at least I wasn't pretending. I did what I did without guilt for what I didn't do. I found a few renegades with whom I connected. Between them and the MA fellowship, I developed a new support system.

I hoped we'd never have to give up our place in New York; I still had mad love for that city—its restaurants, theatres, architecture, shopping and energy. Not to mention the people—intense, sharp and challenging.

How lucky we were to have two coasts, two homes, two kids, two cars... no gigs? Well, that was about to change.

———— Restored to Insanity ————

Riding high with hope and possibilities, Lenny and I were working our asses off and loving every minute of it.

With another sometime-writing partner, Michael, Lenny was working on no fewer than a half-dozen side projects. With the beginnings of an idea, at my suggestion, the three of us wrote a pitch for an independent feature for Bill Plant. Nothing like being busy to take on more.

My development meetings were yielding gratifying results. Bruce had come up with a few workable alternatives to our original format. Brian and I had attached a handful of A-list celebrities and the definitive charity. At Bruce's request we'd also hooked up a couple of C-listers, just in case we ended up on cable.

Convinced that we were ready, Jason set up a meeting where we would put forth our product to the "suits" to determine if it was time to pitch the networks. The meeting was set for the following Wednesday.

Brian had been trying to reach Stephen Kay and had finally connected. His meeting was scheduled for two weeks down the road. We had a good feeling. It wasn't with his people, it was with the man himself. Even though Stephen wasn't as enormous a star as he once was, he was still very famous and beloved. We were sure this news would further our cause.

That Monday, right before dinner, Lenny got an email from the producer of *The Erin McDonald Show*.

"Hey there... is there a number we can reach you at?"

There was no interpretation other than good news. If Lenny wasn't getting the job surely they would've simply told his agent. "Hey there" was friendly—playful even.

We danced, we kissed. We ate, anxiously waiting for the call. By 9:00 p.m., when the phone still hadn't rung, Lenny was getting nervous. By 3:00 the next afternoon, he was insane.

At 4:00, his guard momentarily dropped, he answered the ringing phone matter-of-factly.

"Hello..."

"Oh... hi," he stammered, racing up the stairs for privacy.

I followed and stood behind the closed bedroom door, waiting for his jubilant exit.

"Uh huh. I understand."

Silence.

Gingerly, I opened the door

"What happened?" I asked, stifling tears, afraid to hear the answer.

"They said it was a chemistry thing, nothing to do with my work; a personal connection between Erin and one of the other candidates. They said she couldn't hire me as a staff writer as the budget wouldn't allow for my salary quote but, if things went well, they'd try to bring me in later. They told me they were sorry; they hoped we'd work together in the future."

Another fucking heartbreak.

There was nothing else.

This disappointment, Holloran, Randa, were all primarily due to a lack of political savvy. As talented and learned as Lenny is, he's equally inept at playing the game. He just can't do it. A total non-manipulator, he's a straight shooter—shy, modest, no bullshit—my opposite. Although often overshadowed by flamboyant types, Lenny always lands on his feet. I knew he would again. *But when?*

Back to zero.

Wait...there's my show.

"Maybe it's my turn, Lenny. Maybe you're meant to make up for lost time with the kids, finish up your mom's story, and I'm meant to do some earning for a change. Even though Buckley-Shapiro hasn't returned the contract, they said it'd be retroactive. In a few weeks I'll get my first check, and when we sell the thing, I'm due to make a bundle."

"If you sell the thing," Lenny, mumbled.

"We'll sell it!"

As much as I believed, negativity bred fear.

After yet another sleepless night, I got a call from Jason's assistant, postponing my Wednesday meeting to Friday.

On Friday, moments before I was about to leave the house, Jason's assistant called.

"Sorry, Andi, something's come up. The meeting will be rescheduled for next week."

I had a bad feeling. Greg, my acting agent, assured me this happened all the time. "It's nothing to be concerned about." Regardless, my guts were flipping.

By Tuesday, when I hadn't heard from them, I put a call in to Jason. By this time I knew. This was not good. *But why?* The show was progressing better than any of us had hoped.

On Wednesday afternoon, Jason returned my call.

"Sorry for the delay getting back to you Andi. There's been a bit of a shake-up around here."

Here it comes…

"Last Friday, the day of your scheduled meeting, we had a corporate restructuring. I'm no longer involved with prime time programming. I'll be working only with daytime. A newly formed company will be handling prime time, headed up by Kelly."

"Oh…"

"Don't worry, Andi," said Jason, sounding worried. "This won't affect your show. Your contract's still good. It just moves to the new company. Of the four shows we have in development right now, yours is the furthest along with the most potential. You just won't be doing it with me."

"That's awful Jason. You get it. You've shared my passion from the start. This stinks."

"It does for me too."

I put a call in to Greg, who assured me it would not affect my deal. He also informed me that my contract, which Buckley-Shapiro was supposed to have returned weeks prior, had only gone back that Monday, after the restructuring. It was still not signed. My stomachache ached.

"The contract is retroactive to the first development meeting," Greg explained. "We still have a few weeks to go before the money period kicks in. Don't worry."

Easy for him to fuckin' say.

Kelly was professional and cool. Other than the first meeting and a few email updates, she'd had no direct involvement in the project. For the next couple of days, Greg played phone-tag with her. On Friday afternoon at 3:15, picking Syd and Jack up from school, amidst the insanity of hundreds of kids celebrating their two-day emancipation, my phone rang.

The school was up in the foothills; cell reception was awful at best. Amid the crackle of static I barely heard—

"Hi… K…y"

Guessing, I responded, "Hi, Kelly."

I barely got what followed. Having to fill in the blanks, the gist was they had made some calls and there wasn't interest in my show due to a very recent, very huge failure of a celebrity cooking show. I pressed for specifics. The only one she offered was Lori's cable station. She said they'd heard the idea before.

"Of course they have. I pitched it to them before I came to you. We were going back and forth for months before you optioned it."

I could barely make out what she was saying, and was getting increasingly frustrated and angry.

"There's interest in a "docu-soap." Maybe you and Bruce can get together and work on that."

"A docu-soap?"

As she began to explain, the reception got worse.

"Andi, why don't you call me next week and we can talk about it."

I called Bruce.

He explained, "A docu-soap follows a celebrity in hopes they'll crash and burn." The antithesis of what I aspired to with my show.

I had no interest.

The next Friday, while reading the trades with my morning coffee, there was an announcement that one of television's most successful producers was developing a show unmistakably close to mine.

So that was, as they say, that.

As quickly and suddenly as it had come, so it went. No longer a player, now a loser. What was worse? Having an option and being dropped, or never having it at all?

Were the weeks of contract negotiations, talking crazy-huge numbers of adjusted gross net, and "Created by" vs. "Original idea by," worth the heartbreak and humiliation of having it all go away? Was the cost of having to answer, "Hey, Andi, how's your show going?" to everyone I knew, worth those weeks of facing my fears and watching my dream take form?

Hell, yes!

Regrets? I have a few. Not too few to mention. They all concern my BIG mouth. Why can't I live without an audience? Why do I always need applause? Why must I end up apologizing before the final curtain?

Because, I have zero restraint of pen and tongue.

When will I fucking learn?

Ending, a new beginning

I don't believe in accidents. When something desired isn't obtained, almost without fail, a really good reason eventually surfaces why it was better not to have gotten it in the first place.

Our friend who landed the head writing job for Erin McDonald was let go in the middle of his first cycle, immediately after moving his family out here. Shortly thereafter, the show was cancelled.

Lenny's had a half dozen or so jobs in the last couple of years and is negotiating a new gig now—there's no way to know if it'll be a short run or the start of something big. What job comes with a guarantee these days? Ironically, his "best of" clip reel from Randa is what enticed them. One man's poison...

A friend of a friend is a pal of Vinny's. We reconnected by email recently and we plan to meet for coffee. How great is that? It's been almost twenty years. He never married, didn't have kids... turns out my years-long obsession wasn't the right man for me. I didn't know it, but the universe and Vinny did.

I'm easing back into the professional arena. With a resume older than dirt, it gets pretty scary. Recovery saves me. It's not about the pot anymore, it's getting through the day with a modicum of peace. Still an addict, with or without the weed, I can overdo just about anything—food, exercise, horoscopes, the computer, even love. Especially love. My obsessive desire to be loved and appreciated is the real drug that fuels me.

There's an old wives' tale about a Cherokee who tells his grandson about a battle that goes on inside people. He says, "My son, the battle is between two wolves. One is Evil. It is anger, envy, sorrow, regret, greed, arrogance, self-pity, guilt, resentment, inferiority, lies, superiority and ego. The other is Good. It is joy, peace, love, hope, serenity, humility, kindness, benevolence, empathy, generosity, truth, compassion and faith." The grandson asks, "Which wolf wins?" The old Cherokee replies, "The one you feed."

My natural inclination is to feed the bad wolf. Obsession, jealousy and greed will all drive me to make poor choices. Recovery keeps me in check. I'd like to say it's ruined me for bad behavior, but I still manage to do my share. Hopefully, I catch myself quicker and self-correct sooner. I had to sit down and write this to halt the revenge I was plotting against a ~~pain-in-the-ass~~ poor lost soul.

Try as I might, I can't control people, places or things. That doesn't stop me from giving it a go—constantly. When left to my own devices, my overly organized, compulsive life quickly becomes unmanageable. I get plenty done, but it's never enough. In my quest for perfection, I'm impossible to please—making myself, and those around me, miserable. The proverbial bite in the ass is almost instantaneous these days. Perhaps it's merely a sharpened awareness. The check and balance system has become impossible to ignore. It's annoying in the moment, but makes for better sleep.

I can't even adjust my own attitude, dammit. I can affirm, pray and meditate, but I can't think myself happy. I struggle to get out of my head; it's such a dangerous place for me to hang. Without permission, doubt creeps in, arm-in-arm with the critic. Pretty soon I'm paralyzed in quicksand. The only thing that silences the chatter is taking action. No matter how mundane the task—washing the dishes, paying a bill, calling Maryann—can serve to right my course. When I get moving, everything sort of works out. And I suffer less. As soon as I try to solve it in my head, I'm on the hamster wheel with a one-way ticket to Crazytown.

The illusion of control fucks with me constantly. Nothing ever goes the way I think it will. Life is filled with variables that I can't anticipate. I can spend hours, days, weeks concocting the best plan ever and then one of the kids gets sick, my car gets hit, the deal falls through... all that time spent planning—in the toilet. Why the fuck do I bother? Be here now, motherfucker. Man that shit is hard.

I've come to believe that someone—something—always has my back. Having faith is murder, but worry has never amassed me anything but a migraine and a stomachache. I'm not sure any of my worst fears have ever been realized, and if they were, I got through them. There's no evidence that I won't again.

Playing "Let's Make A Deal" with God doesn't net me what I want, or what I think I want. But everything that's happened, even the crap, has pretty much always paved the way for something better.

A major control freak from way back, I'm trying to let go. The tighter I hold the reins, the more elusive my desire becomes. As soon as I relax my grip, good tends to flow.

Too often I live in fear and resentment. When left unchecked, it grows to enormous proportion, taking up vast space in my head. Instead of anesthetizing myself or squashing the feelings, if I dig deep, talk it out, and do my damndest to keep a loving focus, I can usually gain some understanding and compassion. With guidance, I can find my part in almost every perceived slight, allowing me forgiveness, which releases the baggage stored in my head, making room for more fruitful endeavors and feelings.

When I explore the qualities that don't serve me (obsession, envy, jealousy, self-righteousness, perfectionism, to name but a few) and become willing to part with them, they don't magically disappear, but they do become less crippling. If I choose to indulge them, as I'm often wont to do, I pay the price, as does everyone in my path. When I act from fear, everyone's fucked. When I focus on love, things seem to work out.

After forty-plus years of always being right, slowly, I'm gaining acceptance of my humanity. Humility eludes me, but I mustered just enough to get me through a pretty thorough *My Name is Earl* amends process. To prevent further wreckage, I have to be vigilant. Sorry may be the hardest word, but, with practice, it's beginning to roll a bit more effortlessly off my tongue.

I don't get through a day without apologizing to someone, for something—usually the kids or Lenny. I still can't behave in my pajamas. My progress in my most intimate relationships is ridiculously slow, almost indiscernible. When my guard's down, I'm still intolerant, impatient and a perfection-seeking pain in the ass. It's not that I'm inauthentic with the rest of the world... it's just that I try to take a beat, to think before I speak. I don't do that at home. I aspire to. I talk about it ad nauseam. I can't seem to get the hang of it until after I've yelled, nagged and complained.

Help—a word I only used when singing along to the Beatles—is coming a bit more naturally to this "Don't worry. I got it" girl. And with that, relief—I don't have to do everything, all the time, for everybody. Not that I ever could, but it never stopped me from trying.

I'm finding life is only worth living honestly, with vulnerability. I hid out for so long behind my bullshit and my supposed strength. All it did was isolate me.

I want what I want when I want it, but I'm learning to be grateful, even when things don't go my way. I usually have to be reminded... again and again and again. It's progress, a long way from perfection.

I strive to remember to keep the faith and trust that I'm doing exactly what I'm meant to do, every moment—even when I fuck up. I'm not in the habit of learning lessons when things are going my way.

Every day's a do-over, an opportunity to start fresh. As long as I stay willing I'm a little bit less of a lunatic. It doesn't make pain any easier to bear in the midst of it, nor fear any less scary, but it's my choice how long I suffer. Every down is followed by an up, every disappointment with an opportunity, every hurt, with love. The sooner I remember that shit, the quicker I heal.

Thanks in large part to The Facebook, I've networked myself into a few cool scenes and created a little something of my own—literary soirees in my home that are gathering steam and creating a bit of buzz. I utilize all my skills and I'm of service to others. Even though I haven't managed to make a friggin' dime yet, I hold hope that if I keep doing what I love, what I seem to be good at, the money will follow. Who knows? Maybe *this* is that big thing the psychic spoke of.

Back in the day, Lenny was living his dream. Clutching his coattails, I was along for the ride. We were young, in love and hopeful of the future that lay before us. On our way to one of Lenny's stand-up-hell gigs, we idled away some of the long highway hours listening to self-help tapes, at my insistence. One of them directed us to write down where we wanted to be in five years. Lenny grudgingly dictated his responses to me, over his protests of "This is bullshit!" As his list grew, he got into it, imagining all that was possible. It's been years since then, but damn if not every one of those dreams has come to pass. They don't all look like we imagined, and it didn't happen in the exact timeline. Some of my dreams I've only experienced vicariously through Lenny, but hey! I ain't dead yet.

My not working all those years put a lot of pressure on Lenny. Having been the major earner through my first marriage, justified or not, I had no guilt. Working since I was twelve, moving away from home at seventeen, I was unaccustomed to being taken care of. I discovered that I liked it. A lot. Unfortunately, I was not the first damsel Lenny supported. Eventually, it created quite a rub. The psychic's words came back to haunt me. "Always work and stay focused on your career. Stocks and bonds are sexy. If you abandon your dreams, it will cost you in love." She knew. That bitch! Arrogant me never thought her premonition would come to pass. When it did, I defended my decision to the hilt. What kept getting lost were the intangibles, the non-accountables that millions of wives and mothers thanklessly provide every day. I felt it my duty to constantly refresh Lenny's memory.

Starting over in middle age is a pain in the ass, but it's also an incredible opportunity to try on a new life. As scary and unsettling as things are, I haven't felt this awake in a long time. I finally finished my manuscript. The daily discipline and accomplishment is a gift of sobriety. This one isn't going in the bottom of a drawer.

On the flipside, Lenny and I still aren't sure if we can find our way back to each other without the buzz. We don't have a clue how to revive the passion and intimate connection that've taken a beating while life's been in session. We're giving the counseling thing another go, this time with a different focus—on what's best for all of us, especially Jack and

Syd. We made them, and that life, together. We were crazy happy for a whole lot of years. And we're sober. That ain't chopped liver. Maybe the rest is gravy...

Complacent is an awful way to live. I'd rather invite the unknown, as scary as it is—and it's friggin' terrifying—because I need to shake it up and see what comes. I'd gotten to the point where I stopped being grateful; I was so caught up with the things that were failing me. This forced re-evaluation has made so much more possible. I am, once again, counting my blessings and re-thinking my priorities. We've had to learn to live with less—less money, less stuff. Ouch. Yet, there's so much more—more acceptance, support, understanding and growth.

I've come to believe that the things I'm really passionate and unwavering about, the "must haves" that I'll stop at nothing to achieve, are my destiny. My desire amps up so that I can persevere and make them happen. When I think about my childhood dreams, those I held onto and those I let go, as much as I might have wanted something for a time, if it passed, I now believe it wasn't meant to be; no amount of pushing was going to make it so. Likewise, when something is truly meant to be, nothing I can do will fuck it up. I take great comfort in that.

Why is Julia Roberts living my life? She's not.

I realize now I'd like to know her—not be her. My best is yet to come, dammit. Cue Tony Bennett.

I'm still insecure—wanting... needing... approval and validation. But once I have my career in place, get raucously laid and have a tummy tuck, everything's going to be jake—I think.

The only thing I know for certain is that I have absolutely no idea what's going to happen. I just pray that what I make of my life is better than I dare to dream.

As we say in "the rooms," thanks for letting me share.

Not The End

Acknowledgements:

Heartfelt thanks to my publishers, Lawrence O'Flahaven, for offering a safe place to land while skillfully and magnificently facilitating the manifestation of my dream beyond my dream, and Carl Reiner, for modeling creative genius, coupled with inspiring ethics, as a man and as an artist. I remain hopeful some will rub off; D.J. Markuson for his keen eye, technical wizardry and mastery; David Tabatsky, editor extraordinaire—brilliant, complex and innovative—who challenged me to expand my vision and stretch beyond my reach and, Bruce Kluger for facilitating the introduction and injecting wise opinion all over the friggin' place; Mary Novaria, who patiently and meticulously exposed the gazillion misplaced commas, apostrophes and other assaults on the written page; Linda Edell Howard, J David Farrell and Alan Bail for invaluable friendship and counsel; Merrilee Heifetz for requesting first read and advising on next steps; Gordon Gebert for always believing and, offering... twice; Lynn Jones Johnston for saying "yes" in spite of the challenges; Tina Cole, who proved that five minutes a day was oft enough; Liz Martinez who's silently kept me accountable for 3784 days and counting; Jackie Collins for so generously taking me under her wing and introducing me around; Adriana Trigiani and Scott Carter, who unknowingly sparked me; Rory Rosegarten, Ralph Della Cava and Richard Brown, whose right words at the right time gave me the courage to try; Henry Jaglom, who pushed me to defend my voice and in so doing helped me to own it; Stephen King for *On Writing* and for being my ideal reader, unbeknownst to him; Phil Rosenthal, whose fearlessness inspired me to foster my own, although mine no doubt mortifies him; Joanne Milazzo, who always has my back and my heart; readers Colin Broderick, Renata Love, Hubert O'Hearn and Josie Brown for their insights, Carol McDonald for hand holding, Kathy Boyett for cheerleading; the generous error hunters, Judy Moore, who I owe a birthday... not a gift... or a dinner... the day. She spent hers on this— fabulous, crazy friend. Laura Craig, Susan Sweetman, Jennifer Bradshaw, Ken La Kier, Julie Hasse, Susan Berger, Peggy Glenn and Lori Nelson... blame them; Liz Mintzer, Susanne Crummy and Craig Ames for shoring my foundation and supplying wisdom, guidance and tools; Michael Pohl and David Hitt for sharing their paradise retreat; my girl Zoe Moon, for celestial empowerment; Gabe Abelson for affording me time and freedom; Honey Leopold and Jan Katz for challenging me to be my better self; Harry and Samantha Abelson for gifting me with unconditional love and more pride and joy than I know what to do with; Larry Katz for putting stars in my eyes and love in my heart; the writers on West 96th Street who schooled me from the inside; the wominz of *Women Who Write*, who listened and validated at every turn; and the peoples of The Facebook, who helped me... find... me.